MILITARY
AIRCRAFT
MARKINGS
1994

PETER R. MARCH

IAN ALLAN
Publishing

NA P-51D Mustang 474008/N51RR is privately owned and based at North Weald. *PRM*

Contents

Photographs by Peter R. March (PRM) unless otherwise credited

This fifteenth edition published 1994

ISBN 0 7110 2233 X

Published by Ian Allan Ltd
Printed by Ian Allan Printing Ltd at its works
at Coombelands in Runnymede, England

Front cover:
F-27 of the Royal Netherlands Air Force. *PRM*

Rear cover, top:
Fairey Swordfish. *PRM*

Introduction

This fifteenth edition of *abc Military Aircraft Markings*, a companion to *abc Civil Aircraft Markings*, again sets out to list in alphabetical and numerical order all the aircraft which carry a United Kingdom military serial, and which are based, or might be seen, in the UK. The term **aircraft** used here covers powered, manned aeroplanes, helicopters and gliders. Included are all the current Royal Air Force, Royal Navy, Army Air Corps, Ministry of Defence (Procurement Executive), manufacturers' test aircraft and civilian-owned aircraft with military markings.

Aircraft withdrawn from operational use but which are retained in the UK for ground training purposes or otherwise preserved by the Services and in museums and collections are listed. The serials of some incomplete aircraft have been included, such as the cockpit sections of machines displayed by the RAF Exhibition Flight, aircraft used by airfield fire sections and for service battle damage repair training (BDRT), together with significant parts of aircraft held by preservation groups and societies. Many of these aircraft are allocated, and sometimes wear, a secondary identity, such as an RAF Support Command 'M' maintenance number. These numbers are listed against those aircraft to which they have been allocated.

A serial 'missing' is either because it was never issued as it formed part of a 'black-out block', or because the aircraft is written off, scrapped, sold, abroad or allocated an alternative marking. Aircraft used as targets on MoD ranges to which access is restricted, and un-manned target drones, are omitted, as are UK military aircraft that have been permanently grounded overseas and unlikely to return to Britain.

In the main, the serials listed are those markings presently displayed on the aircraft. Aircraft which bear a false serial are quoted in *italic type*. The manufacturer and aircraft type are given, together with recent alternative, previous, secondary or civil identity shown in round brackets. Complete records of multiple previous identities are only included where space permits. The operating unit and its based location, along with any known unit and base code markings in square brackets, are given as accurately as possible. The unit markings are normally carried boldly on the sides of the fuselage or on the aircraft's fin. In the case of RAF and AAC machines currently in service, they are usually one or two letters or numbers, while the RN continues to use a well-established system of three-figure codes between 000 and 999 together with a fin letter code denoting the aircraft's operational base. RN squadrons, units and bases are allocated blocks of numbers from which individual aircraft codes are issued. To help identification of RN bases and landing platforms on ships, a list of tail-letter codes with their appropriate base, helicopter code number, ship pennant number and type of vessel is included; as is a helicopter code number/ships' tail-letter code grid cross-reference.

Codes change, for example when aircraft move between units, and therefore the markings currently painted on a particular aircraft might not be those shown in this edition because of subsequent events. The effect of the on-going 'Options for Change' RAF re-organisation accounts for the large number of changes in this edition to Tornado GR1s/F3s, Jaguars, Phantoms, Pumas and Chinooks. They will continue to be noticeable for several years. Those airframes which may not appear in the next edition because of sale, accident, etc, have their fates, where known, given in italic type in the *locations* column.

The Irish Army Air Corps fleet is listed, together with the serials of other overseas air arms whose aircraft might be seen visiting the UK from time to time. The serial numbers are as usually presented on the individual machine or as they are normally identified. Where possible, the aircraft's base and operating unit have been shown.

USAF, US Army and US Navy aircraft based in the UK and in Western Europe, and of types which regularly visit the UK from the USA, are each listed in separate sections by aircraft type. The serial number actually displayed on the aircraft is shown in full, with additional Fiscal Year (FY) or full serial information also provided. Where appropriate, details of the operating wing, squadron allocation and base are added. The USAF is, like the RAF, continuing a major reorganisation which is producing new unit titles, many squadron changes and the closure of bases worldwide. Only details that concern changes effected by December 1993 are shown.

Veteran and Vintage aircraft which carry overseas military markings but which are based in the UK have been separately listed showing their principal means of identification.

Information shown is believed to be correct at 31 January 1994, and significant changes can be monitored through the monthly 'Military Markings' column in *Aircraft Illustrated*.

Acknowledgements

The compiler again wishes to thank the many people who have taken trouble to send comments, criticism and other useful information following the publication of the previous editions of *abc Military Aircraft Markings*. In particular the following correspondents: D. Braithwaite, P. F. Burton, G. Fraser, A.Helden, I. Logan, P.- J. Martin, A.P. March, P.Moonen, I. Polson, P. C. Ridgwell, R. Robinson, M. K. Thompson and P. Wiggins.

This compilation has relied heavily on the publications of the following aviation groups and societies: *Air North, British Aviation Review* (British Aviation Research Group), *Macclesfield Historical Aviation Society*, *North-West Air News* (Air Britain, Merseyside Branch), *Osprey* (Solent Aviation Society), *Prestwick Airport Letter* (Prestwick Airport Aviation Group), *Scottish Air News* (Central Scotland Aviation Group), *Stansted Aviation Newsletter* (The Stansted Aviation Society), *Strobe* (The East of England Aviation Group), *Ulster Air Mail* (Ulster Aviation Society), *Upper Heyford News* (Upper Heyford Aviation Society) and *VAS News* (Valley Aviation Society).

The new edition of *abc Military Aircraft Markings* would not have been possible without considerable research and collating by Howard Curtis and checking by Wal Gandy, to whom I am indebted.

Peter R. March   **January 1994**

Auster 5 RT486 (G-AJGJ) is civilian owned at Old Sarum. *PRM*

Restored in USAAC colours, Stearman G-ILLE flies as '379'. *PRM*

Abbreviations

AAC	Army Air Corps
A&AEE	Aeroplane & Armament Experimental Establishment
AAS	Aeromedical Airlift Squadron
ABS	Air Base Squadron
ABW	Air Base Wing
ACCGS	Air Cadets Central Gliding School
ACCS ⎫	Airborne Command and Control
ACCW ⎭	Squadron/Wing
ACR	Armoured Cavalry Regiment
AEF	Air Experience Flight
AES	Air Engineering School
AEW	Airborne Early Warning
AFRES	Air Force Reserve
AFSC	Air Force System Command
AG	Airlift Group
AHB	Attack Helicopter Battalion
AIU	Accident Investigation Unit
AKG	Aufklärürngsgeschwader (Reconnaissance Wing)
ALS	Airlift Squadron
AMD-BA	Avions Marcel Dassault-Breguet Aviation
AMG	Aircraft Maintenance Group
AMS	Air Movements School
ANG	Air National Guard
APS	Aircraft Preservation Society
ARRS ⎫	Aerospace Rescue and Recovery
ARRW ⎭	Squadron/Wing
ARS	Air Refuelling Squadron
ARW	Air Refuelling Wing
ARWS	Advanced Rotary Wing Squadron
ASF	Aircraft Servicing Flight
AS&RU	Aircraft Salvage and Repair Unit
ATC	Air Training Corps
ATCC	Air Traffic Control Centre
ATS	Aircrewman Training Squadron
AvCo	Aviation Company
AW	Airlift Wing
AW	Armstrong Whitworth Aircraft
AWG	Amt für Wehrgeophysik
AW&CS ⎫	Airborne Warning & Control
AW&CW ⎭	Squadron/Wing
BAC	British Aircraft Corporation
BAe	British Aerospace PLC
BAOR	British Army of the Rhine
BAPC	British Aviation Preservation Council
BATUS	British Army Training Unit Support
BBMF	Battle of Britain Memorial Flight
BDRF	Battle Damage Repair Flight
BDRT	Battle Damage Repair Training
Be	Beech
Bf	Bayerische Flugzeugwerke
BFME	British Forces Middle East
BFWF	Basic Fixed Wing Flight
BGA	British Gliding & Soaring Association
BHC	British Hovercraft Corporation
BNFL	British Nuclear Fuels Ltd
BP	Boulton & Paul
B-V	Boeing-Vertol
BW	Bomber Wing
CAC	Commonwealth Aircraft Corporation
CARG	Cotswold Aircraft Restoration Group
CASA	Construcciones Aeronauticas SA
CATCS	Central Air Traffic Control School
CBAS	Commando Brigade Air Squadron
CC	County Council
CCF	Combined Cadet Force
CDE	Chemical Defence Establishment
CEAM	Centre d'Expérimentation Aériennes Militaires
CEV	Centre d'Essais en Vol
CFS	Central Flying School
CGMF	Central Glider Maintenance Flight
CIFAS	Centre d'Instruction des Forces Aériennes Stratégiques
CinC	Commander in Chief
Co	Company
CSDE	Central Servicing Development Establishment
CT	College of Technology
CTE	Central Training Establishment
CTTS	Civilian Technical Training School
CV	Chance-Vought
D-BD	Dassault-Breguet Dornier
Det	Detachment
DH	de Havilland
DHC	de Havilland Canada
DRA	Defence Research Agency
DTI	Department of Trade and Industry
EABDR	Engineering and Battle Damage Repair
EAP	European Aircraft Project
ECS/ECW	Electronic Countermeasures Squadron/Wing
EDA	Escadre de Detection Aéroportée
EE	English Electric
EFTS	Elementary Flying Training Squadron
EHI	European Helicopter Industries
EMA	East Midlands Airport
EoN	Elliot's of Newbury
ERV	Escadre de Ravitaillement en Vol
ETPS	Empire Test Pilots' School
ETS	Engineering Training School
EWAU	Electronics Warfare Avionics Unit
FAA	Fleet Air Arm/Federal Aviation Administration
FACF	Forward Air Control Flight
FBS	Flugbereitschaftstaffel
FBW	Fly by wire
FCS	Facility Checking Squadron
FE	Further Education
FEWSG	Fleet Electronic Warfare Support Group
FG	Fighter Group
FGF	Flying Grading Flight
FH	Fairchild-Hiller
FI	Falkland Islands
Flt	Flight
FMA	Fabrica Militar de Aviones
FOL	Forward Operating Location
FONA	Flag Officer Naval Aviation
FRADU	Fleet Requirements and Air Direction Unit
FRL	Flight Refuelling Ltd
FS	Fighter Squadron
FSCTE	Fire School Central Training Establishment
FTS	Flying Training School
FW	Fighter Wing
FW	Foster Wikner
FY	Fiscal Year
F3 OCU	Tornado F3 Operational Conversion Unit
GAL	General Aircraft Ltd
GD	General Dynamics
GI	Ground Instruction
HFR	Heeresfliegerregiment (Corps transport regiment)

7

HFWS	Heeresflieger Waffenschule
HMS	Her Majesty's Ship
HOCU	Harrier OCU
HP	Handley-Page
HQ	Headquarters
HS	Hawker Siddeley
HSF	Harrier Servicing Flight
IAF	Israeli Air Force
IAM	Institute of Aviation Medicine
IHM	International Helicopter Museum
IWM	Imperial War Museum
JATE	Joint Air Transport Establishment
JbG	Jagd Bomber Geschwader (Fighter Bomber Wing)
JG	Jagd Geschwader (Fighter Wing)
JMU	Jaguar Maintenance Unit
JTU	Joint Trials Unit
LOFTU	Lynx Operational Flying Trials Unit
LTG	Luft Transport Geschwader (Air Transport Wing)
LTV	Ling-Temco-Vought
LVG	Luftwaffen Versorgungs Geschwader (Air Force Maintenance Wing)
McD	McDonnell Douglas
MFG	Marine Flieger Geschwader (Naval Air Wing)
MGSP	Mobile Glider Servicing Party
MH	Max Holste
MIB	Military Intelligence Battalion
MiG	Mikoyan — Gurevich
MoD(PE)	Ministry of Defence (Procurement Executive)
Mod	Modified
MR	Maritime Reconnaissance
MRF	Meteorological Research Flight
MS	Morane-Saulnier
MSMW	Military Special Missions Wing
MU	Maintenance Unit
NA	North American
NACDS	Naval Air Command Driving School
NAEWF	NATO Airborne Early Warning Force
NAF	Naval Air Facility
NASU	Naval Air Support Unit
NE	North-East
NHTU	Naval Hovercraft Trials Unit
NI	Northern Ireland
NMSU	Nimrod Major Servicing Unit
NYARC	North Yorks Aircraft Restoration Centre
OCU	Operational Conversion Unit
OEU	Operational Evaluation Unit
OTD	Overseas Training Division
OTS	Operational Training Squadron
PAX	Passenger procedural trainer
PRU	Photographic Reconnaissance Unit
RAeS	Royal Aeronautical Society
RAF	Royal Aircraft Factory/Royal Air Force
RAFC	Royal Air Force College
RAFM	Royal Air Force Museum
RAFGSA	Royal Air Force Gliding and Soaring Association
RAOC	Royal Army Ordnance Corps
RCAF	Royal Canadian Air Force
RE	Royal Engineers
Regt	Regiment
REME	Royal Electrical & Mechanical Engineers
RGE	Ridge Gliding Establishment
RM	Royal Marines
RMC of S	Royal Military College of Science
RN	Royal Navy
RNAS	Royal Naval Air Station
RNAW	Royal Naval Aircraft Workshop
RNAY	Royal Naval Aircraft Yard
RNEC	Royal Naval Engineering College
RNEFTS	Royal Naval Elementary Flying Training School
RNGSA	Royal Navy Gliding and Soaring Association
ROF	Royal Ordnance Factory
R-R	Rolls-Royce
RS	Reid & Sigrist/Reconnaissance Squadron
RS&RE	Royal Signals and Radar Establishment
RSV	Reparto Sperimentale Volo
RW	Reconnaissance Wing
SA	Scottish Aviation
Saab	Svenska Aeroplan Aktiebolag
SAC	Strategic Air Command
SAE	School of Aircraft Engineering
SAH	School of Air Handling
SAL	Scottish Aviation Limited
SAOEU	Strike/Attack Operational Evaluation Unit
SAR	Search and Rescue
Saro	Saunders-Roe
SARTU	Search and Rescue Training Unit
SCF	Scout Conversion Flight
SEPECAT	Société Europ´enne de Production de l'avion Ecole de Combat et d'Appui Tactique
SHAPE	Supreme Headquarters Allied Forces Europe
SIF	Servicing Instruction Flight
SKTU	Sea King Training Unit
SNCAN	Société Nationale de Constructions Aéronautiques du Nord
SOS	Special Operations Squadron
SoTT	School of Technical Training
SPAD	Société Pour les Appareils Deperdussin
Sqn	Squadron
SSF	Station Servicing Flight
SSTF	Small Ships Trials Flight
SW	Strategic Wing
T&EE	Test & Evaluation Establishment
TMTS	Trade Management Training School
TSLw	Technische Schule der Luftwaffe
TTTE	Tri-national Tornado Training Establishment
TW	Test Wing
TWU	Tactical Weapons Unit
UAS	University Air Squadron
UK	United Kingdom
UKAEA	United Kingdom Atomic Energy Authority
UNFICYP	United Nations' Forces in Cyprus
US	United States
USAF	United States Air Force
USAFE	United States Air Forces in Europe
USAREUR	US Army Europe
USEUCOM	United States European Command
USN	United States Navy
VGS	Volunteer Gliding School
VQ	Air Reconnaissance Squadron
VR	Logistic Support Squadron
VS	Vickers-Supermarine
WG	Wing
WLT	Weapons Loading Training
WRG	Weather Reconnaissance Group
WRS	Weather Reconnaissance Squadron
WS	Westland
WW2	World War II

A Guide to the Location of Operational Bases in the UK

This section is to assist the reader to locate the places in the United Kingdom where operational military aircraft are based. The term *aircraft* also includes helicopters and gliders.

The alphabetical order listing gives each location in relation to its county and to its nearest classified road(s) (*by* means adjoining; *of* means proximate to), together with its approximate direction and mileage from the centre of a nearby major town or city.

Some civil airports are included where active military units are also based, but **excluded** are MoD sites with non-operational aircraft (eg *gate guardians*), the bases of privately-owned civil aircraft which wear military markings and museums.

User	Base name	County/Region	Location	Distance/direction from (town)
DRA	Aberporth	Dyfed	N of A487	6m ENE of Cardigan
USAF	Alconbury	Cambridgeshire	E by A1/A14	4m NW of Huntingdon
RAF	Aldergrove/Belfast	Co Antrim	W by A26	13m W of Belfast Airport
RAF	Benson	Oxfordshire	E by A423	1m NE of Wallingford
A&AEE	Boscombe Down	Wiltshire	S by A303, W of A338	6m N of Salisbury
RAF	Boulmer	Northumberland	E of B1339	4m E of Alnwick
RAF	Brawdy	Dyfed	N of A487	9m NW of Haverfordwest
RAF	Brize Norton	Oxfordshire	W of A4095	5m SW of Witney
RAF	Cambridge Airport/	Cambridgeshire	S by A1303	2m E of Cambridge Teversham
RAF	Catterick	Yorkshire North	E by A1	7m WNW of Northallerton
RAF	Chivenor	Devon	S of A361	4m WNW of Barnsta
RAF	Church Fenton	Yorkshire North	S of B1223	7m WNW of Selby
RAF	Colerne	Wiltshire	S of A420, E of Fosse Way	5m NE of Bath
RAF	Coltishall	Norfolk	W of B1150	9m NNE of Norwich
RAF	Coningsby	Lincolnshire	S of A153, W by B1192	10m NW of Boston
RAF	Cosford	Shropshire	W of A41, N of A464	9m WNW of Wolverhampton
RAF	Cottesmore	Leicestershire	W of A1, N of B668	9m NW of Stamford
RAF	Cranwell	Lincolnshire	N by A17, S by B1429	5m WNW of Sleafor
RNAS	Culdrose	Cornwall	E by A3083	1m SE of Helston
AAC	Dishforth	Yorkshire North	E by A1	4m E of Ripon
BAe	Dunsfold	Surrey	W of A281, S of B2130	9m S of Guildford
RAF	Exeter Airport	Devon	S by A30	4m ENE of Exeter
DRA	Farnborough	Hampshire	W of A325, N of A323	2m W of Farnboroug
BAe	Filton	Avon	E by M5 jn 17, W by A38	4m N of Bristol
RAF	Finningley	Yorkshire South	W of A614, S of B1396	6m ESE of Doncaste
RNAY	Fleetlands	Hampshire	E by A32	2m SE of Fareham
RAF	Glasgow Airport	Strathclyde	N by M8 jn 28	7m W of city
RAF	Halton	Buckinghamshire	N of A4011, S of B4544	4m ESE of Aylesbur
RAF	Henlow	Bedfordshire	E of A600, W of A6001	1m SW of Henlow
RAF	Honington	Suffolk	E of A134, W of A1088	6m S of Thetford
RAF	Hullavington	Wiltshire	W of A429	1m N of M4 jn 17
RAF	Kenley	Greater London	W of A22	1m W of Warlingham
RAF	Kinloss	Grampian	E of B9011, N of B9089	3m NE of Forres
RAF	Kirknewton	Lothian	E by B7031, N by A70	8m SW of Edinburgh
USAF	Lakenheath	Suffolk	W by A1065	8m W of Thetford
RAF	Leeming	Yorkshire North	E by A1	5m SW of Northaller
RAF	Leuchars	Fife	E of A919	7m SE of Dundee
RAF	Linton-on-Ouse	Yorkshire North	E of B6265	10m NW of York
T&EE	Llanbedr	Gwynedd	W of A496	7m NNW of Barmou
RAF	Lossiemouth	Grampian	W of B9135, S of B9040	4m N of Elgin
RAF	Lyneham	Wiltshire	W of A3102, S of A420	10m WSW of Swind
DRA	Machrihanish	Strathclyde	W of A83	3m W of Cambletow
RAF	Manston	Kent	N by A253	3m W of Ramsgate
RAF	Marham	Norfolk	N by A1122	6m W of Swaffham
AAC	Middle Wallop	Hampshire	S by A343	6m SW of Andover
USAF	Mildenhall	Suffolk	S by A1101	9m NNE of Newmar
AAC	Netheravon	Wiltshire	E of A345	5m N of Amesbury
RAF	Newton	Nottinghamshire	N of A52, W of A46	7m E of Nottingham
RAF	Northolt	Greater London	N by A40	3m E of M40 jn 1
RAF	Odiham	Hampshire	E of A32	2m S of M3 jn 5
RNAS	Portland	Dorset	E by A354	3m S of Weymouth
RN	Predannack	Cornwall	W by A3083	7m S of Helston
RN	Prestwick Airport	Strathclyde	E by A79	3m N of Ayr
RAF	St Athan	South Glamorgan	N of B4265	13m WSW of Cardi

9

UK Operational Bases – continued

User	Base name	County/Region	Location	Distance/direction from (town)
RAF	St Mawgan/Newquay	Cornwall	N of A3059	4m ENE of Newquay Airport
RAF	Scampton	Lincolnshire	W by A15	6m N of Lincoln
RAF	Sealand	Clwyd	W by A550	6m WNW of Chester
RAF	Shawbury	Shropshire	W of B5063	7m NNE of Shrewsbury
RAF	South Cerney	Gloucestershire	W by A419	3m SE of Cirencester
RAF	Swansea Airport/	West Glamorgan	W by A4118	6m W of Swansea
	Fairwood Common			
RAF	Swanton Morley	Norfolk	W of B1147	4m NNE of Dereham
RAF	Swinderby	Lincolnshire	SE by A46	9m SW of Lincoln
RAF/	Sydenham/	Co Down	W by A2	2m E of city
Shorts	Belfast City Airport			
RAF	Ternhill	Shropshire	SW by A41	3m SW of Market Drayton
DRA	Thurleigh/Bedford	Bedfordshire	E of A6, W of B660	7m N of Bedford
AAC	Topcliffe	Yorkshire North	E of A167, W of A168	3m SW of Thirsk
RAF	Turnhouse/Edinburgh	Lothian	N of A8, E of M8 J2	6m W of Edinburgh Airport
RAF	Upavon	Wiltshire	S by A342	14m WNW of Andover
RAF	Valley	Gwynedd	S of A5 on Anglesey	5m SE of Holyhead
RAF	Waddington	Lincolnshire	E by A607, W by A15	5m S of Lincoln
BAe	Warton	Lancashire	S by A584	8m SE of Blackpool
AAC	Wattisham	Suffolk	N of B1078	5m SSW of Stowmarket
DRA	West Freugh	Dumfries & Galloway	S by A757, W by A715	5m SE of Stranraer
RAF	Weston-on-the-Green	Oxfordshire	E by A43	9m N of Oxford
RAF	Wittering	Cambridgeshire	W by A1, N of A47	3m S of Stamford
RAF	Woodvale	Merseyside	W by A565	5m SSW of Southport
RAF	Wyton	Cambridgeshire	E of A141, N of B1090	3m NE of Huntingdon
WS	Yeovil	Somerset	N of A30, S of A3088	1m W of Yeovil
RNAS	Yeovilton	Somerset	S by B3151, S of A303	5m N of Yeovil

BAe Hawk 200 Radar Development Aircraft ZJ201, with Royal Air Force of Oman Hawk 103 101/ZH699.
Geoff Lee/BAe Defence

British Military Aircraft Serials

The Committee of Imperial Defence through its Air Committee introduced a standardised system of numbering aircraft in November 1912. The Air Department of the Admiralty was allocated the first batch 1-200 and used these to cover aircraft already in use and those on order. The Army was issued with the next block from 201-800, which included the number 304 which was given to the Cody Biplane now preserved in the Science Museum. By the outbreak of World War 1 the Royal Navy was on its second batch of serials 801-1600 and this system continued with alternating allocations between the Army and Navy until 1916 when number 10000, a Royal Flying Corps BE2C, was reached.

It was decided not to continue with five digit numbers but instead to start again from 1, prefixing RFC aircraft with the letter A and RNAS aircraft with the prefix N. The RFC allocations commenced with A1 an FE2D and before the end of the year had reached A9999 an Armstrong Whitworth FK8. The next group commenced with B1 and continued in logical sequence through the C, D, E and F prefixes. G was used on a limited basis to identify captured German aircraft, while H was the last block of wartime-ordered aircraft. To avoid confusion I was not used, so the new postwar machines were allocated serials in the J range. A further minor change was made in the serial numbering system in August 1929 when it was decided to maintain four numerals after the prefix letter, thus omitting numbers 1 to 999. The new K series therefore commenced at K1000, which was allocated to an AW Atlas.

The Naval N prefix was not used in such a logical way. Blocks of numbers were allocated for specific types of aircraft such as seaplanes or flying-boats. By the late 1920s the sequence had largely been used up and a new series using the prefix S was commenced. In 1930 separate naval allocations were stopped and subsequent serials were issued in the 'military' range which had by this time reached the K series. A further change in the pattern of allocations came in the L range. Commencing with L7272 numbers were issued in blocks with smaller blocks of serials between not used. These were known as black-out blocks. It would appear that this policy is being reintroduced at the present time. As M had already been used as a suffix for Maintenance Command instructional airframes it was not used as a prefix. Although N had previously been used for naval aircraft it was used again for serials allocated from 1937.

With the build-up to World War 2 the rate of allocations quickly accelerated and the prefix R was being used when war was declared. The letters O and Q were not allotted, nor was S which had been used up to S1865 for naval aircraft before integration into the RAF series. By 1940 the serial Z9999 had been reached, as part of a blackout block, with the letters U and Y not used to avoid confusion. The option to recommence serial allocation at A1000 was not taken up; instead it was decided to use an alphabetical two-letter prefix with three numerals running from 100 to 999. Thus AA100 was allocated to a Blenheim IV.

This two-letter, three-numeral serial system which started in 1940 continues today with the current issue being in the later part of the ZH range. The letters C, I, O, Q, U and Y were, with the exception of NC, not used. For various reasons the following letter combinations were not issued: DA, DB, DH, EA, GA to GZ, HA, HT, JE, JH, JJ, KR to KT, MR, NW, NZ, SA to SK, SV, TN, TR and VE. The first postwar serials issued were in the VP range while the end of the WZs had been reached by the Korean War. At the current rate of issue the Z range will last well into the next century.

Note: Whilst every effort has been made to ensure the accuracy of this publication, no part of the contents has been obtained from official sources. The compiler will be pleased to continue to receive comments, corrections and further information for inclusion in subsequent editions of *Military Aircraft Markings*. A monthly up-date of additions and amendments is published in *Aircraft Illustrated*.

McDonnell Douglas KC10A Extender 30082 of 458 OG Barksdale AFB, LA. *Andrew P. March*

Panavia Tornado GR1A ZA405 of No 2 Sqn based at RAF Marham. *PRM*

British Military Aircraft Markings

A serial in *italics* denotes that it is not the genuine marking for that airframe.

Serial	Type	Owner or Operator	Notes
164	Bleriot Type XI (BAPC 106)	RAF Museum, Hendon	
168	Sopwith Tabloid Scout Replica (G-BFDE)	RAF Museum, Hendon	
215	DH Vampire T55 (U-1215/G-HELV)	Jet Heritage, Bournemouth	
304	Cody Biplane (BAPC 62)	Science Museum, South Kensington	
433	Bleriot Type XXVII (BAPC 107)	RAF Museum, Hendon	
687	RAF BE2b Replica (BAPC 181)	RAF Museum, Hendon	
1701	RAF BE2c Replica (BAPC 117)	Brooklands Museum, Weybridge	
2345	Vickers FB5 Gunbus Replica (G-ATVP)	RAF Museum, Hendon	
2699	RAF BE2c	Imperial War Museum, Lambeth	
3066	Caudron GIII (G-AETA)	RAF Museum, Hendon	
5492	Sopwith LC-1T Triplane Replica (G-PENY)	Privately owned, stored Ballymoney	
5844	Avro 504K Replica (BAPC 42)	*Painted as H1968*	
5894	DH2 Replica (G-BFVH) [FB2]	Wessex Aviation & Transport, Chalmington	
5964	DH2 Replica (BAPC 112)	Museum of Army Flying, Middle Wallop	
6232	RAF BE2c Replica (BAPC 41)	RAF, stored St Athan	
8359	Short 184	FAA Museum, RNAS Yeovilton	
A1325	RAF BE2e	Mosquito Aircraft Museum, London Colney	
A1742	Bristol Scout D Replica (BAPC 38)	The Aircraft Restoration Co, Duxford	
A4850	RAF SE5 Replica (BAPC 176)	South Yorkshire Aviation Museum, Firbeck	
A7317	Sopwith Pup Replica (BAPC 179)	Midland Air Museum, Coventry	
A8226	Sopwith 1½ Strutter Replica (G-BIDW)	RAF Museum, Hendon	
B415	AFEE 10/42 Rotabuggy Replica (BAPC 163)	Museum of Army Flying, Middle Wallop	
B1807	Sopwith Pup (G-EAVX) [A7]	Privately owned, Keynsham, Avon	
B2458	Sopwith F1 Camel Replica (G-BPOB) [R]	Privately owned, Booker	
B4863	Eberhardt SE5E (G-BLXT) [G]	The Old Flying Machine Co, Duxford	
B6291	Sopwith F1 Camel (G-ASOP)	The Shuttleworth Collection, Old Warden	
B6401	Sopwith F1 Camel Replica (G-AWYY/C1701)	FAA Museum, RNAS Yeovilton	
B7270	Sopwith F1 Camel Replica (G-BFCZ)	Brooklands Museum, Weybridge	
B9708	Sopwith 1½ Strutter Replica	Macclesfield Historical Aviation Society, Marthall	
C1904	RAF SE5A Replica (G-PFAP) [Z]	Privately owned, Syerston	
C3011	Phoenix Currie Super Wot (G-SWOT) [S]	Privately owned, Breighton	
C4451	Avro 504J Replica (BAPC 210)	Southampton Hall of Aviation	
C4912	Bristol M1C Replica (BAPC 135)	Northern Aeroplane Workshops	
C4994	Bristol M1C Replica (G-BLWM)	RAF Museum, Hendon	
D2700	RAF SE5A Replica (BAPC 208)	Prince's Mead Centre, Farnborough	
D3419	Sopwith F1 Camel Replica (BAPC 59)	RAF, stored St Athan	
D5329	Sopwith F5 Dolphin	RAF Museum Store, Cardington	
D7560	Avro 504K	Museum of Army Flying, Middle Wallop	
D7889	Bristol F2B Fighter (G-AANM/BAPC 166)	Privately owned, St Leonards-on-Sea	
D8084	Bristol F2B Fighter (G-ACAA/F4516) [S]	The Fighter Collection, Duxford	
D8096	Bristol F2B Fighter (G-AEPH) [D]	The Shuttleworth Collection, Old Warden	
E373	Avro 504K Replica (BAPC 178)	Privately owned, Eccleston, Lancs	
E449	Avro 504K (G-EBJE)	RAF Museum, Hendon	
E2466	Bristol F2B Fighter (BAPC 165) [I]	RAF Museum, Hendon	
E2581	Bristol F2B Fighter	Imperial War Museum, Duxford	

Notes	Serial	Type	Owner or Operator
	F141	RAF SE5A Replica (G-SEVA) [G]	Privately owned, Boscombe Down
	F344	Avro 504K Replica	RAF Museum Store, Henlow
	F760	SE5A Microlight Replica [A]	Privately owned, Redhill
	F904	RAF SE5A (G-EBIA)	The Shuttleworth Collection, Old Warden
	F938	RAF SE5A (G-EBIC)	RAF Museum, Hendon
	F943	RAF SE5A Replica (G-BIHF) [S]	Privately owned, White Waltham
	F943	RAF SE5A Replica (G-BKDT)	Yorkshire Air Museum, Elvington
	F1010	Airco DH9A [C]	RAF Museum, Hendon
	F3556	RAF RE8	Imperial War Museum, Duxford
	F4013	Sopwith F1 Camel Replica	Privately owned, Coventry
	F5447	RAF SE5A Replica (G-BKER) [N]	Privately owned, Cumbernauld
	F5459	RAF SE5A Replica (BAPC 142) [11-Y]	Flambards Village Theme Park, Helston
	F5459	RAF SE5A Replica (G-INNY) [Y]	Privately owned, Old Sarum
	F6314	Sopwith F1 Camel [B]	RAF Museum, Hendon
	F8010	RAF SE5A Replica (G-BDWJ) [Z]	Privately owned, Graveley
	F8614	Vickers Vimy Replica (G-AWAU)	RAF Museum, Hendon
	H1968	Avro 504K Replica (BAPC 42)	RAF, stored St Athan
	H2311	Avro 504K (G-ABAA)	Greater Manchester Museum of Science and Industry
	H3426	Hawker Hurricane Replica (BAPC 68)	Midland Air Museum, stored Coventry
	H5199	Avro 504K (BK892/3118M/ G-ACNB/G-ADEV)	The Shuttleworth Collection, Old Warden
	J7326	DH Humming Bird (G-EBQP)	Privately owned, Bishops Stortford
	J8067	Westland Pterodactyl 1a	Science Museum, South Kensington
	J9941	Hawker Hart 2 (G-ABMR)	RAF Museum, Hendon
	K1786	Hawker Tomtit (G-AFTA)	The Shuttleworth Collection, Old Warden
	K2050	Isaacs Fury II (G-ASCM)	Privately owned, Boscombe Down
	K2059	Isaacs Fury II (G-PFAR)	Privately owned, Dunkeswell
	K2075	Isaacs Fury II (G-BEER)	Privately owned, Sturgate
	K2227	Bristol Bulldog IIA (G-ABBB) (wreck)	RAF Museum Restoration Centre, Cardington
	K2567	DH Tiger Moth (G-MOTH) (really DE306/7035M)	Russavia Collection, Dunstable
	K2571	DH Tiger Moth Replica	Privately owned, RAF Hereford
	K2572	DH Tiger Moth (G-AOZH) (really NM129)	Privately owned, Shoreham
	K2572	DH Tiger Moth Replica	The Aeroplane Collection, Warmingham
	K3215	Avro Tutor (G-AHSA)	The Shuttleworth Collection, Old Warden
	K3584	DH Queen Bee (BAPC 186)	Mosquito Aircraft Museum, London Colney
	K3661	Hawker Nimrod II (G-BURZ)	Privately owned, Rye
	K3731	Isaacs Fury Replica (G-RODI)	Privately owned, Hailsham
	K4232	Avro Rota I (SE-AZB)	RAF Museum, Hendon
	K4235	Avro Rota I (G-AHMJ)	The Shuttleworth Collection, Old Warden
	K4972	Hawker Hart Trainer IIA (1764M)	RAF Museum, Hendon
	K5054	Supermarine Spitfire Replica	Southampton Hall of Aviation
	K5054	Supermarine Spitfire Replica (G-BRDV)	Privately owned, Hullavington
	K5054	Supermarine Spitfire Replica (BAPC 214)	Southampton Airport
	K5414	Hawker Hind (G-AENP/BAPC 78) [XV]	The Shuttleworth Collection, Old Warden
	K6035	Westland Wallace II (2365M)	RAF Museum, Hendon
	K7271	Hawker Fury II Replica (BAPC 148)	RAF Cosford Aerospace Museum, stored
	K8042	Gloster Gladiator II (8372M)	RAF Museum, Hendon
	K8203	Hawker Demon I (G-BTVE/2292M)	Privately owned, Rye
	K9926	VS Spitfire I Replica (BAPC 217) [JH-C]	RAF Bentley Priory, on display
	K9942	VS Spitfire IA (8383M) [SD-V]	RAF Museum, Hendon
	L1070	VS Spitfire I Replica (BAPC 227) [XT-A]	RAF Turnhouse, on display
	L1096	VS Spitfire I Replica (BAPC 229) [PR-O]	RAF Digby, on display
	L1592	Hawker Hurricane I [KW-Z]	Science Museum, South Kensington
	L1592	Hawker Hurricane I Replica (BAPC 63) [KW-Z]	Kent Battle of Britain Museum, Hawkinge
	L1679	Hawker Hurricane I Replica [JX-G]	Museum of Army Flying, Middle Wallop

Serial	Type	Owner or Operator	Notes
L1710	Hawker Hurricane I Replica (BAPC 219) [AL-D]	RAF Biggin Hill, on display	
L2301	VS Walrus I (G-AIZG)	FAA Museum, RNAS Yeovilton	
L2940	Blackburn Skua I	FAA Museum, RNAS Yeovilton	
L5343	Fairey Battle I [VO-S]	RAF Museum, Hendon	
L6906	Miles Magister I (G-AKKY/T9841) (BAPC 44)	Museum of Berkshire Aviation, Woodley	
L7775	Vickers Wellington IA (fuselage)	Privately owned, Moreton-in-Marsh	
L8756	Bristol Bolingbroke IVT (RCAF 10001) [XD-E]	RAF Museum, Hendon	
N248	Supermarine S6A	Southampton Hall of Aviation	
N546	Wright Quadruplane Type 1 Replica (BAPC 164)	Southampton Hall of Aviation	
N1671	Boulton Paul Defiant I (8370M) [EW-D]	RAF Museum, Hendon	
N1854	Fairey Fulmar II (G-AIBE)	FAA Museum, RNAS Yeovilton	
N2078	Sopwith Baby	FAA Museum, RNAS Yeovilton	
N2276	Gloster Sea Gladiator II [H] (was N5226; really N5903)	The Shuttleworth Collection, FAA Museum, Yeovilton	
N2308	Gloster Gladiator I (G-AMRK) (really L8032) [HP-B]	The Shuttleworth Collection, Old Warden	
N2980	Vickers Wellington IA [R]	Brooklands Museum, Weybridge	
N3194	VS Spitfire I Replica [BAPC 220] [GR-Z]	RAF Biggin Hill, on display	
N3289	VS Spitfire I Replica (BAPC 65) [DW-K]	Kent Battle of Britain Museum, Hawkinge	
N3313	VS Spitfire Replica (BAPC 69) [QV-K]	Kent Battle of Britain Museum, Hawkinge	
N4389	Fairey Albacore [4M] (really N4172)	FAA Museum, RNAS Yeovilton	
N4877	Avro Anson I (G-AMDA) [VX-F]	Skyfame Collection, Duxford	
N5180	Sopwith Pup (G-EBKY)	Repainted as N6181, April 1993	
N5182	Sopwith Pup Replica (G-APUP)	RAF Museum, Hendon	
N5195	Sopwith Pup (G-ABOX)	Museum of Army Flying, Middle Wallop	
N5419	Bristol Scout D Replica (N5419)	RAF Museum/Skysport Engineering, Hatch	
N5492	Sopwith Triplane Replica (BAPC 111)	FAA Museum, RNAS Yeovilton	
N5628	Gloster Gladiator II	RAF Museum, Hendon	
N5912	Sopwith Triplane (8385M)	RAF Museum, Hendon	
N6004	Short Stirling I	RAeS Medway Branch, Rochester	
N6181	Sopwith Pup (G-EBKY/N5180)	The Shuttleworth Collection, Old Warden	
N6290	Sopwith Triplane Replica (G-BOCK)	The Shuttleworth Collection, Old Warden	
N6452	Sopwith Pup Replica (G-BIAU)	FAA Museum, RNAS Yeovilton	
N6466	DH Tiger Moth (G-ANKZ)	Privately owned, Barton	
N6720	DH Tiger Moth (7014M) [RUO-B]	No 1940 Sqn ATC, Levenshulme	
N6797	DH Tiger Moth (G-ANEH)	Privately owned, Chilbolton	
N6812	Sopwith F1 Camel	Imperial War Museum, Lambeth	
N6847	DH Tiger Moth (G-APAL)	Privately owned, Little Gransden	
N6848	DH Tiger Moth (G-BALX)	Privately owned, Headcorn	
N6965	DH Tiger Moth (G-AJTW) [FL-J]	Written off at Tibenham, 28 August 1993	
N6985	DH Tiger Moth (G-AHMN)	Museum of Army Flying, Middle Wallop	
N9191	DH Tiger Moth (G-ALND)	Privately owned, Shobdon	
N9389	DH Tiger Moth (G-ANJA)	Privately owned, Shipmeadow, Suffolk	
N9899	Supermarine Southampton I	RAF Museum Restoration Centre, Cardington	
P1344	HP Hampden I (9175M) [PL-K]	RAF Museum Restoration Centre, Cardington	
P1344	HP Hampden I (tail only) (parts from Hereford L6012)	RAF Museum, Hendon	
P2617	Hawker Hurricane I (8373M) [AF-A]	RAF Museum, Hendon	
P2793	Hawker Hurricane I Replica [SD-M]	Privately owned, Malton	
P3059	Hawker Hurricane I Replica (BAPC64) [SD-N]	Kent Battle of Britain Museum, Hawkinge	
P3175	Hawker Hurricane I (wreck)	RAF Museum, Hendon	
P3386	Hawker Hurricane I Replica (BAPC 218) [FT-A]	RAF Bentley Priory, on display	
P3395	Hawker Hurricane IV [JX-B] (really KX829)	Birmingham Museum of Science and Technology	
P3554	Hawker Hurricane I (composite)	The Air Defence Collection, Salisbury	

Notes	Serial	Type	Owner or Operator
	P4139	Fairey Swordfish II [5H] (really HS618/A2001)	FAA Museum, RNAS Yeovilton
	P5865	CCF Harvard 4 (G-BKCK) [LE-W]	Privately owned, North Weald
	P6382	Miles M.14A Hawk Trainer 3 (G-AJRS) [C]	The Shuttleworth Collection, Old Warden
	P7350	VS Spitfire IIA (G-AWIJ) [YT-F]	RAF Battle of Britain Memorial Flight, Coningsby
	P7540	VS Spitfire IIA [DU-W]	Dumfries & Galloway Aviation Museum, Tinwald Downs
	P8140	VS Spitfire II Replica (BAPC 71) [ZF-K]	Norfolk & Suffolk Av'n Museum, Flixton
	P8448	VS Spitfire II Replica (BAPC 225) [UM-D]	RAF Swanton Morley, on display
	P9444	VS Spitfire IA [RN-D]	Science Museum, South Kensington
	R1914	Miles Magister (G-AHUJ)	Privately owned, Strathallan
	R4897	DH Tiger Moth II (G-ERTY)	Privately owned, Hamstreet
	R4907	DH Tiger Moth II (G-ANCS)	Privately owned, Wreningham, Norfolk
	R5250	DH Tiger Moth II (G-AODT)	Privately owned, Tibenham
	R5868	Avro Lancaster I (7325M) [PO-S]	RAF Museum, Hendon
	R6915	VS Spitfire I	Imperial War Museum, Lambeth
	R9125	Westland Lysander III (8377M) [LX-L]	RAF Museum, Hendon
	R9371	HP Halifax II (cockpit)	Cotswold Aircraft Restoration Group, Innsworth
	S1287	Fairey Flycatcher Replica (G-BEYB) [5]	Privately owned, Duxford
	S1579	Hawker Nimrod I Replica (G-BBVO) [571]	Privately owned, Dunkeswell
	S1595	Supermarine S6B	Science Museum, South Kensington
	T5424	DH Tiger Moth II (G-AJOA)	Privately owned, Chiseldon
	T5493	DH Tiger Moth II (G-ANEF)	Privately owned, Cranwell North
	T5672	DH Tiger Moth II (G-ALRI)	Privately owned, Chalmington
	T5854	DH Tiger Moth II (G-ANKK)	Privately owned, Halfpenny Green
	T5879	DH Tiger Moth II (G-AXBW)	Privately owned, Tongham
	T5968	DH Tiger Moth II (G-ANNN)	Privately owned, Hollybush
	T6099	DH Tiger Moth II (G-AOGR/XL714)	Privately owned, Clacton
	T6256	DH Tiger Moth II	Privately owned, Cranfield
	T6269	DH Tiger Moth II (G-AMOU) [FOR-T]	Privately owned, Coventry
	T6296	DH Tiger Moth II (8387M)	RAF Museum, Hendon
	T6313	DH Tiger Moth II (G-AHVU)	Privately owned, Liphook
	T6818	DH Tiger Moth II (G-ANKT) [91]	The Shuttleworth Collection, Old Warden
	T6991	DH Tiger Moth II (G-ANOR/DE694)	Privately owned, Paddock Wood
	T7230	DH Tiger Moth II (G-AFVE)	Privately owned, Denham
	T7281	DH Tiger Moth II (G-ARTL)	Privately owned, Egton, nr Whitby
	T7404	DH Tiger Moth II (G-ANMV)	Privately owned, Booker
	T7471	DH Tiger Moth II (G-AJHU)	Privately owned, Compton Abbas
	T7909	DH Tiger Moth II (G-ANON)	Privately owned, Sherburn-in-Elmet
	T7997	DH Tiger Moth II (G-AOBH)	Repainted as G-AOBH
	T8191	DH Tiger Moth II	RN Historic Flight, stored Lee-on-Solent
	T9707	Miles Magister I (G-AKKR/8378M/ T9708)	Greater Manchester Museum of Science and Industry
	T9738	Miles Magister I (G-AKAT)	Privately owned, Breighton
	V1075	Miles Magister I (G-AKPF)	Privately owned, Shoreham
	V3388	Airspeed Oxford I (G-AHTW)	Imperial War Museum, Duxford
	V6028	Bristol Bolingbroke IVT (G-MKIV) (really RCAF 10038) [GB-D]	British Aerial Museum, Duxford (rear fuselage only)
	V7350	Hawker Hurricane I (fuselage)	Brenzett Aeronautical Museum
	V7467	Hawker Hurricane I Replica (BAPC 223) [LE-D]	RAF Coltishall, on display
	V7767	Hawker Hurricane I Replica (BAPC 72)	Privately owned, Sopley, Hants
	V9281	WS Lysander IIIA (G-BCWL) [RU-M]	Wessex Aviation & Transport, Henstridge
	V9300	WS Lysander IIIA (G-LIZY) [MA-J]	Painted as V9673
	V9441	WS Lysander IIIA (RCAF2355/ G-AZWT) [AR-A]	Privately owned, stored Strathallan
	V9673	WS Lysander IIIA (V9300/G-LIZY) [MA-J]	British Aerial Museum, Duxford

Serial	Type	Owner or Operator	Notes
W1048	HP Halifax II (8465M) [TL-S]	RAF Museum, Hendon	
W2718	VS Walrus I (G-RNLI)	Privately owned, Micheldever	
W4041	Gloster E28/39 [G]	Science Museum, South Kensington	
W4050	DH Mosquito	Mosquito Aircraft Museum, London Colney	
W5856	Fairey Swordfish IV (G-BMGC) [A2A]	RN Historic Flight, Yeovilton	
X4277	VS Spitfire LF.XVIe (7244M) (really TB382) [XT-M]	RAF Exhibition Flight, St Athan	
X4474	VS Spitfire LF.XVIe (7241M) (really TE311) [QV-I]	RAF Exhibition Flight, St Athan	
X4590	VS Spitfire I (8384M) [PR-F]	RAF Museum, Hendon	
X7688	Bristol Beaufighter I (3858M/ G-DINT)	Privately owned, Hatch	
Z2033	Fairey Firefly I (G-ASTL) [275]	Imperial War Museum, Duxford	
Z5722	Bristol Bolingbroke IVT (G-BPIV) (really RCAF 10201) [WM-Z]	British Aerial Museum, Duxford	
Z7015	Hawker Sea Hurricane IB (G-BKTH)	The Shuttleworth Collection, Duxford	
Z7197	Percival Proctor III (G-AKZN/ 8380M)	RAF Museum, Hendon	
Z7381	Hawker Hurricane XII (G-HURI) [XR-T]	The Fighter Collection, Duxford	
AA908	VS Spitfire Vb Replica (BAPC 230) [UM-W]	Eden Camp Theme Park, Malton	
AB130	VS Spitfire Va (parts)	Privately owned, Ludham	
AB910	VS Spitfire Vb [MD-E]	RAF BBMF, Coningsby	
AD540	VS Spitfire Vb (wreck)	Dumfries and Galloway Air Museum	
AE436	HP Hampden I (parts)	RAFM Restoration Centre, Cardington	
AL246	Grumman Martlet I	FAA Museum, RNAS Yeovilton	
AM561	Lockheed Hudson V (remains)	Cornwall Aero Park, Helston	
AP506	Cierva C30A (G-ACWM)	International Helicopter Museum, Weston-super-Mare	
AP507	Cierva C30A (G-ACWP) [KX-P]	Science Museum, South Kensington	
AR213	VS Spitfire Ia (G-AIST) [PR-O]	Privately owned, Booker	
AR501	VS Spitfire LF.Vc (G-AWII) (NN-A]	The Shuttleworth Collection, Old Warden	
AR614	VS Spitfire Vc (G-BUWA/7555M/ 5378M)	The Old Flying Machine Company, Duxford	
BB807	DH Tiger Moth (G-ADWO)	Southampton Hall of Aviation	
BE417	Hawker Hurricane XIIb (G-HURR) [AE-K]	Privately owned, Brooklands	
BE421	Hawker Hurricane IIc Replica (BAPC 205) [XP-G]	RAF Museum, Hendon	
BH229	Hawker Hurricane IIb	Privately owned, Lancing	
BL370	VS Spitfire Vb	Privately owned, Oxford	
BL614	VS Spitfire Vb (4354M) [ZD-F]	Greater Manchester Museum of Science and Industry	
BL628	VS Spitfire Vb (G-BTTN)	Privately owned, Thruxton	
BM597	VS Spitfire Vb (5718M/G-MKVB) [PR-O]	Privately owned, Audley End	
BN230	Hawker Hurricane IIc (5466M) (really LF751) [FT-A]	RAF Manston, Memorial Pavilion	
BR600	VS Spitfire IX Replica (BAPC 222) [SH-V]	RAF Uxbridge, on display	
BR600	VS Spitfire IX Replica (BAPC 224)	Ambassador Hotel, Norwich	
BR601	VS Spitfire IX	*To USA Nov 1992*	
BW853	Hawker Sea Hurricane XA (G-BRKE)	Privately owned, Milden	
BW881	Hawker Sea Hurricane XA	Privately owned, Milden	
DD931	Bristol Beaufort VIII (9131M) [L]	RAF Museum, Hendon	
DE208	DH Tiger Moth II (G-AGYU)	Privately owned, Ronaldsway	
DE363	DH Tiger Moth II (G-ANFC)	Military Aircraft Preservation Group, Hadfield, Derbyshire	
DE623	DH Tiger Moth II (G-ANFI)	Privately owned, St Athan	
DE673	DH Tiger Moth II (6948M/G-ADNZ)	Privately owned, Hampton	
DE970	DH Tiger Moth II (G-AOBJ)	Privately owned, Cardiff	
DE992	DH Tiger Moth II (G-AXXV)	Privately owned, Membury	
DF128	DH Tiger Moth II (G-AOJJ) [RCO-V]	Privately owned, Abingdon	

Notes	Serial	Type	Owner or Operator
	DF155	DH Tiger Moth II (G-ANFV)	Privately owned, Shempston Fm, Lossiemouth
	DF198	DH Tiger Moth II (G-BBRB)	Privately owned, Biggin Hill
	DG202	Gloster F9/40 (5758M) [G]	RAF Cosford Aerospace Museum
	DG590	Miles Hawk Major (8379M/ G-ADMW)	RAF Museum/Skysport Engineering Hatch
	DP872	Fairey Barracuda II (fuselage)	FAA Museum, stored Wroughton
	DR393	Hawker Hurricane IIa (P3351)	Privately owned, Lancing, W Sussex
	DR613	FW Wicko GM1 (G-AFJB)	Privately owned, stored Berkswell
DR628	Beech D.17S (N18V) [PB-1]	*Sold to the USA*
	DV372	Avro Lancaster I (cockpit)	Imperial War Museum, Lambeth
	EE416	Gloster Meteor F3 (cockpit)	Science Museum, Wroughton
	EE425	Gloster Meteor F3 (cockpit)	Rebel Air Museum, Earls Colne
	EE531	Gloster Meteor F4 (7090M)	Midland Air Museum, Coventry
	EE549	Gloster Meteor F4 (7008M)	Tangmere Military Aviation Museum
	EF545	VS Spitfire Vc	Privately owned, High Wycombe
	EJ693	Hawker Tempest V [SA-J]	Privately owned
	EM720	DH Tiger Moth II (G-AXAN)	Privately owned, Little Gransden
	EM727	DH Tiger Moth II (G-AOXN)	Privately owned, Yeovil
	EM903	DH Tiger Moth II (G-APBI)	Privately owned, Halstead
	EN224	VS Spitfire F.XII (G-FXII)	Privately owned, Newport Pagnell
EN343	VS Spitfire PR.XI Replica (BAPC 226)	RAF Benson, on display
EN398	VS Spitfire F.IX Replica (BAPC 190) [JE-J]	Aces High Ltd, North Weald
	EP120	VS Spitfire Vb (5377M/8070M)	Privately owned, Duxford
	EX976	NA Harvard III	FAA Museum, RNAS Yeovilton
	EZ259	NA Harvard IIA (G-BMJW)	Privately owned, Bracknell
	EZ407	NA Harvard IIA	RN Historic Flight, stored Lee-on-Solent
FB226	Bonsall Mustang Replica (G-BDWM) [MT-A]	Privately owned, Gamston
	FE695	NA Harvard IIB (Sw AF 16105/ G-BTXI)	The Fighter Collection, Duxford
	FE905	NA Harvard IIB (LN-BNM/12392)	Newark Air Museum, Winthorpe
	FE992	NA Harvard IIB (G-BDAM) [KT]	Privately owned, North Weald
	FH153	NA Harvard IIB (G-BBHK) [GW-A]	Privately owned, stored Cardiff
FR870	Curtiss Kittyhawk IV (NL1009N) [GA-S]	The Fighter Collection, Duxford
	FS728	NA Harvard IIB (G-BAFM)	Privately owned, Denham
	FS890	NA Harvard IIB (7554M)	A&AEE, stored Boscombe Down
	FT239	NA Harvard IV (G-BIWX)	Privately owned, North Weald
	FT375	NA Harvard IIB [5]	MoD(PE), A&AEE Boscombe Down
	FT391	NA Harvard IIB (G-AZBN)	Privately owned, Shoreham
FX301	NA Harvard III (G-JUDI) (really EX915)	Privately owned, Bryngwyn Bach, Clwyd
FX360	NA Harvard IIB (really KF435)	Booker Aircraft Museum
	FX442	NA Harvard IIB ♥	Privately owned, Bournemouth
FX760	Curtiss Kittyhawk IV (9150M) [GA-?]	RAF Museum, Hendon
HB275	Beech C-45 Expeditor II (N5063N/G-BKGM)	Privately owned, North Weald
	HB751	Fairchild Argus III (G-BCBL)	Privately owned, Little Gransden
	HH379	GAL48 Hotspur II (rear fuselage)	Museum of Army Flying, Middle Wallop
	HJ711	DH Mosquito NF.II [VI-C]	Night Fighter Preservation Tm, Elvington
	HM354	Percival Proctor III (G-ANPP)	Privately owned, Stansted
	HM580	Cierva C-30A (G-ACUU)	Imperial War Museum, Duxford
	HR792	HP Halifax II	*To LV907, July 1993*
	HS503	Fairey Swordfish IV (BAPC 108)	RAF Cosford Aerospace Museum, stored
HX922	DH Mosquito TT35 (G-AWJV) (really TA634) [EG-F]	*Repainted as TA634*
	JV482	Grumman Wildcat V	Ulster Aviation Society, Langford Lodge
JV928	PBY-5A Catalina (G-BLSC) [Y]	*Repainted as RCAF 9754*
	KB889	Avro Lancaster X (G-LANC) [NA-I]	Imperial War Museum, Duxford
	KB976	Avro Lancaster X (G-BCOH)	*Sold in the USA, February 1993*
	KB994	Avro Lancaster X (G-BVBP)	Aces High, North Weald
	KD431	CV Corsair IV [E2-M]	FAA Museum, RNAS Yeovilton
	KE209	Grumman Hellcat II	FAA Museum, RNAS Yeovilton
KE418	Hawker Tempest (rear fuselage)	RAF Museum Store, Cardington

Serial	Type	Owner or Operator	Notes
KF183	NA Harvard IIB [3]	MoD(PE) A&AEE Boscombe Down	
KF388	NA Harvard IIB (cockpit)	Privately owned, Bournemouth	
KF487	NA Harvard IIB (for spares)	The Fighter Collection, Duxford	
KF532	NA Harvard IIB (cockpit)	Newark Air Museum, Winthorpe	
KG374	Douglas Dakota IV [YS] (really KN645/8355M)	RAF Cosford Aerospace Museum	
KJ351	Airspeed Horsa II (BAPC 80) [23] (really TL659)	Museum of Army Flying, Middle Wallop	
KK995	Sikorsky Hoverfly I [E]	RAF Museum, Hendon	
KL161	NA Mitchell II (N88972)[VO-B]	The Fighter Collection, Duxford	
KN448	Douglas Dakota C4 (cockpit)	Science Museum, South Kensington	
KN751	Consolidated Liberator C.VI [F]	RAF Cosford Aerospace Museum	
KP208	Douglas Dakota IV [YS]	Airborne Forces Museum, Aldershot	
KZ191	Hawker Hurricane IV (frame only)	Privately owned, North Weald	
KZ321	Hawker Hurricane IV (G-HURY) [JV-N]	The Fighter Collection, Duxford	
LA198	VS Spitfire F21 (7118M) [RAI-G]	RAF, stored St Athan	
LA226	VS Spitfire F21 (7119M)	RAF, stored At Athan	
LA255	VS Spitfire F21 (6490M) [JX-U]	RAF No 1 Sqn, Wittering	
LA546	VS Seafire F46 (cockpit)	Privately owned, Colchester	
LA564	VS Seafire F46	Privately owned, Newport Pagnell	
LB294	Taylorcraft Plus D (G-AHWJ)	Museum of Army Flying, Whitchurch	
LB312	Taylorcraft Plus D (G-AHXE)	Privately owned, Shoreham	
LB335	Taylorcraft Plus D (G-AHGW)	Privately owned, Edge Hill	
LF363	Hawker Hurricane IIc (wreck)	RAF BBMF, stored Coningsby	
LF738	Hawker Hurricane IIc (5405M)	RAF, RAeS Medway Branch, Rochester	
LF858	DH Queen Bee (G-BLUZ)	Privately owned, Hatch	
LH208	Airspeed Horsa I (parts only) (8596M)	Museum of Army Flying, Middle Wallop	
LS326	Fairey Swordfish II (G-AJVH) [L2]	RN Historic Flight, RNAS Yeovilton	
LV907	HP Halifax III (HR792) [NP-F]	Yorkshire Air Museum, Elvington	
LZ551	DH Vampire [G]	FAA Museum, RNAS Yeovilton	
LZ766	Percival Proctor III (G-ALCK)	Skyfame Collection, Duxford	
LZ842	VS Spitfire IX	Privately owned, Battle, Sussex	
MF628	Vickers Wellington T10	RAF Museum, Hendon	
MH434	VS Spitfire HF.IXb (G-ASJV)] [ZD-B]	The Old Flying Machine Company, Duxford	
MH486	VS Spitfire LF.IX Replica (BAPC 206) [FF-A]	RAF Museum, Hendon	
MH603	VS Spitfire IX	Privately owned, Stretton, Cheshire	
MH777	VS Spitfire IX Replica (BAPC 221) [RF-N]	RAF Northolt, on display	
MJ627	VS Spitfire T.IX (G-ASOZ/ G-BMSB)	Privately owned, Coventry	
MJ730	VS Spitfire HF.IXe (G-HFIX) [GZ-?]	Privately owned, East Midlands Airport	
MK356	VS Spitfire IX (5690M)	RAF BBMF, St Athan	
MK732	VS Spitfire LF.IX (G-HVDM/ 8633M)	To The Netherlands as H-25, June 1993	
MK805	VS Spitfire LF.IX Replica [SH-B]	Privately owned, Lowestoft	
MK912	VS Spitfire LF.IXe (SM-29/ G-BRRA) [MN-P]	Privately owned, Paddock Wood	
ML407	VS Spitfire T.IX (G-LFIX) [OU-V]	Privately owned, Duxford	
ML417	VS Spitfire LF.IXe (G-BJSG) [21-T]	Privately owned, Duxford	
ML427	VS Spitfire IX (6457M) [I-ST]	Birmingham Museum of Science & Industry	
ML796	Short Sunderland V	Imperial War Museum, Duxford	
ML814	Short Sunderland III (G-BJHS)	Sold to USA, 20 July 1993	
ML824	Short Sunderland V [NS-Z]	RAF Museum, Hendon	
MN235	Hawker Typhoon IB	RAF Museum, Hendon	
MP425	Airspeed Oxford I (G-AITB)	Newark Air Museum, Winthorpe	
MT438	Auster III (G-AREI)	Museum of Army Flying, Middle Wallop	
MT719	VS Spitfire LF.VIIIc (G-VIII) [YB-J]	Sold to USA as N719MT, June 1993	
MT847	VS Spitfire FR.XIVe (6960M) [AX-H]	RAF Cosford Aerospace Museum	
MT928	VS Spitfire HF.VIII (G-BKMI/ A58-671/MV154) [ZX-M]	Privately owned, Filton	
MV154	VS Spitfire HF.VIII	Repainted as MT928, April 1993	
MV262	VS Spitfire FR.XIV (G-CCVV)	Privately owned, Booker	
MV293	VS Spitfire FR.XIV (G-SPIT/ G-BGHB) (MV363) [OI-C]	Privately owned, Duxford	

19

Notes	Serial	Type	Owner or Operator
	MV370	VS Spitfire FR.XIV (G-FXIV) [EB-Q]	Sold to Germany, 1992
	MW376	Hawker Tempest II (G-BSHW/ IAFHA564)	Privately owned, Audley End
	MW401	Hawker Tempest II (G-PEST/ IAF HA604)	Privately owned, Brooklands
	MW404	Hawker Tempest II (IAF HA557)	Privately owned, Brooklands
	MW467	VS Spitfire V Replica (BAPC 202)	Privately owned, Llanbedr
	MW758	Hawker Tempest II (IAF HA580)	Privately owned, Chichester
	MW763	Hawker Tempest II (G-TEMT/ IAF HA586)	Privately owned, Brooklands
	NF370	Fairey Swordfish III	Imperial War Museum, Duxford
	NF389	Fairey Swordfish III [5B]	RN Historic Flight, BAe Brough
	NF875	DH Dominie (G-AGTM) [603/CH]	Reverted to G-AGTM, 1993
	NH238	VS Spitfire LF.IX (N238V/G-MKIX)	Sold to the USA, 1992
	NH799	VS Spitfire FR.XIV (G-BUZU) [AP-V]	Privately owned, Audley End
	NJ673	Auster 5D (G-AOCR)	Privately owned, Wellesbourne Mountford
	NJ695	Auster 4 (G-AJXV)	Privately owned, Tollerton
	NJ703	Auster 5 (G-AKPI)	Privately owned, Ingoldmells
	NJ719	Auster 5 (G-ANFU) (really TW385)	North-East Aircraft Museum, Usworth
	NL750	DH Tiger Moth II (T7997/G-AOBH)	Privately owned, Compton Abbas
	NL879	DH Tiger Moth II (G-AVPJ)	Repainted as G-AVPJ
	NL985	DH Tiger Moth I (7015M)	Vintage Aircraft Team, Cranfield
	NM181	DH Tiger Moth I (G-AZGZ)	Privately owned, Rush Green
	NP181	Percival Proctor IV (G-AOAR)	Privately owned, Biggin Hill
	NP184	Percival Proctor IV (G-ANYP) [K]	Privately owned, Chatteris
	NP294	Percival Proctor IV [TB-M]	Lincolnshire Aviation Heritage Centre, East Kirkby
	NP303	Percival Proctor IV (G-ANZJ)	Privately owned, Byfleet, Surrey
	NV778	Hawker Tempest TT5 (8386M)	RAFM Restoration Centre, Cardington
	NX611	Avro Lancaster B.VII (8375M/ G-ASXX) [YF-C]	Lincolnshire Aviation Heritage Centre, East Kirkby
	PA474	Avro Lancaster B.I [PM-M²]	RAF BBMF, Coningsby
	PF179	HS Gnat T1 (XR541/8602M)	Privately owned, Worksop
	PK624	VS Spitfire F22 (8072M) [RAU-T]	RAF, stored St Athan
	PK664	VS Spitfire F22 (7759M) [V6-B]	RAF, stored St Athan
	PK683	VS Spitfire F24 (7150M)	Southampton Hall of Aviation
	PK724	VS Spitfire F24 (7288M)	RAF Museum, Hendon
	PL344	VS Spitfire LF.IXe (G-IXCC)	Privately owned, Booker
	PL965	VS Spitfire PR.XI (G-MKXI) [F]	The Old Flying Machine Co, Duxford
	PL983	VS Spitfire PR.XI (G-PRXI) ▶	Warbirds of GB, Bournemouth
	PM631	VS Spitfire PR.XIX [N]	RAF BBMF, Coningsby
	PM651	VS Spitfire PR.XIX (7758M) [X]	RAF, stored St Athan
	PN323	HP Halifax VII (cockpit)	Imperial War Museum, Lambeth
	PP566	Fairey Firefly I (fuselage)	South Yorkshire Av'n Museum, Firbeck
	PP972	VS Seafire L.IIIc (G-BUAR)[6M-D]	To USA, March 1993
	PR536	Hawker Tempest II (IAF HA457) [OQ-H]	RAF Museum, Hendon
	PS853	VS Spitfire PR.XIX [C]	RAF BBMF, Coningsby
	PS915	VS Spitfire PR.XIX (7548M/7711M) [P]	RAF BBMF, Coningsby
	PT462	VS Spitfire T.IX (G-CTIX)	Privately owned, Duxford
	PV202	VS Spitfire T.IX (G-TRIX) [VZ-M]	Privately owned, Denham
	PZ865	Hawker Hurricane IIc (G-AMAU) [J]	RAF BBMF, Coningsby
	RA848	Slingsby Cadet TX1	Privately owned, Leeds
	RA854	Slingsby Cadet TX1	Privately owned, Harrogate
	RA897	Slingsby Cadet TX1	Newark Air Museum store, Hucknall
	RD253	Bristol Beaufighter TF.X (7931M)	RAF Museum, Hendon
	RF342	Avro Lincoln B.II (G-29-1/G-APRJ)	To USA, November 1992
	RF398	Avro Lincoln B.II (8376M)	RAF Cosford Aerospace Museum
	RG333	Miles Messenger IIA (G-AIEK)	Privately owned, Felton, Bristol
	RG333	Miles Messenger IIA (G-AKEZ)	Privately owned, Chelmsford
	RH377	Miles Messenger 4A (G-ALAH)	Privately owned, Stretton, Cheshire
	RH746	Bristol Brigand TF1	North-East Aircraft Museum, Usworth
	RL962	DH Dominie II (G-AHED)	RAF Museum Store, Cardington
	RM221	Percival Proctor IV (G-ANXR)	Privately owned, Biggin Hill
	RN201	VS Spitfire F.XIV (SG-31/G-BSKP)	Privately owned, Paddock Wood

Serial	Type	Owner or Operator	Notes
RN218	Isaacs Spitfire Replica (G-BBJI)[N]	Privately owned, Langham	
RR232	VS Spitfire HF.IXc (G-BRSF)	Privately owned, Lancing, Sussex	
RR299	DH Mosquito T.III (G-ASKH) [HT-E]	British Aerospace, Hawarden	
RT486	Auster 5 (G-AJGJ) [PF-A]	Privately owned, Old Sarum	
RT520	Auster 5 (G-ALYB)	South Yorkshire Av'n Museum, Firbeck	
RW382	VS Spitfire LF.XVIe (7245M/ 8075M/G-XVIA) [NG-C]	Privately owned, Audley End	
RW386	VS Spitfire LF.XVIe (6944M/ G-BXVI) [RAK-A]	Privately owned, Audley End	
RW388	VS Spitfire LF.XVIe (6946M) [U4-U]	Stoke-on-Trent City Museum, Hanley	
RW393	VS Spitfire LF.XVIe (7293M) [XT-A]	RAF, stored St Athan	
RX168	VS Seafire L.IIIc	Privately owned, High Wycombe	
SL542	VS Spitfire LF.XVIe (8390M) [4M-N]	Privately owned, Hatch	
SL674	VS Spitfire LF.IX (8392M) [RAS-H]	RAF, stored St Athan	
SM520	VS Spitfire LF.IX	Privately owned, Oxford	
SM832	VS Spitfire F.XIV (G-WWII)	The Fighter Collection, Duxford	
SM845	VS Spitfire FR.XVIII (G-BUOS)	Privately owned, Mitcheldever	
SM969	VS Spitfire F.XVIIIe (G-BRAF) [D-A]	To USA, November 1992	
SX137	VS Seafire F.XVII	FAA Museum, RNAS Yeovilton	
SX300	VS Seafire F.XVII (A646/A696/ A2054)	Privately owned, Warwick	
SX336	VS Seafire F.XVII (A2055/ G-BRMG)	Privately owned, Twyford, Berks	
TA122	DH Mosquito FB.VI [UP-G]	Mosquito Aircraft Museum, London Colney	
TA634	DH Mosquito TT35 (G-AWJV) [8K-K]	Mosquito Aircraft Museum, London Colney	
TA639	DH Mosquito TT35 (7806M) [AZ-E]	RAF Cosford Aerospace Museum	
TA719	DH Mosquito TT35 (G-ASKC) [6T]	Skyfame Collection, Duxford	
TA805	VS Spitfire IX	Privately owned, Battle, East Sussex	
TB252	VS Spitfire LF.XVIe (G-XVIE) (7257M/7281M/8073M) [GW-H]	Privately owned, Audley End	
TB752	VS Spitfire LF.XVIe (7256M/ 7279M/8086M) [KH-Z]	RAF Manston, Memorial Pavilion	
TB885	VS Spitfire LF.XVIe	Shoreham Aircraft Preservation Society	
TD248	VS Spitfire LF.XVIe (7246M/ G-OXVI) [D]	Privately owned, Earls Colne	
TE184	VS Spitfire LF.XVIe (G-MXVI)	Privately owned, East Midlands	
TE392	VS Spitfire LF.XVIe (7000M/ 8074M)	To USA, November 1992	
TE462	VS Spitfire LF.XVIe (7243M)	Royal Scottish Museum of Flight, East Fortune	
TE476	VS Spitfire LF.XVIe (G-XVIB/ N476TE)	Privately owned, Booker	
TE517	VS Spitfire LF.IX (G-BIXP/G-CCIX)	To USA, November 1992	
TE566	VS Spitfire LF.IXe (G-BLCK) [DU-A]	Privately owned, Audley End	
TG263	Saro SR.A1 (G-12-1) [P]	Southampton Hall of Aviation	
TG511	HP Hastings C1 (8554M)	RAF Cosford Aerospace Museum	
TG517	HP Hastings T5 [517]	Newark Air Museum, Winthorpe	
TG528	HP Hastings C1A	Skyfame Collection, Duxford	
TJ118	DH Mosquito TT35 (cockpit)	Mosquito Aircraft Museum, stored	
TJ138	DH Mosquito B35 (7607M) [VO-L]	RAF Museum, Hendon	
TJ343	Auster 5 (G-AJXC)	Privately owned, stored Hook	
TJ398	Auster 5 (BAPC 70)	Aircraft Preservation Society of Scotland, East Fortune	
TJ569	Auster 5 (G-AKOW)	Museum of Army Flying, Middle Wallop	
TJ672	Auster 5D (G-ANIJ)	Privately owned, RAF Swanton Morley	
TJ704	Beagle A.61 Terrier 2 (G-ASCD) [JA]	Yorkshire Air Museum, Elvington	
TK718	GAL Hamilcar I	Royal Tank Museum, Bovington	
TK777	GAL Hamilcar I (fuselage)	Museum of Army Flying, Middle Wallop	
TL615	Airspeed Horsa II	Robertsbridge Aviation Society	
TP298	VS Spitfire FR.XVIII	Sold to USA as N41702	
TS291	Slingsby Cadet TX1 (BGA852)	Royal Scottish Museum of Flight, East Fortune	

Notes	Serial	Type	Owner or Operator
	TS423	Douglas Dakota C3 (G-DAKS)	Aces High Ltd, North Weald
	TS798	Avro York C1 (G-AGNV/*MW100*)	RAF Cosford Aerospace Museum
	TV959	DH Mosquito T.III [AF-V]	The Fighter Collection, stored Duxford
	TV959	DH Mosquito T.III Replica	Privately owned, Heald Green, Cheshire
	TW384	Auster 5 (G-ANHZ)	Privately owned, Headcorn
	TW439	Auster 5 (G-ANRP)	Privately owned, Exeter
	TW448	Auster 5 (G-ANLU)	Privately owned, Hedge End
	TW467	Auster 5 (G-ANIE) [ROD-F]	Privately owned, Abingdon
	TW511	Auster 5 (G-APAF)	Privately owned, Skegness
	TW536	Auster AOP6 (7704M/G-BNGE) [TS-V]	Privately owned, Middle Wallop
	TW591	Auster 6A (G-ARIH) [N]	Privately owned, Abbots Bromley
	TW641	Beagle A.61 Terrier 2 (G-ATDN)	Privately owned, Biggin Hill
	TX183	Avro Anson C.XIX (G-BSMF)	Privately owned, Arbroath
	TX213	Avro Anson C.XIX (G-AWRS)	North-East Aircraft Museum, Usworth
	TX214	Avro Anson C.XIX (7817M)	RAF Cosford Aerospace Museum
	TX226	Avro Anson C.XIX (7865M)	Imperial War Museum, Duxford
	TX228	Avro Anson C.XIX	City of Norwich Aviation Museum
	TX235	Avro Anson C.XIX	Caernarfon Air World
	VD165	Slingsby T7 Kite	Privately owned, Dunstable
	VF301	DH Vampire F1 (7060M) [RAL-B]	Midland Air Museum, Coventry
	VF516	Beagle A.61 Terrier 2 (G-ASMZ) [T]	Privately owned, Crediton
	VF526	Auster 6A (G-ARXU) [T]	Privately owned, Middle Wallop
	VF548	Beagle A.61 Terrier 1 (G-ASEG)	Privately owned, Dunkeswell
	VH127	Fairey Firefly TT4 [200/R]	FAA Museum, stored RNAS Yeovilton
	VL348	Avro Anson C19 (G-AVVO)	Newark Air Museum, Winthorpe
	VL349	Avro Anson C19 (G-AWSA)	Norfolk & Suffolk Aviation Museum, Flixton
	VM325	Avro Anson C19	Midland Air Museum, Coventry
	VM360	Avro Anson C19 (G-APHV)	Royal Scottish Museum of Flight, East Fortune
	VM791	Slingsby Cadet TX3 (really XA312) (8876M)	No 135 Redhill & Reigate Sqn ATC, RAF Kenley
	VN148	Grunau Baby IIb (BAPC 33/ BGA2400)	Privately owned, Dunstable
	VN485	VS Spitfire F24 (7326M)	Imperial War Museum, Duxford
	VP519	Avro Anson C19 (G-AVVR) (cockpit)	Macclesfield Historical Aviation Society, Marthall
	VP952	DH Devon C2 (8820M)	RAF Cosford Aerospace Museum
	VP955	DH Devon C2 (G-DVON)	Privately owned, Old Sarum
	VP957	DH Devon C2 (8822M) (cockpit)	No 1137 Sqn ATC, Belfast
	VP959	DH Devon C2 [L]	MoD(PE), DRA West Freugh
	VP967	DH Devon C2 (G-KOOL)	East Surrey Technical College, Redhill
	VP968	DH Devon C2	A&AEE Boscombe Down, derelict
	VP971	DH Devon C2 (8824M)	FSCTE, RAF Manston
	VP975	DH Devon C2 [M]	Science Museum, Wroughton
	VP976	DH Devon C2 (8784M)	RAF Northolt Fire Section
	VP977	DH Devon C2 (G-ALTS)	DRA West Freugh Fire Section
	VP978	DH Devon C2 (8553M)	RAF Brize Norton, instructional use
	VP981	DH Devon C2	RAF BBMF, Coningsby
	VR137	Westland Wyvern TF1	FAA Museum, RNAS Yeovilton
	VR192	Pervical Prentice T1 (G-APIT)	Second World War Aircraft Preservation Society, Lasham
	VR249	Percival Prentice T1 (G-APIY) [FA-EL]	Newark Air Museum, Winthorpe
	VR259	Percival Prentice T1 (G-APJB)	Privately owned, Coventry
	VR930	Hawker Sea Fury FB11 (8382M)	RN Historic Flight, stored Lee-on-Solent
	VS356	Percival Prentice T1 (G-AOLU)	Privately owned, Stonehaven
	VS517	Avro Anson T20	RN, stored Lee-on-Solent
	VS562	Avro Anson T21 (8012M)	Maes Artro Craft Village, Llanbedr
	VS610	Percival Prentice T1 (G-AOKL) [K-L]	Privately owned, Nayland
	VS623	Percival Prentice T1 (G-AOKZ) [KQ-F]	Midland Air Museum, Coventry
	VT260	Gloster Meteor F4 (8813M) [67]	South Yorks Aircraft Preservation Society, Firbeck
	VT409	Fairey Firefly AS5 (mostly WD889)	North-East Aircraft Museum, Usworth
	VT812	DH Vampire F3 (7200M) [N]	RAF Museum, Hendon
	VT935	Boulton Paul P111A (VT769)	Midland Air Museum, Coventry
	VT987	Auster AOP6 (G-BKXP)	Privately owned, Little Gransden, Cambs
	VV106	Supermarine 510 (7175M)	RN, stored Lee-on-Solent

Serial	Type	Owner or Operator	Notes
VV119	Supermarine 535 (7285M) (cockpit)	Lincolnshire Aviation Museum, East Kirkby	
VV217	DH Vampire FB5 (7323M)	North-East Aircraft Museum, Usworth	
VV901	Avro Anson T21	Yorkshire Air Museum, Elvington	
VW453	Gloster Meteor T7 (8703M)	RAF Innsworth, on display	
VW985	Auster AOP6 (G-ASEF)	Privately owned, Upper Arncott, Oxon	
VX118	Auster AOP6 (G-ASNB)	Privately owned, Kingston Deverill	
VX147	Alon A2 Aircoupe (G-AVIL)	Privately owned, Headcorn	
VX185	EE Canberra B(I)8 (7631M) (cockpit)	Science Museum, Wroughton	
VX250	DH Sea Hornet 21 [48] (rear fuselage)	Mosquito Aircraft Museum, London Colney	
VX272	Hawker P1052 (7174M)	RN, Lee-on-Solent, stored	
VX275	Slingsby Sedbergh TX1 (8884M) (BGA 572)	RAF Museum Restoration Centre, Cardington	
VX461	DH Vampire FB5 (7646M)	RAF Cosford Aerospace Museum, stored	
VX573	Vickers Valetta C2 (8389M)	RAF Cosford Aerospace Museum, stored	
VX577	Vickers Valetta C2	North-East Aircraft Museum, Usworth	
VX580	Vickers Valetta C2	Norfolk & Suffolk Av'n Museum, Flixton	
VX595	WS51 Dragonfly HR1 [29]	Gosport Aviation Society, HMS *Sultan*	
VX653	Hawker Sea Fury FB11 (G-BUCM)	The Fighter Collection, Duxford	
VX926	Auster T7 (G-ASKJ)	Privately owned, Little Gransden	
VZ304	DH Vampire FB6 (G-MKVI/ J-1167)[A-T]	Vintage Aircraft Team, Bruntingthorpe	
VZ345	Hawker Sea Fury T20S	RN Historic Flight, Yeovilton	
VZ462	Gloster Meteor F8	Second World War Aircraft Preservation Society, stored	
VZ467	Gloster Meteor F8 (G-METE)	Privately owned, RAF Cosford	
VZ477	Gloster Meteor F8 (7741M) (cockpit)	Midland Air Museum, Coventry	
VZ608	Gloster Meteor FR9	Newark Air Museum, Winthorpe	
VZ634	Gloster Meteor T7 (8657M)	Newark Air Museum, Winthorpe	
VZ638	Gloster Meteor T7 (G-JETM) [HF]	Privately owned, Charlwood, Surrey	
VZ728	RS4 Desford Trainer (G-AGOS)	Leicestershire Museum of Science & Technology, Coalville	
VZ962	WS51 Dragonfly HR1 [904]	International Helicopter Museum, Weston-super-Mare	
VZ965	WS51 Dragonfly HR5	FAA Museum, at RNAS Culdrose	
WA473	VS Attacker F1 [102/J]	FAA Museum, stored RNAS Yeovilton	
WA576	Bristol Sycamore 3 (7900M/ G-ALSS)	Dumfries & Galloway Aviation Museum, Tinwald Downs	
WA577	Bristol Sycamore 3 (7718M/ G-ALST)	North-East Aircraft Museum, Usworth	
WA591	Gloster Meteor T7 (7917M) [W]	Meteor Flight, stored Yatesbury	
WA630	Gloster Meteor T7 [69] (cockpit)	Robertsbridge Aviation Museum, Mayfield	
WA634	Gloster Meteor T7/8	RAF Cosford Aerospace Museum	
WA638	Gloster Meteor T7	Martin Baker Aircraft, Chalgrove	
WA662	Gloster Meteor T7	Derby WW2 Avionics Museum	
WA984	Gloster Meteor F8 [A]	Tangmere Military Aviation Museum	
WB188	Hawker Hunter F3 (7154M)	Tangmere Military Aviation Museum	
WB271	Fairey Firefly AS5 [204/R]	RN Historic Flight, RNAS Yeovilton	
WB440	Fairey Firefly AS6 (cockpit)	South Yorkshire Aviation Museum, Firbeck	
WB491	Avro Ashton 2 (TS897/G-AJJW) (cockpit)	Wales Aircraft Museum, Cardiff	
WB550	DH Chipmunk T10 [F]	RAF No 6 AEF, Benson	
WB556	DH Chipmunk T10	RAFGSA, Bicester	
WB560	DH Chipmunk T10	RAF No 4 AEF, Exeter	
WB565	DH Chipmunk T10 [X]	AAC BFWF, Middle Wallop	
WB567	DH Chipmunk T10	RAF No 12 AEF, Turnhouse	
WB569	DH Chipmunk T10 [R]	RAF No 5 AEF, Cambridge	
WB575	DH Chipmunk T10 [907]	RN Flying Grading Flt, Plymouth	
WB584	DH Chipmunk T10 PAX (7706M)	No 327 Sqn ATC, Kilmarnock	
WB585	DH Chipmunk T10 (G-AOSY) [RCU-X]	Privately owned, Blackbushe	
WB586	DH Chipmunk T10 [A]	RAF No 6 AEF, Benson	
WB588	DH Chipmunk T10 (G-AOTD) [D]	Shuttleworth Collection, Old Warden	
WB615	DH Chipmunk T10 [E]	AAC BFWF, Middle Wallop	
WB624	DH Chipmunk T10 PAX	The Aeroplane Collection, Long Marston	
WB626	DH Chipmunk T10 PAX	Privately owned, Swanton Morley	
WB627	DH Chipmunk T10 [N]	RAF No 5 AEF, Cambridge	
WB647	DH Chipmunk T10 [R]	AAC BFWF, Middle Wallop	

Notes	Serial	Type	Owner or Operator
	WB652	DH Chipmunk T10 [V]	RAF No 5 AEF, Cambridge
	WB654	DH Chipmunk T10 [T]	RAF No 3 AEF, Colerne
	WB657	DH Chipmunk T10 [908]	RN Flying Grading Flt, Plymouth
	WB660	DH Chipmunk T10 (G-ARMB)	Privately owned, Shipdham
	WB670	DH Chipmunk T10 (8361M)	No 1312 Sqn ATC, Southend
	WB671	DH Chipmunk T10 [910]	RN Flying Grading Flt, Plymouth
	WB685	DH Chipmunk T10 PAX	North-East Aircraft Museum, Usworth
	WB693	DH Chipmunk T10 [S]	AAC BFWF, Middle Wallop
	WB697	DH Chipmunk T10 [90]	RAF No 10 AEF, Woodvale
	WB702	DH Chipmunk T10 (G-AOFE)	Privately owned, Goodwood
	WB703	DH Chipmunk T10 (G-ARMC)	Privately owned, White Waltham
	WB732	DH Chipmunk T10 (G-AOJZ/ G-ASTD)	Repainted as G-AOJZ
	WB739	DH Chipmunk T10 [8]	RAF No 8 AEF, Shawbury
	WB754	DH Chipmunk T10 [H]	AAC BFWF, Middle Wallop
	WB758	DH Chipmunk T10 (7729M) [P]	Privately owned, Torbay
	WB763	DH Chipmunk T10 (G-BBMR) [14]	Southall Technical College
	WB971	Slingsby T21B (BGA 3324)	Became BGA 3324
	WB981	Slingsby T21B (BGA3238)	Privately owned, Aston Down
	WB990	Slingsby T21B (BGA 3148)	Became BGA 3148
	WD286	DH Chipmunk T10 (G-BBND) [J]	Privately owned, Bourn
	WD288	DH Chipmunk T10 (G-AOSO) [38]	Privately owned, Charlton Park, Wilts
	WD289	DH Chipmunk T10 [N]	RAF No 3 AEF, Colerne
	WD292	DH Chipmunk T10 (G-BCRX)	Privately owned, Old Sarum
	WD293	DH Chipmunk T10 PAX (7645M)	No 1367 Sqn ATC, Caerleon
	WD305	DH Chipmunk T10 (G-ARGG)	Privately owned, Coventry
	WD310	DH Chipmunk T10 [H]	RAF No 3 AEF, Colerne
	WD318	DH Chipmunk T10 PAX (8207M)	RAF No 1 SoTT, Halton
	WD325	DH Chipmunk T10 [N]	AAC BFWF, Middle Wallop
	WD331	DH Chipmunk T10 [A,6]	RAF Benson (on repair)
	WD355	DH Chipmunk T10 PAX	No 1955 Sqn ATC, Wells, Somerset
	WD356	DH Chipmunk T10 (7625M)	Privately owned, St Ives, Cambridgeshire
	WD363	DH Chipmunk T10 (G-BCIH) [5]	Privately owned, Andrewsfield
	WD370	DH Chipmunk T10 PAX	No 176 Sqn ATC, Hove
	WD373	DH Chipmunk T10 [12]	RAF No 2 AEF, Bournemouth
	WD374	DH Chipmunk T10 [903]	RN Flying Grading Flt, Plymouth
	WD379	DH Chipmunk T10 (WB696/ G-APLO) [K]	Privately owned, Jersey
	WD386	DH Chipmunk T10 PAX (cockpit)	Wiltshire Historic Aviation Group
	WD388	DH Chipmunk T10 (G-BDIC)	Privately owned, Woodvale
	WD390	DH Chipmunk T10 [68]	RAF No 9 AEF, Finningley
	WD413	Avro Anson T21 (7881M/G-BFIR)	Privately owned, Lee-on-Solent
	WD646	Gloster Meteor TT20 (8189M) [R]	Privately owned, North Weald
	WD686	Gloster Meteor NF11	Muckleburgh Collection, Weybourne
	WD790	Gloster Meteor NF11 (8743M) (cockpit)	North-East Aircraft Museum, Usworth
	WD931	EE Canberra B2 (cockpit)	RAF Cosford Aerospace Museum
	WD935	EE Canberra B2 (8440M) (cockpit)	Privately owned, Egham
	WD954	EE Canberra B2 (cockpit)	Privately owned, Romford, Essex
	WD955	EE Canberra T17A [EM]	RAF No 360 Sqn, Wyton
	WE113	EE Canberra T4 (cockpit)	Privately owned, Woodhurst, Cambs
	WE122	EE Canberra TT18 (845) (cockpit)	Privately owned, North Weald
	WE139	EE Canberra PR3 (8369M)	RAF Museum, Hendon
	WE168	EE Canberra PR3 (8049M) (cockpit)	Privately owned, Colchester
	WE188	EE Canberra T4	Solway Aviation Society, Carlisle
	WE402	DH Venom FB50 (G-VENI/J-1523)	Privately owned, Bournemouth
	WE569	Auster T7 (G-ASAJ)	Privately owned, Middle Wallop
	WE600	Auster T7(mod) (7602M)	RAF Cosford Aerospace Museum
	WE925	Gloster Meteor F8	Privately owned, Yatesbury
	WE982	Slingsby Prefect TX1 (8781M)	RAF Cosford Aerospace Museum
	WE990	Slingsby Prefect TX1 (BGA 2583)	Privately owned, RAF Swanton Morley
	WF118	Percival Sea Prince T1 (G-DACA)	Privately owned, Charlwood, Surrey
	WF122	Percival Sea Prince T1 (A2673) [575/CU]	Flambards Village Theme Park, Helston
	WF125	Percival Sea Prince T1 (A2674) [576]	RN Predannack Fire School
	WF128	Percival Sea Prince T1 (8611M) Flixton	Norfolk & Suffolk Aviation Museum,

Serial	Type	Owner or Operator	Notes
WF137	Percival Sea Prince C1	Second World War Aircraft Preservation Society, Lasham	
WF225	Hawker Sea Hawk F1 (A2645) [CU]	RNAS Culdrose, at main gate	
WF259	Hawker Sea Hawk F2 (A2483) [171/A]	Royal Scottish Museum of Flight, East Fortune	
WF369	Vickers Varsity T1 [F]	Newark Air Museum, Winthorpe	
WF372	Vickers Varsity T1 [T]	Brooklands Museum, Weybridge	
WF376	Vickers Varsity T1	Bristol Airport Fire Section	
WF408	Vickers Varsity T1 (8395M)	RAF Northolt, for ground instruction	
WF410	Vickers Varsity T1 [F]	Brunel Technical College, Lulsgate	
WF425	Vickers Varsity T1	*Scrapped at Duxford, October 93*	
WF643	Gloster Meteor F8 [X]	Norfolk & Suffolk Aviation Museum, Flixton	
WF714	Gloster Meteor F8 (really WK914)	The Old Flying Machine Co, Duxford	
WF784	Gloster Meteor T7 (7895M)	RAF Quedgeley, at main gate	
WF825	Gloster Meteor T7 (8359M) [A]	Avon Aviation Museum, stored Yatesbury	
WF877	Gloster Meteor T7 (G-BPOA)	Aces High Ltd, North Weald	
WF890	EE Canberra T17 [EJ]	RAF Wyton, Fire Section	
WF911	EE Canberra B2 (cockpit)	Pennine Aviation Museum, store	
WF916	EE Canberra T17 [EL]	RAF No 360 Sqn, Wyton	
WF922	EE Canberra PR3	Midland Air Museum, Coventry	
WG300	DH Chipmunk T10 PAX	RAFGSA, Bicester	
WG303	DH Chipmunk T10 PAX (8208M)	RAFGSA, Bicester	
WG307	DH Chipmunk T10 (G-BCYJ)	Privately owned, Shempston Farm, Lossiemouth	
WG308	DH Chipmunk T10 [71]	RAF No 7 AEF, Newton	
WG316	DH Chipmunk T10 (G-BCAH)	Privately owned, Shoreham	
WG321	DH Chipmunk T10 [G]	AAC BFWF, Middle Wallop	
WG323	DH Chipmunk T10 [F]	AAC BFWF, Middle Wallop	
WG348	DH Chipmunk T10 (G-BBMV)	Privately owned, Moulton St Mary	
WG350	DH Chipmunk T10 (G-BPAL)	Privately owned, Popham	
WG362	DH Chipmunk T10 PAX (8437M/ 8630M)	RAF Swinderby, instructional use	
WG403	DH Chipmunk T10 [O] (wreck)	AAC, Middle Wallop	
WG407	DH Chipmunk T10 [67]	RAF No 9 AEF, Finningley	
WG418	DH Chipmunk T10 PAX (8209M/ G-ATDY)	RAF No 10 AEF, Woodvale	
WG419	DH Chipmunk T10 PAX (8206M)	No 1053 Sqn ATC, Armthorpe	
WG422	DH Chipmunk T10 (8394M/ G-BFAX) [16]	Privately owned, St Just	
WG430	DH Chipmunk T10 [3]	RAF No 1 AEF, Manston	
WG432	DH Chipmunk T10 [L]	AAC BFWF, Middle Wallop	
WG458	DH Chipmunk T10 [B]	RAF No 4 AEF, Exeter	
WG463	DH Chipmunk T10 PAX (8363M/ G-ATDX)	No 188 Sqn ATC, Ipswich	
WG465	DH Chipmunk T10 (G-BCEY)	Privately owned, White Waltham	
WG466	DH Chipmunk T10	RAF Gatow Station Flight, Berlin	
WG469	DH Chipmunk T10 [72]	RAF No 7 AEF, Newton	
WG471	DH Chipmunk T10 PAX (8210M)	No 301 Sqn ATC, Bury St Edmunds	
WG472	DH Chipmunk T10 (G-AOTY)	Privately owned, Netherthorpe	
WG477	DH Chipmunk T10 PAX (8362M/ G-ATDI/G-ATDP)	No 281 Sqn ATC, Birkdale	
WG478	DH Chipmunk T10 [L]	RAF, stored Shawbury	
WG479	DH Chipmunk T10 [K]	RAF No 12 AEF, Turnhouse	
WG480	DH Chipmunk T10 [D]	RAF No 7 AEF, Newton	
WG486	DH Chipmunk T10	RAF Gatow Station Flight, Berlin	
WG511	Avro Shackleton T4 (fuselage)	Flambards Village Theme Park, Helston	
WG718	WS51 Dragonfly HR3 (A2531) [934]	Privately owned, Long Marston	
WG719	WS51 Dragonfly HR5 (G-BRMA) [902]	International Helicopter Museum, Weston-super-Mare	
WG724	WS51 Dragonfly HR5 [932]	North-East Aircraft Museum, Usworth	
WG751	WS51 Dragonfly HR5	Privately owned, Ramsgreave, Lancs	
WG754	WS51 Dragonfly HR3 (7703M) (really WG725) [912/CU]	Flambards Village Theme Park, Helston	
WG760	EE P1A (7755M)	RAF Cosford Aerospace Museum	
WG763	EE P1A (7816M)	Greater Manchester Museum of Science and Industry	
WG768	Short SB5 (8005M)	RAF Cosford Aerospace Museum	
WG774	BAC 221	Science Museum, RNAS Yeovilton	
WG777	Fairey FD2 (7986M)	RAF Cosford Aerospace Museum	
WG789	EE Canberra B2/6 (cockpit)	Booker Aircraft Museum	

Notes	Serial	Type	Owner or Operator
	WH132	Gloster Meteor T7 (7906M) [J]	No 276 Sqn ATC, Chelmsford
	WH166	Gloster Meteor T7 (8052M)	Privately owned, Birlingham, Worcs
	WH291	Gloster Meteor F8	Second World War Aircraft Preservation Society, Lasham
	WH301	Gloster Meteor F8 (7930M) [T]	RAF Museum, Hendon
	WH364	Gloster Meteor F8 (8169M)	Avon Aviation Museum, stored Yatesbury
	WH453	Gloster Meteor D16 [L]	MoD(PE), stored T&EE Llanbedr
	WH646	EE Canberra T17A [EG]	RAF No 360 Sqn, Wyton
	WH657	EE Canberra B2	Brenzett Aeronautical Museum
	WH665	EE Canberra T17 (8763M) [J]	BAe Filton, Fire Section
	WH699	EE Canberra B2T (8755M) (really WJ637)	RAFC Cranwell, Trenchard Hall on display
	WH724	EE Canberra T19 (cockpit)	RAF Shawbury Fire Section
	WH725	EE Canberra B2	Imperial War Museum, Duxford
	WH734	EE Canberra TT18	MoD(PE) T&EE, Llanbedr
	WH740	EE Canberra T17 (8762M) [K]	East Midlands Airport Aero Park
	WH773	EE Canberra PR7 (8696M)	Privately owned, Charlwood, Surrey
	WH775	EE Canberra PR7 (8128M/8868M) [O]	RAF No 2 SoTT, Cosford
	WH779	EE Canberra PR7 [BP]	RAF No 360 Sqn, Wyton
	WH780	EE Canberra T22 (minus cockpit)	RAF St Athan, Fire Section
	WH791	EE Canberra PR7 (8165M/8176M/ 8187M)	RAF Cottesmore, at main gate
	WH797	EE Canberra T22 (minus cockpit)	RAF St Athan, Fire Section
	WH840	EE Canberra T4 (8350M)(cockpit)	Staffordshire Aviation Museum, Seighford
	WH846	EE Canberra T4	Yorkshire Air Museum, Elvington
	WH849	EE Canberra T4 [BE]	RAF St Athan, stored
	WH850	EE Canberra T4	Macclesfield Historical Aviation Society, Marthall
	WH854	EE Canberra T4 (cockpit)	Martin Baker Aircraft, Chalgrove
	WH863	EE Canberra T17 (8693M) (cockpit)	Newark Air Museum, Winthorpe
	WH869	EE Canberra B2 (8515M)	*Scrapped by June 1992*
	WH887	EE Canberra TT18 [847]	MoD(PE) stored, T&EE Llanbedr
	WH902	EE Canberra T17 [EK]	RAF No 360 Sqn, Wyton
	WH903	EE Canberra B2 (5854M) (cockpit)	Privately owned, Charlwood, Surrey
	WH904	EE Canberra T19 [04]	Newark Air Museum, Winthorpe
	WH946	EE Canberra B6(mod)(8185M) (cockpit)	Privately owned, Tetney, Grimsby
	WH952	EE Canberra B6	Royal Arsenal, Woolwich
	WH953	EE Canberra B6(mod)	MoD(PE), DRA Bedford
	WH957	EE Canberra E15 (8869M) (cockpit)	Privately owned, Bruntingthorpe
	WH960	EE Canberra B15 (8344M) (cockpit)	Privately owned, Bruntingthorpe
	WH964	EE Canberra E15 (8870M) (cockpit)	Privately owned, Bruntingthorpe
	WH981	EE Canberra E15 [CN]	RAF Wyton, Fire Section
	WH984	EE Canberra B15 (8101M) (cockpit)	Privately owned, Bruntingthorpe
	WH991	WS51 Dragonfly HR3	Privately owned, Storwood, East Yorks
	WJ231	Hawker Sea Fury FB11 [115/O] (really WE726)	FAA Museum, Yeovilton
	WJ237	WAR Sea Fury Replica (G-BLTG) [113/O]	Privately owned, Langham
	WJ350	Percival Sea Prince C2	*Burned by April 1993*
	WJ358	Auster AOP6 (G-ARYD)	Museum of Army Flying, stored Middle Wallop
	WJ565	EE Canberra T17 (8871M) (cockpit)	Privately owned, Bruntingthorpe
	WJ574	EE Canberra TT18 [844]	MoD(PE), stored T&EE Llanbedr
	WJ576	EE Canberra T17	Wales Aircraft Museum, Cardiff
	WJ607	EE Canberra T17A [EB]	RAF No 360 Sqn, Wyton
	WJ614	EE Canberra TT18 [846]	RAF, stored St Athan
	WJ629	EE Canberra TT18 (8747M) [845]	RAF Chivenor, BDRT
	WJ630	EE Canberra T17 [ED]	RAF Wyton, Fire Section
	WJ633	EE Canberra T17A [EF]	*Scrapped at Wyton*
	WJ636	EE Canberra TT18 [CX]	RAF Wyton, Fire Section
	WJ639	EE Canberra TT18 [39]	North-East Aircraft Museum, Usworth
	WJ676	EE Canberra B2 (7796M) (cockpit)	Science Museum, Wroughton
	WJ677	EE Canberra B2 (cockpit)	RN, stored Culdrose
	WJ678	EE Canberra B2 (8864M) [CF]	*Scrapped by June 1992*

Serial	Type	Owner or Operator	Notes
WJ680	EE Canberra TT18 (G-BURM) [CT]	Privately owned, Duxford	
WJ717	EE Canberra TT18 (9052M)	RAF CTTS, St Athan	
WJ721	EE Canberra TT18 [21]	Pennine Aviation Museum, Bacup	
WJ731	EE Canberra B2T [BK]	RAF Wyton	
WJ756	EE Canberra E15 [BB]	RAF Wyton, Fire Section	
WJ775	EE Canberra B6 (8581M) [J] (fuselage)	FSCTE, RAF Manston	
WJ815	EE Canberra PR7 (8729M)	RAF Coningsby Fire Section	
WJ817	EE Canberra PR7 (8695M) [FU2]	RAF Wyton, Fire Section	
WJ821	EE Canberra PR7 (8668M)	Bassingbourn, on display	
WJ861	EE Canberra T4 [BF]	RAF St Athan, Fire Section	
WJ863	EE Canberra T4 (cockpit)	Cambridge Airport Fire Section	
WJ865	EE Canberra T4	MoD(PE) Farnborough, Fire Section	
WJ866	EE Canberra T4 [BL]	RAF No 360 Sqn, Wyton	
WJ872	EE Canberra T4 (8492M) (cockpit)	No 327 Sqn ATC, Kilmarnock	
WJ874	EE Canberra T4 [BM]	RAF No 360 Sqn, Wyton	
WJ876	EE Canberra T4 (cockpit)	RAF Exhibition Flight, St Athan	
WJ880	EE Canberra T4 (8491M) [39] (cockpit)	South Yorkshire Aviation Museum, Firbeck	
WJ893	Vickers Varsity T1	T&EE Aberporth Fire Section	
WJ903	Vickers Varsity T1 [C] (cockpit)	Dumfries & Galloway Aviation Museum, Tinwald Downs	
WJ944	Vickers Varsity T1	Wales Aircraft Museum, Cardiff	
WJ945	Vickers Varsity T1 (G-BEDV) [21]	IWM, Duxford	
WJ975	EE Canberra T19 [S]	Bomber County Aviation Museum, Hemswell	
WJ981	EE Canberra T17A [EN]	RAF No 360 Sqn, Wyton	
WJ986	EE Canberra T17A [EP]	RAF No 360 Sqn, Wyton	
WJ992	EE Canberra T4	MoD(PE), stored Bedford	
WK102	EE Canberra T17 (8780M) [EQ] (cockpit)	Privately owned, Bruntingthorpe	
WK111	EE Canberra T17 [EA]	RAF No 360 Sqn, Wyton	
WK119	EE Canberra B2 (cockpit)	RAF Wyton, Fire Section	
WK122	EE Canberra TT18 [22]	Flambards Village Theme Park, Helston	
WK124	EE Canberra TT18 (9093M) [CR]	FSCTE, RAF Manston	
WK126	EE Canberra TT18 [843]	RN, stored St Athan	
WK127	EE Canberra TT18 (8985M) [FO] (minus cockpit)	*Scrapped at Wyton, September 1993*	
WK127	EE Canberra TT18 (cockpit)	RAF Wyton Fire Section	
WK128	EE Canberra B2	MoD(PE) T&EE, Llanbedr	
WK142	EE Canberra TT18 [848]	RN, stored St Athan	
WK143	EE Canberra B2	T&EE Llanbedr Fire Section	
WK162	EE Canberra B2 (8887M) [CA]	RAF Wyton Fire Section	
WK163	EE Canberra B6	MoD(PE) DRA Bedford	
WK198	VS Swift F4 (7428M)	North-East Aircraft Museum, Usworth	
WK275	VS Swift F4	Privately owned, Upper Hill, nr Leominster	
WK277	VS Swift FR5 (7719M) [N]	Newark Air Museum, Winthorpe	
WK281	VS Swift FR5 (7712M) [S]	RAF Museum, Hendon	
WK511	DH Chipmunk T10 (G-BVBT) [905]	Kennet Aircraft, Cranfield	
WK512	DH Chipmunk T10 [A]	AAC BFWF, Middle Wallop	
WK517	DH Chipmunk T10 [84]	RAF No 11 AEF, Leeming	
WK518	DH Chipmunk T10	RAF BBMF, Coningsby	
WK522	DH Chipmunk T10 (G-BCOU)	Privately owned, High Easter	
WK549	DH Chipmunk T10 (G-BTWF) [Y]	Privately owned, Rufforth	
WK550	DH Chipmunk T10 [J]	RAF No 8 AEF, Shawbury	
WK554	DH Chipmunk T10 [4]	RAF No 1 AEF, Manston	
WK558	DH Chipmunk T10 (G-ARMG)	Privately owned, Wellesbourne Mountford	
WK559	DH Chipmunk T10 [M]	AAC BFWF, Middle Wallop	
WK562	DH Chipmunk T10 [91]	RAF No 10 AEF, Woodvale	
WK570	DH Chipmunk T10 PAX (8211M)	No 424 Sqn ATC, Southampton	
WK572	DH Chipmunk T10 [92]	RAF No 10 AEF, Woodvale	
WK574	DH Chipmunk T10	RN, stored Shawbury	
WK576	DH Chipmunk T10 PAX (8357M)	No 1206 Sqn ATC, Lichfield	
WK585	DH Chipmunk T10	RAF No 12 AEF, Turnhouse	
WK586	DH Chipmunk T10 [X]	RAF No 3 AEF, Colerne	
WK587	DH Chipmunk T10 PAX (8212M)		
WK589	DH Chipmunk T10 [C]	RAF No 6 AEF, Benson	
WK590	DH Chipmunk T10 [69]	RAF No 9 AEF, Finningley	
WK608	DH Chipmunk T10 [906]	RN Historic Flt, Yeovilton	
WK609	DH Chipmunk T10 [93]	RAF No 10 AEF, Woodvale	
WK611	DH Chipmunk T10 (G-ARWB)	Privately owned, White Waltham	

Notes	Serial	Type	Owner or Operator
	WK613	DH Chipmunk T10 [P]	Pennine Aviation Museum, Bacup
	WK620	DH Chipmunk T10 [T]	AAC, Middle Wallop
	WK621	DH Chipmunk T10 (G-BDBL)	Privately owned, Shoreham
	WK622	DH Chipmunk T10 (G-BCZH)	Privately owned, Horsford
	WK624	DH Chipmunk T10 [N]	RAF No 3 AEF, Colerne
	WK626	DH Chipmunk T10 PAX (8213M)	No 358 Sqn ATC, Welling, Kent
	WK628	DH Chipmunk T10 (G-BBMW)	Privately owned, Shoreham
	WK630	DH Chipmunk T10 [11] ●	RAF No 2 AEF, Bournemouth
	WK633	DH Chipmunk T10 [B]	RAF, stored Shawbury
	WK634	DH Chipmunk T10 [902]	RN Flying Grading Flt, Plymouth
	WK635	DH Chipmunk T10	RN, stored Shawbury
	WK638	DH Chipmunk T10 [83]	RAF No 11 AEF, Leeming
	WK639	DH Chipmunk T10 [L]	RAF No 3 AEF, Colerne
	WK640	DH Chipmunk T10 [C]	RAF No 3 AEF, Colerne
	WK642	DH Chipmunk T10 [94]	RAF No 10 AEF, Woodvale
	WK643	DH Chipmunk T10 [G]	RAF No 7 AEF, Newton
	WK654	Gloster Meteor F8 (8092M) [X]	RAF Neatishead, at main gate
	WK800	Gloster Meteor D16 [Z]	MoD(PE) T&EE, Llanbedr
	WK864	Gloster Meteor F8 (7750M) [C] (really WL168)	RAF Finningley on display
	WK935	Gloster Meteor Prone Pilot (7869M)	RAF Cosford Aerospace Museum
	WK991	Gloster Meteor F8 (7825M)	Imperial War Museum, Duxford
	WL131	Gloster Meteor F8 (7751M) (cockpit)	4th Guernsey (Forest) Air Scouts, Guernsey Airport
	WL181	Gloster Meteor F8 [X]	North-East Aircraft Museum, Usworth
	WL332	Gloster Meteor T7	Stratford Aircraft Collection, Long Marston
	WL345	Gloster Meteor T7	Privately owned, Hollington, E Sussex
	WL349	Gloster Meteor T7 [Z]	Gloucestershire Airport, on display
	WL360	Gloster Meteor T7 (7920M) [G]	Gloucestershire Aviation Collection, Hucclecote
	WL375	Gloster Meteor T7	Dumfries & Galloway Aviation Museum, Tinwald Downs
	WL405	Gloster Meteor T7 (spares)	Martin Baker Aircraft, Chalgrove
	WL419	Gloster Meteor T7	Martin Baker Aircraft, Chalgrove
	WL505	DH Vampire FB9 (7705M/G-FBIX)	Privately owned, Cranfield
	WL626	Vickers Varsity T1 (G-BHDD) [P]	East Midlands Airport Aero Park
	WL627	Vickers Varsity T1 (8488M) [D] (cockpit)	Privately owned, Preston, Humberside
	WL635	Vickers Varsity T1	RAF Machrihanish Police School
	WL679	Vickers Varsity T1 (9155M)	RAF Cosford Aerospace Museum
	WL732	BP Sea Balliol T21	RAF Cosford Aerospace Museum
	WL756	Avro Shackleton AEW2 (9101M)	RAF St Mawgan, Fire Section
	WL790	Avro Shackleton AEW2	Shackleton Preservation Trust, Coventry
	WL795	Avro Shackleton MR2C (8753M)	RAF St Mawgan, on display
	WL798	Avro Shackleton MR2C (8114M) [T] (cockpit)	Privately owned, Elgin
	WL925	Slingsby Cadet TX3 (cockpit) (really WV925)	RAF No 633 VGS, Cosford
	WM145	AW Meteor NF11 (cockpit)	N Yorks Aircraft Recovery Centre, Chop Gate
	WM167	AW Meteor NF11 (G-LOSM) ●	Jet Heritage Ltd, Bournemouth
	WM223	AW Meteor TT20	Second World War Aircraft Preservation Society, Lasham
	WM267	Gloster Meteor NF11 (cockpit)	Night Fighter Preservation Group, Elvington
	WM292	AW Meteor TT20 [841]	Wales Aircraft Museum, Cardiff
	WM311	AW Meteor TT20 (8177M) (really WM224)	Privately owned, North Weald
	WM366	AW Meteor NF13 (4X-FNA)	Second World War Aircraft Preservation Society, Lasham
	WM367	AW Meteor NF13 (cockpit)	Privately owned, North Weald
	WM571	DH Sea Venom FAW21 [VL]	Southampton Hall of Aviation
	WM729	DH Vampire NF10 (pod) [A]	Privately owned, Ruislip
	WM913	Hawker Sea Hawk FB5 (A2510/ 8162M) [456/J]	Newark Air Museum, Winthorpe
	WM961	Hawker Sea Hawk FB5 (A2517) [J]	Caernarfon Air World
	WM969	Hawker Sea Hawk FB5 (A2530) [10/Z]	Imperial War Museum, Duxford
	WM993	Hawker Sea Hawk FB5 (A2522) [034]	Privately owned, Peasedown St John, Avon

Serial	Type	Owner or Operator	Notes
WM994	Hawker Sea Hawk FB5 (A2503/ ● G-SEAH)	Jet Heritage Ltd, Bournemouth	
WN105	Hawker Sea Hawk FB3 (A2662/ A2509/8164M) (really WF299)	Privately owned, Birlingham, Worcs	
WN108	Hawker Sea Hawk FB5 [033]	Ulster Aviation Society, Langford Lodge	
WN149	BP Balliol T2 (cockpit)	Boulton-Paul Society, Wolverhampton	
WN493	WS51 Dragonfly HR5	FAA Museum, RNAS Yeovilton	
WN499	WS51 Dragonfly HR5 [Y]	Caernarfon Air World	
WN516	BP Balliol T2 (cockpit)	North-East Aircraft Museum, Usworth	
WN534	BP Balliol T2 (cockpit)	Boulton-Paul Society, Wolverhampton	
WN890	Hawker Hunter F2 (cockpit)	Privately owned, Chandlers Ford, Hants	
WN904	Hawker Hunter F2 (7544M) [3]	RE 39 Regt, Waterbeach, on display	
WN907	Hawker Hunter F2 (7416M) (cockpit)	Blyth Valley Aviation Collection, Walpole	
WP180	Hawker Hunter F5 (7582M/8473M) [K] (really WP190)	RAF Stanbridge, at main gate	
WP185	Hawker Hunter F5 (7583M)	RAF Abingdon, on display	
WP250	DH Vampire NF10 (cockpit)	Privately owned, Tamworth	
WP255	DH Vampire NF10 (pod)	South Yorkshire Aviation Museum, Firbeck	
WP270	EoN Eton TX1 (8598M)	Greater Manchester Museum of Science and Industry	
WP271	EoN Eton TX1	Privately owned, stored, Keevil	
WP309	Percival Sea Prince T1 [570/CU]	RNAS Yeovilton Fire Section	
WP313	Percival Sea Prince T1 [568/CU]	FAA Museum, stored	
WP314	Percival Sea Prince T1 (8634M) [573/CU]	Privately owned, Preston, Humberside	
WP321	Percival Sea Prince T1 (G-BRFC) [750/CU]	Privately owned, Bourn	
WP503	WS51 Dragonfly HR3 [901]	Privately owned, Storwood, East Yorks	
WP515	EE Canberra B2 (cockpit)	Wales Aircraft Museum, Cardiff	
WP772	DH Chipmunk T10 [Q]	AAC, stored St Athan	
WP776	DH Chipmunk T10 [817/CU]	RN, stored Shawbury	
WP784	DH Chipmunk T10 PAX	Privately owned, Boston	
WP786	DH Chipmunk T10 [G]	RAF No 6 AEF, Benson	
WP788	DH Chipmunk T10 (G-BCHL)	Privately owned, Sleap	
WP790	DH Chipmunk T10 (G-BBNC) [T]	Mosquito Aircraft Museum, London Colney	
WP795	DH Chipmunk T10 [901]	RN Flying Grading Flt, Plymouth	
WP800	DH Chipmunk T10 (G-BCXN) [2]	Privately owned, Halton	
WP801	DH Chipmunk T10 [911]	RN Flying Grading Flt, Plymouth	
WP803	DH Chipmunk T10 [C]	RAF No 4 AEF, Exeter	
WP805	DH Chipmunk T10 [D]	RAF No 6 AEF, Benson	
WP808	DH Chipmunk T10 (G-BDEU)	Privately owned, Binham	
WP809	DH Chipmunk T10 [778]	RN stored, Shawbury	
WP833	DH Chipmunk T10 [A]	RAF No 4 AEF, Exeter	
WP835	DH Chipmunk T10 (G-BDCB)	Privately owned, Rochester	
WP837	DH Chipmunk T10 [A]	RAF No 5 AEF, Cambridge	
WP839	DH Chipmunk T10 [A]	RAF No 8 AEF, Shawbury	
WP840	DH Chipmunk T10 [9] ●	RAF No 6 AEF, Bournemouth	
WP843	DH Chipmunk T10 (G-BDBP) [F]	Based at Rotterdam, The Netherlands	
WP844	DH Chipmunk T10 [85]	RAF No 11 AEF, Leeming	
WP845	DH Chipmunk T10 PAX	No 1329 Sqn ATC, Stroud	
WP855	DH Chipmunk T10 [5]	RAF No 1 AEF, Manston	
WP856	DH Chipmunk T10 [904]	RN Flying Grading Flt, Plymouth	
WP857	DH Chipmunk T10 (G-BDRJ)[24]	Privately owned, Elstree	
WP859	DH Chipmunk T10 [E]	RAF No 8 AEF, Shawbury	
WP860	DH Chipmunk T10	RAF No 12 AEF, Turnhouse	
WP863	DH Chipmunk T10 PAX (8360M/G-ATJI)	No 2293 Sqn ATC, Marlborough	
WP864	DH Chipmunk T10 PAX (8214M)	RAF No 7 AEF, Newton	
WP869	DH Chipmunk T10 PAX (8215M)	RAF	
WP871	DH Chipmunk T10 [W]	AAC BFWF, Middle Wallop	
WP872	DH Chipmunk T10	RAF No 12 AEF, Turnhouse	
WP896	DH Chipmunk T10 [M]	RAF No 3 AEF, Colerne	
WP900	DH Chipmunk T10 [V]	RAF No 3 AEF, Colerne	
WP901	DH Chipmunk T10 [B]	RAF No 6 AEF, Benson	
WP903	DH Chipmunk T10 (G-BCGC)	RN Gliding Club, Culdrose	
WP904	DH Chipmunk T10 [909]	RN Flying Grading Flt, Plymouth	
WP906	DH Chipmunk T10 [816/CU]	RN, stored Shawbury	
WP907	DH Chipmunk T10 PAX (7970M)	Privately owned, Reading	
WP912	DH Chipmunk T10 (8467M)	RAF Cosford Aerospace Museum	
WP914	DH Chipmunk T10 [E]	RAF No 6 AEF, Benson	
WP920	DH Chipmunk T10 [10]	RAF No 2 AEF, Bournemouth	

Notes	Serial	Type	Owner or Operator
	WP921	DH Chipmunk T10 PAX	No 1924 Sqn ATC, Croydon
	WP925	DH Chipmunk T10 [C]	AAC BFWF, Middle Wallop
	WP927	DH Chipmunk T10 PAX (8216M/G-ATJK)	No 247 Sqn ATC, Ashton-under-Lyne
	WP928	DH Chipmunk T10 [D]	AAC BFWF, Middle Wallop
	WP929	DH Chipmunk T10 [F]	RAF No 8 AEF, Shawbury
	WP930	DH Chipmunk T10 [J]	AAC BFWF, Middle Wallop
	WP962	DH Chipmunk T10 [C]	RAF No 5 AEF, Teversham
	WP964	DH Chipmunk T10 [Y]	AAC BFWF, Middle Wallop
	WP967	DH Chipmunk T10	RAF No 12 AEF, Turnhouse
	WP970	DH Chipmunk T10 [T]	RAF No 5 AEF, Cambridge
	WP971	DH Chipmunk T10 (G-ATHD)	Privately owned, Denham
	WP972	DH Chipmunk T10 PAX(8667M)	CSDE, RAF Swanton Morley
	WP974	DH Chipmunk T10 [96]	RAF No 10 AEF, Woodvale
WP976	DH Chipmunk T10 (G-APTS) (really WP791)	Privately owned, Booker
	WP977	DH Chipmunk T10 (G-BHRD) [N]	Privately owned, Kidlington
	WP978	DH Chipmunk T10 PAX (7467M) ◗	RAF No 2 AEF, Bournemouth
	WP979	DH Chipmunk T10 [J]	CSDE, RAF Swanton Morley
	WP980	DH Chipmunk T10 [E]	*Crashed RAF St Athan, 26 August 1993*
	WP981	DH Chipmunk T10 [D]	RAF No 5 AEF, Cambridge
	WP983	DH Chipmunk T10 [B]	AAC BFWF, Middle Wallop
	WP984	DH Chipmunk T10 [73]	RAF No 7 AEF, Newton
	WR410	DH Venom FB54 (J1790/G-BLKA) [N]	Vintage Aircraft Team, Bruntingthorpe
	WR539	DH Venom FB4 (8399M) [F]	Mosquito Aircraft Museum, London Colney
	WR960	Avro Shackleton AEW2 (8772M)	Greater Manchester Museum of Science and Industry
	WR963	Avro Shackleton AEW2	Air Atlantique, Coventry
	WR971	Avro Shackleton MR3 (8119M) [Q]	Privately owned, Narborough, Norfolk
	WR974	Avro Shackleton MR3 (8117M) [K]	Privately owned, Charlwood, Surrey
	WR977	Avro Shackleton MR3 (8186M) [B]	Newark Air Museum, Winthorpe
	WR982	Avro Shackleton MR3 (8106M) [J]	Privately owned, Charlwood, Surrey
	WR985	Avro Shackleton MR3 (8103M)	Stratford Aircraft Collection, Long Marston
	WS103	Gloster Meteor T7 [709/VL]	FAA Museum, Crawley College
	WS692	Gloster Meteor NF12 (7605M) [C]	Newark Air Museum, Winthorpe
	WS726	Gloster Meteor NF14 (7960M) [G]	No 1855 Sqn ATC, Royton
	WS739	Gloster Meteor NF14 (7961M)	Newark Air Museum, Winthorpe
	WS760	Gloster Meteor NF14 (7964M)	Classic Jet Aircraft Collection, Loughborough
	WS774	Gloster Meteor NF14 (7959M)	Privately owned, Fearn, Cambs
	WS776	Gloster Meteor NF14 (7716M) [K]	RAF North Luffenham, at main gate
	WS788	Gloster Meteor NF14 (7967M) [Z]	Yorkshire Air Museum, Elvington
	WS792	Gloster Meteor NF14 (7965M) [K]	Privately owned, Brighouse Bay, D&G
	WS807	Gloster Meteor NF14 (7973M) [N]	Privately owned, Yatesbury
	WS832	Gloster Meteor NF14 [W]	Solway Aviation Society, Carlisle Airport
	WS838	Gloster Meteor NF14	Midland Air Museum, Coventry
	WS843	Gloster Meteor NF14 (7937M) [Y]	RAF Museum, Hendon
	WT121	Douglas Skyraider AEW1 (WT983) [415/CU]	FAA Museum, stored RNAS Yeovilton
	WT212	EE Canberra B2	*Scrapped at Macclesfield*
	WT301	EE Canberra B6(mod)	Defence School, Chattenden
	WT308	EE Canberra B(I)6	RN, Predannack Fire School
	WT309	EE Canberra B(I)6	A&AEE Boscombe Down, Apprentice School
	WT327	EE Canberra B(I)8	MoD(PE) DRA Bedford
	WT333	EE Canberra B(I)8	Privately owned, Bedford
	WT339	EE Canberra B(I)8 (8198M)	RAF Barkston Heath Fire Section
	WT346	EE Canberra B(I)8 (8197M)	*To New Zealand, February 1993*
	WT480	EE Canberra T4 [BC]	RAF No 360 Sqn, Wyton
	WT482	EE Canberra T4 (cockpit)	Stratford Aircraft Collection, Long Marston
	WT483	EE Canberra T4 [83]	Stratford Aircraft Collection, Long Marston
	WT486	EE Canberra T4 (8102M) [C]	Belfast Airport Fire Section
	WT488	EE Canberra T4	BAe Dunsfold Fire Section
	WT507	EE Canberra PR7 (8131M/8548M) [44] (cockpit)	No 384 Sqn ATC, Mansfield
	WT509	EE Canberra PR7 [BR]	RAF No 360 Sqn, Wyton
	WT518	EE Canberra PR7 (8133M/8691M) (rear fuselage only)	Cardiff Airport Fire Section
	WT519	EE Canberra PR7 [CH] .	*Scrapped at Wyton, September 1993*

Serial	Type	Owner or Operator	Notes
WT520	EE Canberra PR7 (8094M/8184M) (cockpit)	Privately owned, Burntwood, Staffs	
WT532	EE Canberra PR7 (8728M/8890M) [Z]	Lovaux Ltd, Bournemouth, derelict	
WT534	EE Canberra PR7 (8549M) [43] (cockpit)	No 492 Sqn ATC, Shirley, W. Midlands	
WT536	EE Canberra PR7 (8063M)	Privately owned, Bruntingthorpe	
WT537	EE Canberra PR7	BAe Samlesbury, on display	
WT555	Hawker Hunter F1 (7499M)	Privately owned, Greenford, London	
WT569	Hawker Hunter F1 (7491M)	No 2117 Sqn ATC, Kenfig Hill, Mid-Glamorgan	
WT612	Hawker Hunter F1 (7496M)	RAF Henlow on display	
WT619	Hawker Hunter F1 (7525M)	Greater Manchester Museum of Science and Industry	
WT648	Hawker Hunter F1 (7530M) (cockpit)	The Air Defence Collection, Salisbury	
WT651	Hawker Hunter F1 [C]	Newark Air Museum, Winthorpe	
WT660	Hawker Hunter F1 (7421M) [C]	RAF, stored Carlisle	
WT680	Hawker Hunter F1 (7533M) [Z]	No 1429 Sqn ATC, at T&EE Aberporth	
WT684	Hawker Hunter F1 (7422M)	RAF Brize Norton Fire Section	
WT694	Hawker Hunter F1 (7510M)	RAF Newton, at main gate	
WT711	Hawker Hunter GA11 [833/DD]	RNAS Culdrose, SAH	
WT720	Hawker Hunter F51 (8565M) [B] (really E-408)	RAF Sealand, on display	
WT722	Hawker Hunter T8C [878/VL]	RN FRADU, Yeovilton	
WT723	Hawker Hunter PR11 [866/VL]	RN SAH, Culdrose	
WT744	Hawker Hunter GA11 [868/VL]	RN FRADU, Yeovilton	
WT745	Hawker Hunter T8C (fuselage)	Scrapped at Bournemouth, 1992	
WT746	Hawker Hunter F4 (7770M) [A]	Army, Saighton, Chester	
WT799	Hawker Hunter T8C [879]	RN, stored Shawbury	
WT804	Hawker Hunter GA11 [831/DD]	RNAS Culdrose, SAH	
WT806	Hawker Hunter GA11	RAF, stored Shawbury	
WT859	Supermarine 544 (cockpit)	Privately owned, South Ruislip	
WT867	Slingsby Cadet TX3	Privately owned, Eaglescott	
WT899	Slingsby Cadet TX3	Privately owned, Rush Green	
WT902	Slingsby Cadet TX3 (BGA 3147)	Privately owned, Lleweni Parc, Clwyd	
WT905	Slingsby Cadet TX3	Aberdeen Technical College	
WT910	Slingsby Cadet TX3	Privately owned, Clapham	
WT933	Bristol Sycamore 3 (G-ALSW/ 7709M)	Newark Air Museum, Winthorpe	
WV106	Douglas Skyraider AEW1 [427/C]	Flambards Village Theme Park, Helston	
WV198	S55 Whirlwind HAR21 (G-BJWY/ A2576) [K]	South Yorkshire Aviation Museum, Firbeck	
WV256	Hawker Hunter GA11 [862/VL]	RN FRADU, Yeovilton	
WV267	Hawker Hunter GA11 [836/DD]	RNAS Culdrose, SAH	
WV276	Hawker Hunter F4 (7847M) [D]	MoD(PE) DRA, Farnborough	
WV309	Hawker Hunter F51 (really E-409)	Wales Aircraft Museum, Cardiff	
WV318	Hawker Hunter T7B [A]	RAF stored Lossiemouth	
WV322	Hawker Hunter T8C (9096M) [Y]	SIF, RAFC Cranwell	
WV332	Hawker Hunter F4 (7673M) (cockpit)	No 1254 Sqn ATC, Godalming	
WV372	Hawker Hunter T7 [877/VL]	RN SAH, Culdrose	
WV381	Hawker Hunter GA11 [732/VL]	BNFL, Culham, Oxon	
WV383	Hawker Hunter T7	MoD(PE) DRA Farnborough	
WV396	Hawker Hunter T8C [879/VL]	RN FRADU, Yeovilton	
WV483	Percival Provost T1 (7693M)[N-E]	Privately owned	
WV486	Percival Provost T1 (7694M)[N-D]	Privately owned, Grazeley, Berks	
WV493	Percival Provost T1 (G-BDYG/ 7696M)	Royal Scottish Museum of Flight, East Fortune	
WV495	Percival Provost T1 (7697M)[P-C]	Vintage Aircraft Team, Bruntingthorpe	
WV499	Percival Provost T1 (7698M)[P-G]	Privately owned, North Weald	
WV562	Percival Provost T1 (7606M)[P-C]	RAF Cosford Aerospace Museum, stored	
WV605	Percival Provost T1 [T-B]	Norfolk & Suffolk Aviation Museum, Flixton	
WV606	Percival Provost T1 (7622M)[P-B]	Newark Air Museum, Winthorpe	
WV666	Percival Provost T1 (7925M/ G-BTDH) [O-D]	Privately owned, Shoreham	
WV679	Percival Provost T1 (7615M)[O-J]	Privately owned, Wellesbourne Mountford	
WV686	Percival Provost T1 (7621M/ G-BLFT) [O-P]	Privately owned, Cranfield	
WV703	Percival Pembroke C1 (8108M) (G-IIIM)	Privately owned, Tattershall Thorpe	

Notes	Serial	Type	Owner or Operator
	WV705	Percival Pembroke C1 (cockpit)	Southampton Hall of Aviation, stored
	WV740	Percival Pembroke C1 (G-BNPH)	Privately owned, Denham
	WV746	Percival Pembroke C1 (8938M)	RAF Cosford Aerospace Museum
	WV753	Percival Pembroke C1 (8113M)	Wales Aircraft Museum, Cardiff
	WV781	Bristol Sycamore HR12 (G-ALTD/ 7839M)	Caernarfon Air World
	WV783	Bristol Sycamore HR12 (G-ALSP/ 7841M)	RNAY Fleetlands Museum
	WV787	EE Canberra B2/8 (8799M)	Newark Air Museum, Winthorpe
	WV797	Hawker Sea Hawk FGA6 (A2637/ 8155M) [491/J]	Midland Air Museum, Coventry
	WV798	Hawker Sea Hawk FGA6 (A2557) [028/CU]	Second World War Aircraft Preservation Society, Lasham
	WV826	Hawker Sea Hawk FGA6 (A2532) [147/Z]	Wales Aircraft Museum, Cardiff
	WV856	Hawker Sea Hawk FGA6 [163]	FAA Museum, stored RNAS Yeovilton
	WV903	Hawker Sea Hawk FGA6 (A2632/ 8153M)	RN, stored Lee-on-Solent
	WV908	Hawker Sea Hawk FGA6 (A2660/ 8154M) [188/A]	RN Historic Flight, stored Yeovilton
	WV911	Hawker Sea Hawk FGA4 (A2526) [115/C]	RN Lee-on-Solent stored
	WW138	DH Sea Venom FAW22 [227/Z]	FAA Museum, stored RNAS Yeovilton
	WW145	DH Sea Venom FAW22 [680/LM]	Royal Scottish Museum of Flight, East Fortune
	WW217	DH Sea Venom FAW22 [736]	Newark Air Museum, Winthorpe
	WW388	Percival Provost T1 (7616M)[O-F]	Privately owned, Long Marston
	WW397	Percival Provost T1 (8060M/ G-BKHP)	*Sold to Australia, Sep 1993*
	WW421	Percival Provost T1 (7688M) [O]	Lincolnshire Aviation Museum, East Kirkby
	WW442	Percival Provost T1 (7618M) [N]	Privately owned, Kings Langley
	WW444	Percival Provost T1 [D]	Privately owned
	WW447	Percival Provost T1	Privately owned, Grazeley, Berks
	WW453	Percival Provost T1 (G-TMKI) [W-S]	Kennet Aircraft, Cranfield
	WW654	Hawker Hunter GA11 [834/DD]	RNAS Culdrose, SAH
	WX660	Hover-Air HA-5 Hoverhawk III (really XW660)	Privately owned, Cheltenham
	WX788	DH Venom NF3	Night Fighter Preservation Team, Elvington
	WX853	DH Venom NF3 (7443M)	Mosquito Aircraft Museum, London Colney
	WX905	DH Venom NF3 (7458M)	Newark Air Museum, Winthorpe
	WZ415	DH Vampire T11 [72]	No 2 Sqn ATC, Leavesden
	WZ425	DH Vampire T11	Privately owned, Birlingham
	WZ450	DH Vampire T11 (pod)	Privately owned, Headcorn
	WZ458	DH Vampire T11 (7728M) [31] (pod)	Blyth Valley Aviation Collection, Walpole
	WZ464	DH Vampire T11 (N62430) [40]	Vintage Aircraft Team, Bruntingthorpe
	WZ476	DH Vampire T11 (really XE985)	Mosquito Aircraft Museum, stored Hatfield
	WZ507	DH Vampire T11 (G-VTII)	Vintage Aircraft Team, Bruntingthorpe
	WZ514	DH Vampire T11	Privately owned, Meols, Merseyside
	WZ515	DH Vampire T11 [60]	Solway Aviation Society, Carlisle
	WZ518	DH Vampire T11	North-East Aircraft Museum, Usworth
	WZ549	DH Vampire T11 (8118M) [F]	Ulster Heritage Centre, Langford Lodge
	WZ550	DH Vampire T11 (7902M) [R]	Booker Aircraft Museum
	WZ553	DH Vampire T11 [40]	Privately owned, Cranfield
	WZ557	DH Vampire T11	N Yorks Aircraft Recovery Centre, Chop Gate
	WZ559	DH Vampire T11 (7736M) [45] (pod)	RAF Halton Fire Section
	WZ581	DH Vampire T11 [77]	Privately owned, Ruislip
	WZ584	DH Vampire T11 [K]	St Albans College of FE
	WZ589	DH Vampire T11 [19]	Lashenden Air Warfare Museum, Headcorn
	WZ590	DH Vampire T11 [19]	Imperial War Museum, Duxford
	WZ608	DH Vampire T11 [56] (pod)	Privately owned, Romford
	WZ620	DH Vampire T11 [68]	Avon Aviation Museum, Yatesbury
	WZ662	Auster AOP9 (G-BKVK)	Privately owned, Cranfield
	WZ679	Auster AOP9 (7863M)	Privately owned, Little Gransden, Cambs
	WZ706	Auster AOP9 (7851M/G-BURR)	Privately owned, Aldershot
	WZ711	Auster 9/Beagle E3 (G-AVHT)	Privately owned, Middle Wallop

Serial	Type	Owner or Operator	Notes
WZ721	Auster AOP9	Museum of Army Flying, Middle Wallop	
WZ724	Auster AOP9 (7432M)	AAC Middle Wallop, at main gate	
WZ736	Avro 707A (7868M)	Greater Manchester Museum of Science and Industry	
WZ744	Avro 707C (7932M)	RAF Cosford Aerospace Museum	
WZ753	Slingsby Grasshopper TX1	Southampton Hall of Aviation	
WZ765	Slingsby Grasshopper TX1	RAFGSA, Bicester	
WZ767	Slingsby Grasshopper TX1	North-East Aircraft Museum, Usworth	
WZ779	Slingsby Grasshopper TX1	Privately owned, Old Sarum	
WZ791	Slingsby Grasshopper TX1 (8944M)	RAF Museum, Hendon	
WZ796	Slingsby Grasshopper TX1	Privately owned, Nympsfield, stored	
WZ819	Slingsby Grasshopper TX1	Became BGA 3498	
WZ822	Slingsby Grasshopper TX1	Robertsbridge Aviation Society, Mayfield	
WZ826	Vickers Valiant B(K)1 (7872M) (cockpit) (really XD826)	Wales Aircraft Museum, Cardiff	
WZ831	Slingsby Grasshopper TX1	Privately owned, Nympsfield	
WZ845	DH Chipmunk T10 [6]	RAF No 1 AEF, Manston	
WZ846	DH Chipmunk T10 PAX (G-BCSC/ 8439M)	No 1404 Sqn ATC, Chatham	
WZ847	DH Chipmunk T10 [F]	RAF No 6 AEF, Benson	
WZ856	DH Chipmunk T10 [74]	RAF No 7 AEF, Newton	
WZ862	DH Chipmunk T10 [W]	RAF No 3 AEF, Colerne	
WZ866	DH Chipmunk T10 PAX (8217M/ G-ATEB)	No 2296 Sqn ATC, Dunoon, Strathclyde	
WZ868	DH Chipmunk T10 (G-BCIW) [H]	Privately owned, Audley End (derelict)	
WZ869	DH Chipmunk T10 PAX (8019M) [R]	No 391 Sqn ATC, Handforth	
WZ872	DH Chipmunk T10 [E]	RAF No 5 AEF, Cambridge	
WZ876	DH Chipmunk T10 (G-BBWN)	Privately owned, Netherthorpe	
WZ877	DH Chipmunk T10 [75]	RAF No 7 AEF, Newton	
WZ878	DH Chipmunk T10 [86]	RAF No 11 AEF, Leeming	
WZ879	DH Chipmunk T10	AAC BFWF, Middle Wallop	
WZ882	DH Chipmunk T10 [K]	AAC BFWF, Middle Wallop	
WZ884	DH Chipmunk T10 [P]	AAC BFWF, Middle Wallop	
XA109	DH Sea Vampire T22	Royal Scottish Museum of Flight, East Fortune	
XA127	DH Sea Vampire T22 (cockpit)	FAA Museum, stored RNAS Yeovilton	
XA129	DH Sea Vampire T22	FAA Museum, stored RNAS Yeovilton	
XA231	Slingsby Grasshopper TX1 (8888M)	E. Cheshire & S. Manchester Wing ATC HQ, RAF Sealand	
XA243	Slingsby Grasshopper TX1 (8886M)	RAF, stored St Athan	
XA244	Slingsby Grasshopper TX1	RAF, stored Cosford	
XA282	Slingsby Cadet TX3	Caernarfon Air World	
XA289	Slingsby Cadet TX3	Privately owned, Eaglescott	
XA292	Slingsby Cadet TX3 (BGA3350)	Brooklands Museum, Weybridge	
XA293	Slingsby Cadet TX3	Stratford Aircraft Collection, Long Marston	
XA302	Slingsby Cadet TX3 (BGA3786)	Privately owned, Winthorpe	
XA454	Fairey Gannet COD4	RNAS Yeovilton Fire Section	
XA459	Fairey Gannet ECM6 (A2608) [E]	Privately owned, Cirencester	
XA460	Fairey Gannet ECM6 [768/BY]	NE Wales Institute of HE, Connah's Quay	
XA466	Fairey Gannet COD4 [777/LM]	FAA Museum, stored Wroughton	
XA508	Fairey Gannet T2 (A2472) [627/GN]	Midland Air Museum, Coventry	
XA553	Gloster Javelin FAW1 (7470M)	RAF Stanmore Park, on display	
XA564	Gloster Javelin FAW1 (7464M)	RAF Cosford Aerospace Museum	
XA571	Gloster Javelin FAW1 (7663M/ 7722M) (cockpit)	Booker Aircraft Museum	
XA634	Gloster Javelin FAW4 (7641M) [L]	RAF Leeming, on display	
XA699	Gloster Javelin FAW5 (7809M)	Midland Air Museum, Coventry	
XA801	Gloster Javelin FAW2 (7739M)	RAF Stafford	
XA847	EE P1B (8371M)	Privately owned, Southampton Docks	
XA862	WS55 Whirlwind HAR1 (A2542/ G-AMJT) [9]	IHM, Weston-super-Mare	
XA864	WS55 Whirlwind HAR1	FAA Museum, stored Wroughton	
XA868	WS55 Whirlwind HAR1	IHM, Weston-super-Mare	
XA870	WS55 Whirlwind HAR1 (A2543)	Flambards Village Theme Park, Helston	
XA880	DH Devon C2	MoD(PE) T&EE, Llanbedr	
XA893	Avro Vulcan B1 (8591M) (cockpit)	RAF Cosford Aerospace Museum	
XA903	Avro Vulcan B1 (cockpit)	Privately owned, Sidcup, Kent	

Notes	Serial	Type	Owner or Operator
	XA909	Avro Vulcan B1 (cockpit)	Lincolnshire Aviation Heritage Centre, East Kirkby
	XA917	HP Victor B1 (7827M) (cockpit)	*Scrapped at RAF Marham, 1993*
	XB259	Blackburn Beverley C1 (G-AOAI)	Museum of Army Transport, Beverley
	XB261	Blackburn Beverley C1 (cockpit)	Imperial War Museum, Duxford
	XB446	Grumman Avenger ECM6B [992/C]	FAA Museum, stored RNAS Yeovilton
	XB480	Hiller HT1 (A2577) [537]	FAA Museum, RNAS Yeovilton
	XB733	Canadair CL-13 Sabre 4 (G-ATBF)	Privately owned
	XB812	Canadair CL-13 Sabre F4 (MM19666) [U]	RAFM, Duxford (restoration by TFM)
	XD145	Saro SR53	RAF Cosford Aerospace Museum
	XD163	WS55 Whirlwind HAR10 (8645M) [X]	International Helicopter Museum, Weston-super-Mare
	XD165	WS55 Whirlwind HAR10 (8673M) [B]	AAC Netheravon, instructional use
	XD186	WS55 Whirlwind HAR10 (8730M)	RAF Chivenor, on display
	XD215	VS Scimitar F1 (A2573) (cockpit)	Privately owned, Ottershaw
	XD219	VS Scimitar F1 (fuselage)	RNAS Yeovilton, Fire Section
	XD234	VS Scimitar F1 [834]	DRA, derelict Farnborough
	XD235	VS Scimitar F1 (cockpit)	Privately owned, Ottershaw
	XD244	VS Scimitar F1 (cockpit)	Privately owned, Ottershaw
	XD317	VS Scimitar F1 [112/R]	FAA Museum, stored RNAS Yeovilton
	XD332	VS Scimitar F1 (A2574) [194/C]	Flambards Village Theme Park, Helston
	XD375	DH Vampire T11 (7887M) [72]	City of Norwich Aviation Museum
	XD377	DH Vampire T11 (8203M) [A] (pod)	Yorkshire Air Museum, Elvington
	XD382	DH Vampire T11 (8033M)	Privately owned, Ripley, Derbys
	XD425	DH Vampire T11 [16]	Dumfries & Galloway Aviation Museum, Tinwald Downs
	XD434	DH Vampire T11 [25]	Fenland Air Museum, Wisbech
	XD435	DH Vampire T11 [26] (pod)	Privately owned, Lapworth, Warwicks
	XD445	DH Vampire T11 [51]	Bomber County Aviation Museum, Hemswell
	XD447	DH Vampire T11 [50]	Vampire Preservation Group, Long Marston
	XD452	DH Vampire T11 (7990M) [66]	Privately owned
	XD453	DH Vampire T11 (7890M) [64]	No 58 Sqn ATC, Elvington
	XD459	DH Vampire T11 [63] (pod)	Privately owned, Bruntingthorpe
	XD463	DH Vampire T11 (8023M)	No 1360 Sqn ATC, Stapleford, Notts
	XD506	DH Vampire T11 (7983M)	RAF Swinderby
	XD515	DH Vampire T11 (7998M/*XM515*)	Newark Air Museum, Winthorpe
	XD525	DH Vampire T11 (7882M) (pod)	Campbell College CCF, Belfast
	XD528	DH Vampire T11 (8159M)	Privately owned, Ottershaw
	XD534	DH Vampire T11 [41]	Military Aircraft Preservation Grp, Marthall
	XD535	DH Vampire T11 (pod)	Aircraft Restoration Flt, North Weald
	XD536	DH Vampire T11 (7734M) [H]	
	XD542	DH Vampire T11 (7604M/*XD429*) [28]	RAF Edzell, Scotland, on display
	XD547	DH Vampire T11 [Z] (pod)	Scotland West Aircraft Investigation Group, stored Aberfoyle
	XD593	DH Vampire T11 [50]	Newark Air Museum, Winthorpe
	XD595	DH Vampire T11 (pod)	Privately owned, Glentham, Lincs
	XD596	DH Vampire T11 (7939M)	Southampton Hall of Aviation
	XD599	DH Vampire T11 [A]	Caernarfon Air World
	XD602	DH Vampire T11 (7737M) (pod)	Privately owned, Brands Hatch
	XD616	DH Vampire T11 [56]	No 1239 Sqn ATC, Hoddesdon, Herts
	XD622	DH Vampire T11 (8160M)	No 2214 Sqn ATC, Usworth
	XD624	DH Vampire T11 [O]	Macclesfield Technical College
	XD626	DH Vampire T11 [Q]	Midland Air Museum, Coventry
	XD674	Hunting Jet Provost T1 (7570M)[T]	RAF Cosford Aerospace Museum
	XD816	Vickers Valiant B(K)1 (cockpit)	Brooklands Museum, Weybridge
	XD818	Vickers Valiant B(K)1 (7894M)	RAF Museum, Hendon
	XD857	Vickers Valiant B(K)1 (cockpit)	Privately owned, Romford
	XD875	Vickers Valiant B(K)1 (cockpit)	South Yorkshire Aviation Museum, Firbeck
	XE317	Bristol Sycamore HR14 (G-AMWO)[S-N]	Newark Air Museum, Winthorpe
	XE327	Hawker Sea Hawk FGA6 (A2556) [644/LH]	Privately owned, Kings Langley, Herts
	XE339	Hawker Sea Hawk FGA6 (8156M/ A2635) [149/E]	RNAS, stored Lee-on-Solent

Serial	Type	Owner or Operator	Notes
XE340	Hawker Sea Hawk FGA6 [131/Z]	Royal Scottish Museum of Flight, East Fortune	
XE368	Hawker Sea Hawk FGA6 (A2534) [200/J]	Flambards Village Theme Park, Helston	
XE369	Hawker Sea Hawk FGA6 (A2580/ 8158M/A2633) [5]	RNAS Yeovilton Fire Section	
XE489	Hawker Sea Hawk FGA6 (G-JETH/ XE364)	Privately owned, Charlwood, Surrey	
XE521	Fairey Rotodyne Y (parts)	International Helicopter Museum, Weston-super-Mare	
XE584	Hawker Hunter FGA9 (cockpit)	Macclesfield Historical Aviation Society, Marthall	
XE597	Hawker Hunter FGA9 (8874M) (cockpit)	RAF Halton	
XE601	Hawker Hunter FGA9	MoD(PE) A&AEE Boscombe Down	
XE624	Hawker Hunter FGA9 (8875M) [G]	RAF Brawdy, on display	
XE627	Hawker Hunter F6A [T]	Imperial War Museum, Duxford	
XE643	Hawker Hunter FGA9 (8586M) (cockpit)	RAF Exhibition Flight, St Athan	
XE650	Hawker Hunter FGA9 (G-9-449) (cockpit)	South Yorkshire Aviation Museum, Firbeck	
XE653	Hawker Hunter F6A (8829M) [S]	RAF TMTS, Scampton	
XE656	Hawker Hunter F6 (8678M)	RAF No 1 SoTT, Halton	
XE665	Hawker Hunter T8C [876]	RN FRADU, Yeovilton	
XE668	Hawker Hunter GA11 [832/DD]	RN Predannack Fire School	
XE670	Hawker Hunter F4 (7762M/8585M) (cockpit)	RAF Exhibition Flight, St Athan	
XE677	Hawker Hunter F4 (G-HHUN) ●	Jet Heritage Ltd, Bournemouth	
XE682	Hawker Hunter GA11	RNAS Culdrose Fire Section	
XE685	Hawker Hunter GA11 [861/VL]	RN FRADU, Yeovilton	
XE689	Hawker Hunter GA11 [864/VL]	RN FRADU, Yeovilton	
XE707	Hawker Hunter GA11 [865/VL]	RN FRADU, Yeovilton	
XE712	Hawker Hunter GA11 [708]	RN Predannack Fire School	
XE793	Slingsby Cadet TX3 (8666M)	RAF St Athan, instructional use	
XE799	Slingsby Cadet TX3 (8943M) [R]	RAF ACCGS Syerston, preserved	
XE802	Slingsby Cadet TX3	Privately owned, Cupar, Fife	
XE849	DH Vampire T11 (7928M) [V3]	Avon Aviation Museum, Calne, Wilts	
XE852	DH Vampire T11 [H]	No 2247 Sqn ATC, Hawarden	
XE855	DH Vampire T11 (pod)	Midland Air Museum, Coventry	
XE856	DH Vampire T11	Stratford Aircraft Collection, Long Marston	
XE864	DH Vampire T11(composite with XD435)	Privately owned, Stretton, Cheshire	
XE872	DH Vampire T11 [62]	Midland Air Museum, Coventry	
XE874	DH Vampire T11 (8582M) [61]	Privately owned, New Blyth, Grampian	
XE897	DH Vampire T11 (really XD403)	Privately owned, RAF Leuchars	
XE920	DH Vampire T11 (8196M) [D]	Allied Aeroplane Collection, RAF Sealand	
XE921	DH Vampire T11 [64]	Avon Aviation Museum, Yatesbury	
XE935	DH Vampire T11 [30]	South Yorks Air Museum, Firbeck	
XE946	DH Vampire T11 (7473M) (pod)	RAF Museum Restoration Centre, Cardington	
XE956	DH Vampire T11	St Albans College of FE	
XE979	DH Vampire T11 [54]	Privately owned, Birlingham, Worcs	
XE982	DH Vampire T11 (7564M)	Privately owned, Dunkeswell	
XE993	DH Vampire T11 (8161M)	Privately owned, Cosford	
XE995	DH Vampire T11 [53]	Privately owned, Marden, Kent	
XE998	DH Vampire T11 [36]	Privately owned, Wisbech	
XF113	VS Swift F7 [19] (cockpit)	The Air Defence Collection, Salisbury	
XF114	VS Swift F7 (G-SWIF) ●	Jet Heritage Ltd, Bournemouth	
XF289	Hawker Hunter T8C [875/VL]	RN FRADU, Yeovilton	
XF300	Hawker Hunter GA11 [860/VL]	RN FRADU, Yeovilton	
XF301	Hawker Hunter GA11 [834/VL]	Privately owned, RAF Shawbury	
XF310	Hawker Hunter T8C [869/VL]	RN SAH, Culdrose	
XF314	Hawker Hunter F51 [N] (really E-412)	Tangmere Military Aviation Museum	
XF321	Hawker Hunter T7	RNEC Manadon	
XF357	Hawker Hunter T8C [871/VL]	RN FRADU, Yeovilton	
XF358	Hawker Hunter T8C [870/VL]	RN FRADU, Yeovilton	
XF368	Hawker Hunter GA11 [863/VL]	RN FRADU, Yeovilton	
XF375	Hawker Hunter F6A (8736M/ G-BUEZ) [05]	The Old Flying Machine Co, Cranwell	
XF382	Hawker Hunter F6A [15]	Midland Air Museum, Coventry	

Notes	Serial	Type	Owner or Operator
	XF383	Hawker Hunter F6 (8706M) [V] (wears *8506M*)	Privately owned, Long Marston
	XF445	Hawker Hunter FGA9 (8715M/ XG264)[T]	*Scrapped at Brawdy*
	XF509	Hawker Hunter F6 (8708M)	RAF Chivenor, at main gate
	XF515	Hawker Hunter F6A (8830M) [C]	TMTS, RAF Scampton
	XF516	Hawker Hunter F6A (8685M) [66]	SIF, RAFC Cranwell
	XF519	Hawker Hunter FGA9 (8677M/ 8738M) (composite with XJ695)	FSCTE, RAF Manston
	XF522	Hawker Hunter F6 (cockpit)	No 1365 Sqn ATC, Aylesbury
	XF526	Hawker Hunter F6 (8679M) [78/E]	RAF St Athan Fire Section
	XF527	Hawker Hunter F6 (8680M)	RAF Halton, on display
	XF545	Percival Provost T1 (7957M) [O-K]	Privately owned, Cranfield
	XF597	Percival Provost T1 (G-BKFW) [AH]	Privately owned, Aldermaston
	XF603	Percival Provost T1 [H]	Rolls-Royce Tech Coll, Filton
	XF690	Percival Provost T1 (8041M/ G-BGKA/G-MOOS)	Privately owned, Cranfield
	XF708	Avro Shackleton MR3 [203/C]	Imperial War Museum, Duxford
	XF785	Bristol 173 (7648M/G-ALBN)	RAF Museum Restoration Centre, Cardington
	XF836	Percival Provost T1 (8043M/ G-AWRY) [JG]	Privately owned, Thatcham
	XF844	Percival Provost T1 [70]	DRA Farnborough Apprentice School
	XF877	Percival Provost T1 (G-AWVF)[JX]	Privately owned, Goodwood
	XF926	Bristol 188 (8368M)	RAF Cosford Aerospace Museum
	XF967	Hawker Hunter T8C (9186M) [T]	SIF, RAF Cranwell
	XF994	Hawker Hunter T8C [873/VL]	RN FRADU, Yeovilton
	XF995	Hawker Hunter T8B	RAF No 208 Sqn, Lossiemouth
	XG154	Hawker Hunter FGA9 (8863M) [54]	RAF Museum, Hendon
	XG160	Hawker Hunter F6A (8831M) [U]	RAF TMTS, Scampton
	XG164	Hawker Hunter F6 (8681M)	RAF No 1 SoTT, Halton
	XG172	Hawker Hunter F6A (8832M) [A]	TMTS, RAF Scampton
	XG194	Hawker Hunter FGA9 (8839M) [55]	RAF North Luffenham Training Area
	XG195	Hawker Hunter FGA9 (composite with XG297)	Bomber County Aviation Museum, Hemswell
	XG196	Hawker Hunter F6A (8702M) [31]	RAF Bracknell, on display
	XG209	Hawker Hunter F6 (8709M) [69]	SIF RAFC, Cranwell
	XG210	Hawker Hunter F6	Privately owned, Beck Row, Suffolk
	XG225	Hawker Hunter F6A (8713M) [S]	RAF Cosford on display
	XG226	Hawker Hunter F6A (8800M)	Privately owned, Long Marston
	XG226	Hawker Hunter F6A (8800M) [28] (cockpit)	Privately owned, Faygate
	XG252	Hawker Hunter FGA9 (8840M) [U]	RAF Credenhill, on display
	XG254	Hawker Hunter FGA9 (8881M)	RAF Coltishall Fire Section
	XG274	Hawker Hunter F6 (8710M) [71]	RAF No 1 SoTT, Halton
	XG290	Hawker Hunter F6 (8711M) [74] ● (fuselage)	Jet Heritage Ltd, Bournemouth
	XG297	Hawker Hunter FGA9 (cockpit)	Pennine Aviation Museum, Bacup
	XG325	EE Lightning F1 (cockpit)	No 1312 Sqn ATC, Southend, Essex
	XG329	EE Lightning F1 (8050M)	Norfolk & Suffolk Aviation Museum, Flixton
	XG331	EE Lightning F1 (cockpit)	Stratford Aircraft Collection, Long Marston
	XG337	EE Lightning F1 (8056M) [M]	RAF Cosford Aerospace Museum
	XG452	Bristol Belvedere HC1 (7997M/ G-BRMB)	IHM, Weston-super-Mare
	XG454	Bristol Belvedere HC1 (8366M)	Greater Manchester Museum of Science and Industry
	XG474	Bristol Belvedere HC1 (8367M) [O]	RAF Museum, Hendon
	XG496	DH Devon C2 (G-ANDX)	Solway Aviation Society, Carlisle
	XG502	Bristol Sycamore HR14	Museum of Army Flying, Middle Wallop
	XG506	Bristol Sycamore HR14 (7852M)	Bomber County Aviation Museum, Hemswell
	XG518	Bristol Sycamore HR14 (8009M) [S-E]	North-East Aircraft Museum, Usworth
	XG540	Bristol Sycamore HR14 (7899M/ 8345M) [Y-S]	Privately owned, Preston, Lancs
	XG544	Bristol Sycamore HR14	Privately owned, Lower Tremar
	XG547	Bristol Sycamore HR14 (8010M/ G-HAPR) [S-T]	IHM, Weston-super-Mare
	XG573	WS55 Whirlwind HAR3	CDE, Porton Down, Wilts
	XG574	WS55 Whirlwind HAR3 (A2575)	FAA Museum, RNAS Yeovilton

Serial	Type	Owner or Operator	Notes
XG577	WS55 Whirlwind HAR3 (A2571/ 9050M)	RAF Leconfield Crash Rescue Training	
XG594	WS55 Whirlwind HAS7 [517/PO]	Royal Scottish Museum of Flight, East Fortune	
XG596	WS55 Whirlwind HAS7 (A2651) [66]	Westland, Yeovil, instructional use	
XG613	DH Sea Venom FAW21	Imperial War Museum, Duxford	
XG629	DH Sea Venom FAW22 (pod)	Stratford Aircraft Collection, Long Marston	
XG680	DH Sea Venom FAW22 [735/VL]	North-East Aircraft Museum, Usworth	
XG691	DH Sea Venom FAW22 [93/J]	Flambards Village Theme Park, Helston	
XG692	DH Sea Venom FAW22 [668/LM]	Midland Warplane Museum, Hatton	
XG730	DH Sea Venom FAW22 [499/A]	Mosquito Aircraft Museum, London Colney	
XG736	DH Sea Venom FAW22	Ulster Aviation Society, Newtownards	
XG737	DH Sea Venom FAW22 [220/Z]	Vampire Preservation Group, Long Marston	
XG743	DH Sea Vampire T22 [597/LM]	Wymondham College, Norfolk	
XG797	Fairey Gannet ECM6 [766/BY]	Imperial War Museum, Duxford	
XG831	Fairey Gannet ECM6 (A2539)[396]	Flambards Village Theme Park, Helston	
XG882	Fairey Gannet T5 (8754M) [771/LM]	Privately owned, Errol	
XG883	Fairey Gannet T5 [773/BY]	Wales Aircraft Museum, Cardiff	
XG888	Fairey Gannet T5 [LM]	RNAS Lee-on-Solent, stored	
XG900	Short SC1	FAA Museum, RNAS Yeovilton	
XG905	Short SC1	Ulster Folk & Transport Museum, Holywood, County Down	
XH131	EE Canberra PR9 [AF]	RAF No 39(1 PRU) Sqn, Marham	
XH133	EE Canberra PR9	Scrapped, 1993	
XH134	EE Canberra PR9 [AA]	RAF No 39(1 PRU) Sqn, Marham	
XH135	EE Canberra PR9 [AG]	RAF No 39(1 PRU) Sqn, Marham	
XH136	EE Canberra PR9 (8782M)	RAF No 2 SoTT, Cosford	
XH165	EE Canberra PR9	RAF St Athan, Fire Section	
XH168	EE Canberra PR9 [AB]	RAF No 39(1 PRU) Sqn, Marham	
XH169	EE Canberra PR9 [AC]	RAF No 39(1 PRU) Sqn, Marham	
XH170	EE Canberra PR9 (8739M)	RAF Wyton, on display	
XH171	EE Canberra PR9 (8746M) [U]	RAF Cosford Aerospace Museum	
XH174	EE Canberra PR9 (cockpit)	RAF, stored St Athan	
XH177	EE Canberra PR9 (cockpit)	Wales Aircraft Museum, Cardiff	
XH278	DH Vampire T11 (8595M/7866M)	No 2482 Sqn ATC, RAF Henlow	
XH312	DH Vampire T11 [18]	Privately owned, Chester	
XH313	DH Vampire T11 [E]	St Albans College of FE	
XH328	DH Vampire T11 (dismantled) ●	Jet Heritage Ltd, Bournemouth	
XH330	DH Vampire T11 [73]	Privately owned, Bridgnorth	
XH537	Avro Vulcan B2MRR (8749M) (cockpit)	Privately owned, Camberley	
XH558	Avro Vulcan B2	Privately owned, Bruntingthorpe	
XH560	Avro Vulcan K2 (cockpit)	Privately owned, Romford	
XH567	EE Canberra B6(mod)	MoD(PE) DRA Bedford	
XH568	EE Canberra B6(mod) (G-BVIC)	Privately owned, Bruntingthorpe	
XH584	EE Canberra T4 (G-27-374) (cockpit)	North-East Aircraft Museum, Usworth	
XH592	HP Victor K1A (8429M) [L]	RAF Cosford Aerospace Museum	
XH648	HP Victor K1A	Imperial War Museum, Duxford	
XH669	HP Victor K2 (9092M)	RAF Waddington Fire Section	
XH670	HP Victor SR2 (cockpit)	Privately owned, Romford, Essex	
XH671	HP Victor K2	Scrapped at RAF Marham	
XH672	HP Victor K2	RAF Cosford Aerospace Museum	
XH673	HP Victor K2 (8911M)	RAF Marham, on display	
XH675	HP Victor K2	RAF Marham Fire Section	
XH767	Gloster Javelin FAW9 (7955M) [A]	City of Norwich Aviation Museum	
XH837	Gloster Javelin FAW7 (8032M) (cockpit)	Caernarfon Air World	
XH892	Gloster Javelin FAW9 (7982M) [J]	Norfolk & Suffolk Aviation Museum, Flixton	
XH897	Gloster Javelin FAW9	Imperial War Museum, Duxford	
XH903	Gloster Javelin FAW9 (7938M)	Gloucestershire Aviation Collection, Hucclecote	
XH980	Gloster Javelin FAW8 (7867M) [A]	RAF West Raynham, at main gate	
XH992	Gloster Javelin FAW8 (7829M) [P]	Newark Air Museum, Winthorpe	
XJ314	RR Thrust Measuring Rig	FAA Museum, RNAS Yeovilton	
XJ380	Bristol Sycamore HR14 (8628M)	Privately owned, New Byth, Grampian	
XJ389	Fairey Jet Gyrodyne (XD759/ G-AJJP)	RAF Cosford Aerospace Museum, stored	

Notes	Serial	Type	Owner or Operator
	XJ393	WS55 Whirlwind HAR3 (A2538)	Privately owned, Codmore Hill, Sussex
	XJ396	WS55 Whirlwind HAR10	DRA Farnborough Fire Section
	XJ409	WS55 Whirlwind HAR10	
	XJ435	WS55 Whirlwind HAR10 (8671M) [V]	AAC Netheravon, instructional use
	XJ445	WS55 Whirlwind HAR5	CDE, Porton Down, Wilts
	XJ476	DH Sea Vixen FAW1 (cockpit)	No 424 Sqn ATC, Southampton Hall of Aviation
	XJ481	DH Sea Vixen FAW1 [VL]	RNAY Fleetlands Museum
	XJ482	DH Sea Vixen FAW1 (A2598) [713/VL]	Norfolk & Suffolk Aviation Museum, Flixton
	XJ488	DH Sea Vixen FAW1 (cockpit)	Privately owned, New Milton, Hants
	XJ494	DH Sea Vixen FAW2	Privately owned, Kings Langley, Herts
	XJ560	DH Sea Vixen FAW2 (8142M) [242]	Newark Air Museum, Winthorpe
	XJ565	DH Sea Vixen FAW2 (127/E)	Mosquito Aircraft Museum, London Colney
	XJ571	DH Sea Vixen FAW2 (8140M) [242/R]	Privately owned, Dunsfold
	XJ575	DH Sea Vixen FAW2 (A2611) (cockpit)	Wellesbourne Wartime Museum
	XJ579	DH Sea Vixen FAW2 (cockpit)	Midland Air Museum, Coventry
	XJ580	DH Sea Vixen FAW2 [131/E]	Christchurch Memorial Group
	XJ582	DH Sea Vixen FAW2 (8139M) [702]	Privately owned, Chelmsford
	XJ607	DH Sea Vixen FAW2 (8171M) [701/VL]	Privately owned, Dunsfold
	XJ634	Hawker Hunter F6A (8684M) [29]	SIF, RAF Cranwell
	XJ639	Hawker Hunter F6A (8687M) [H]	SIF, RAF Cranwell
	XJ676	Hawker Hunter F6A (8844M)	The Old Flying Machine Co, Duxford
	XJ690	Hawker Hunter FGA9	Stratford Aircraft Collection, Long Marston
	XJ723	WS55 Whirlwind HAR10	No 2288 Sqn ATC, Montrose
	XJ726	WS55 Whirlwind HAR10	Caernarfon Air World
	XJ727	WS55 Whirlwind HAR10 (8661M) [L]	AAC Dishforth, BDRT
	XJ729	WS55 Whirlwind HAR10 (8732M/ G-BVGE)	Privately owned, Swindon
	XJ758	WS55 Whirlwind HAR10 (8464M)	Privately owned, Oswestry
	XJ763	WS55 Whirlwind HAR10 (G-BKHA) [P]	Privately owned, Thornicombe, Dorset
	XJ772	DH Vampire T11 [H]	Brooklands Technical College
	XJ823	Avro Vulcan B2A	Solway Aviation Society, Carlisle Airport
	XJ824	Avro Vulcan B2A	Imperial War Museum, Duxford
	XJ917	Bristol Sycamore HR14 [H-S]	Bristol Aero Collection, Banwell
	XJ918	Bristol Sycamore HR14 (8190M)	RAF Cosford Aerospace Museum
	XK149	Hawker Hunter F6A (8714M) [L]	SIF, RAF Cranwell
	XK378	Auster AOP9 (TAD200)	Privately owned
	XK416	Auster AOP9 (7855M/G-AYUA)	Vintage Aircraft Team, Cranfield
	XK417	Auster AOP9 (G-AVXY)	Privately owned, Leicester East
	XK418	Auster AOP9 (7976M)	Second World War Aircraft Preservation Society, Lasham
	XK421	Auster AOP9 (8365M)	Stratford Aircraft Collection, Long Marston
	XK482	Saro Skeeter AOP12 (7840M/ G-BJWC) [C]	Helicopter Museum of GB, Squires Gate
	XK488	Blackburn Buccaneer S1	FAA Museum, RNAS Yeovilton
	XK526	Blackburn Buccaneer S2 (8648M)	RAF Honington, at main gate
	XK527	Blackburn Buccaneer S2D (8818M) (cockpit)	Privately owned, New Milton, Hants
	XK530	Blackburn Buccaneer S1	DRA Bedford Fire Section
	XK531	Blackburn Buccaneer S1 (8403M)	*Scrapped by August 1993*
	XK532	Blackburn Buccaneer S1 (8867M/ A2581) [632/LM]	The Fresson Trust, Inverness Airport
	XK533	Blackburn Buccaneer S1 (cockpit)	Royal Scottish Museum of Flight, East Fortune
	XK590	DH Vampire T11 [V]	Wellesbourne Wartime Museum
	XK623	DH Vampire T11 [56] (*G-VAMP*)	Caernarfon Air World
	XK624	DH Vampire T11 [32]	Norfolk & Suffolk Aviation Museum, Flixton
	XK625	DH Vampire T11 [12]	Brenzett Aeronautical Museum
	XK627	DH Vampire T11	Pennine Aviation Museum, Bacup
	XK632	DH Vampire T11 [67]	No 2 Sqn ATC, Leavesden
	XK637	DH Vampire T11 [56]	No 1855 Sqn ATC, Royton, Greater Manchester

Serial	Type	Owner or Operator	Notes
XK655	DH Comet C2(RC) (G-AMXA)	Privately owned, Carlisle (cockpit)	
XK659	DH Comet C2(RC) (G-AMXC) (cockpit)	Privately owned, Elland, W. Yorks	
XK695	DH Comet C2(RC) (G-AMXH/ 9164M) (fuselage)	RAF Newton, instructional use	
XK699	DH Comet C2 (7971M)	RAF Lyneham on display	
XK724	Folland Gnat F1 (7715M)	RAF Cosford Aerospace Museum	
XK740	Folland Gnat F1 (8396M)	Southampton Hall of Aviation	
XK741	Folland Gnat F1	Midland Air Museum, Coventry	
XK776	ML Utility 1	Museum of Army Flying, Middle Wallop	
XK819	Slingsby Grasshopper TX1	The Aeroplane Collection, Warmingham	
XK822	Slingsby Grasshopper TX1	Privately owned, West Malling	
XK824	Slingsby Grasshopper TX1	Privately owned, Narborough, Norfolk	
XK895	DH Sea Devon C20 (G-SDEV) [19/CU]	Privately owned, North Weald	
XK896	DH Sea Devon C20 (G-RNAS)	Privately owned, Staverton	
XK907	WS55 Whirlwind HAS7 [U]	Midland Air Museum, Coventry	
XK911	WS55 Whirlwind HAS7 (A2603) [519/PO]	Privately owned, Ipswich	
XK936	WS55 Whirlwind HAS7 [62]	Imperial War Museum, Duxford	
XK944	WS55 Whirlwind HAS7 (A2607)	No 617 Sqn ATC, Malpas School, Cheshire	
XK968	WS55 Whirlwind HAR10 (8445M) [E]	FSCTE, RAF Manston	
XK987	WS55 Whirlwind HAR10 (8393M)	MoD Swynnerton, Staffs	
XK988	WS55 Whirlwind HAR10 (A2646) [D]	Museum of Army Flying, Middle Wallop	
XL149	Blackburn Beverley C1 (7988M) (cockpit)	Newark Air Museum, Winthorpe	
XL158	HP Victor K2	*Scrapped at RAF Marham*	
XL160	HP Victor K2 (8910M)	RAF Marham, BDRT	
XL161	HP Victor K2 (91..M)	RAF Lyneham, Fire Section	
XL162	HP Victor K2 (9114M)	FSCTE RAF Manston	
XL164	HP Victor K2 (91..M)	RAF Brize Norton Fire Section	
XL188	HP Victor K2 (9100M) (fuselage)	RAF Kinloss Fire Section	
XL190	HP Victor K2 (91..M)	RAF St Mawgan Fire Section	
XL192	HP Victor K2 (9024M)	RAF Marham Fire Section	
XL231	HP Victor K2	Yorkshire Air Museum, Elvington	
XL318	Avro Vulcan B2 (8733M)	RAF Museum, Hendon	
XL319	Avro Vulcan B2	North-East Aircraft Museum, Usworth	
XL360	Avro Vulcan B2A	Midland Air Museum, Coventry	
XL386	Avro Vulcan B2A (8760M)	*Burned at Manston, September 1992*	
XL388	Avro Vulcan B2 (cockpit)	Blyth Valley Aviation Collection, Waipole	
XL391	Avro Vulcan B2	Privately owned, Blackpool	
XL392	Avro Vulcan B2 (8745M)	*Scrapped at Valley, September 1993*	
XL426	Avro Vulcan B2 (G-VJET)	Vulcan Restoration Trust, Southend	
XL427	Avro Vulcan B2 (8756M)	RAF Machrihanish Fire Section	
XL445	Avro Vulcan K2 (8811M) (cockpit)	Blyth Valley Aviation Collection, Walpole	
XL449	Fairey Gannet AEW3	Wales Aircraft Museum, Cardiff	
XL472	Fairey Gannet AEW3 [044/R]	Privately owned, Charlwood, Surrey	
XL497	Fairey Gannet AEW3 [041/R]	RN, Prestwick, on display	
XL500	Fairey Gannet AEW3 (A2701) [LM]	RN, stored Lee-on-Solent	
XL502	Fairey Gannet AEW3 (8610M/ G-BMYP)	Privately owned, Carlisle,stored	
XL503	Fairey Gannet AEW3 [070/E]	FAA Museum, RNAS Yeovilton	
XL512	HP Victor K2	*Scrapped at RAF Marham*	
XL563	Hawker Hunter T7	MoD(PE) IAM Farnborough	
XL564	Hawker Hunter T7 [4]	MoD(PE) ETPS Boscombe Down	
XL565	Hawker Hunter T7 (parts of WT745)	RAF, stored Shawbury	
XL567	Hawker Hunter T7 (8723M) [84]	Privately owned, Exeter	
XL568	Hawker Hunter T7A [C]	RAF stored, Lossiemouth	
XL569	Hawker Hunter T7 (8833M) [80]	East Midlands Airport Aero Park	
XL572	Hawker Hunter T7 (G-HNTR) [83]	Privately owned, Brough	
XL573	Hawker Hunter T7 (G-BVGH)	Privately owned, Exeter	
XL577	Hawker Hunter T7 (8676M) [W]	SIF, RAF Cranwell	
XL578	Hawker Hunter T7	Privately owned, Cranfield	
XL580	Hawker Hunter T8M [723]	RN, stored Shawbury	
XL586	Hawker Hunter T7	RAF, stored Shawbury	
XL587	Hawker Hunter T7 (8807M) [Z]	TMTS, RAF Scampton	
XL591	Hawker Hunter T7	RAF, stored Shawbury	

XL592 – XM349

Notes	Serial	Type	Owner or Operator
	XL592	Hawker Hunter T7 (8836M) [Y]	TMTS, RAF Scampton
	XL595	Hawker Hunter T7 (G-BTYL) [78]	*Written off, 11 June 1993, Peak District*
	XL598	Hawker Hunter T8C (880/VL)	RN FRADU, Yeovilton
	XL600	Hawker Hunter T7 [Y/FL]	Privately owned, Southall
	XL601	Hawker Hunter T7 [874/VL]	RN SAH, Culdrose
	XL602	Hawker Hunter T8M	MoD(PE) BAe Dunsfold
	XL603	Hawker Hunter T8M [724]	RN, stored Shawbury
	XL609	Hawker Hunter T7 (8866M) [YF]	*Scrapped at Lossiemouth, Oct 1993*
	XL612	Hawker Hunter T7 [2]	MoD(PE) ETPS, Boscombe Down
	XL613	Hawker Hunter T7A	RAF, stored Shawbury
	XL614	Hawker Hunter T7	RAF No 208 Sqn, Lossiemouth
	XL616	Hawker Hunter T7 [D]	RAF stored, Lossiemouth
	XL618	Hawker Hunter T7 (8892M) [05]	RAF Cottesmore Fire Section
	XL623	Hawker Hunter T7 (8770M) [90]	RAF Newton
	XL629	EE Lightning T4	A&AEE Boscombe Down, at main gate
	XL703	SAL Pioneer CC1 (8034M)	RAF Cosford Aerospace Museum, stored
	XL728	WS58 Wessex HAS1	RAF Brawdy, Fire Section
	XL735	Saro Skeeter AOP12	Privately owned, Tattershall Thorpe
	XL738	Saro Skeeter AOP12 (7860M)	Museum of Army Flying, Middle Wallop
	XL762	Saro Skeeter AOP12 (8017M)	Royal Scottish Museum of Flight, East Fortune
	XL763	Saro Skeeter AOP12	Southall Technical College
	XL764	Saro Skeeter AOP12 (7940M)	Newark Air Museum, Winthorpe
	XL765	Saro Skeeter AOP12	Privately owned, Pimlico
	XL770	Saro Skeeter AOP12 (8046M)	Southampton Hall of Aviation
	XL809	Saro Skeeter AOP12 (G-BLIX/PH-HOF)	Privately owned, Wilden, Beds
	XL811	Saro Skeeter AOP12	IHM, Weston-super-Mare
	XL812	Saro Skeeter AOP12 (G-SARO)	Privately owned, Old Buckenham
	XL813	Saro Skeeter AOP12	Museum of Army Flying, Middle Wallop
	XL814	Saro Skeeter AOP12	AAC Historic Aircraft Flight, Middle Wallop
	XL824	Bristol Sycamore HR14 (8021M)	Greater Manchester Museum of Science and Industry
	XL829	Bristol Sycamore HR14	Bristol Industrial Museum
	XL836	WS55 Whirlwind HAS7 (A2642) [65]	RN Predannack Fire School
	XL840	WS55 Whirlwind HAS7	Stratford Aircraft Collection, Long Marston
	XL847	WS55 Whirlwind HAS7 (A2626) [83]	AAC Middle Wallop, Fire Section
	XL853	WS55 Whirlwind HAS7 (A2630) [LS]	RNAY Fleetlands Museum
	XL875	WS55 Whirlwind HAR9	Air Service Training, Perth
	XL880	WS55 Whirlwind HAR9 (A2714) [35]	RN, Lee-on-Solent Fire Section
	XL898	WS55 Whirlwind HAR9 (8654M) [30/ED]	Privately owned, New Byth, Grampian
	XL929	Percival Pembroke C1 (G-BNPU)	Northbrook College, Shoreham Airport
	XL954	Percival Pembroke C1 (9042M/N4234C)	Privately owned, White Waltham
	XL993	SAL Twin Pioneer CC1 (8388M)	RAF Cosford Aerospace Museum
	XM135	BAC Lightning F1 [135]	Imperial War Museum, Duxford
	XM144	BAC Lightning F1 (8417M) [J]	Privately owned, Burntwood, Staffs
	XM169	BAC Lightning F1A (8422M) (cockpit)	N Yorks Aircraft Recovery Centre, Chop Gate
	XM172	BAC Lightning F1A (8427M) [B]	RAF Coltishall, gate guard
	XM173	BAC Lightning F1A (8414M) [A]	RAF Bentley Priory, at main gate
	XM191	BAC Lightning F1A (7854M/8590M) (cockpit)	RAF Exhibition Flight, St Athan
	XM192	BAC Lightning F1A (8413M) [K]	AAC Wattisham, at main gate
	XM223	DH Devon C2 [J]	MoD(PE), DRA West Freugh
	XM279	EE Canberra B(I)8 (cockpit)	South Yorkshire Aviation Museum, Firbeck
	XM296	DH Heron C4	*Sold as G-BVBI, July 1993*
	XM300	WS58 Wessex HAS1	Welsh Industrial and Maritime Museum, Cardiff
	XM327	WS58 Wessex HAS3 [401/KE]	College of Nautical Studies, Warsash
	XM328	WS58 Wessex HAS3	RNAS Culdrose, SAH
	XM329	WS58 Wessex HAS1 (A2609)	RN Predannack Fire School
	XM330	WS58 Wessex HAS1	MoD(PE) DRA Farnborough, stored
	XM349	Hunting Jet Provost T3A (9046M) [T]	RAF No 2 SoTT, Cosford

Serial	Type	Owner or Operator	Notes
XM350	Hunting Jet Provost T3A (9036M) [89]	RAF Church Fenton, Fire Section	
XM351	Hunting Jet Provost T3 (8078M)	RAF No 2 SoTT, Cosford	
XM352	Hunting Jet Provost T3A [21]	RAF, stored Linton-on-Ouse	
XM355	Hunting Jet Provost T3 (8229M) [D]	Privately owned, Cambridge	
XM357	Hunting Jet Provost T3A [45]	RAF, stored Linton-on-Ouse	
XM358	Hunting Jet Provost T3A (8987M) [53]		
XM362	Hunting Jet Provost T3 (8230M)		
XM365	Hunting Jet Provost T3A [37]	RAF, stored Linton-on-Ouse	
XM367	Hunting Jet Provost T3 (8083M) [Z]	RAF No 2 SoTT, Cosford	
XM369	Hunting Jet Provost T3 (8084M) [C]	Privately owned, New Byth, Grampian	
XM370	Hunting Jet Provost T3 [10]	RAF, stored Linton-on-Ouse	
XM371	Hunting Jet Provost T3A (8962M)	Sold to USA as N4427Q September 1992	
XM372	Hunting Jet Provost T3A (8917M) [55]	RAF Linton-on-Ouse Fire Section	
XM374	Hunting Jet Provost T3A [18]	RAF, stored Shawbury	
XM375	Hunting Jet Provost T3 (8231M) [B]	RAF Cottesmore Fire Section	
XM376	Hunting Jet Provost T3A [27]	RAF, stored Linton-on-Ouse	
XM378	Hunting Jet Provost T3A [34]	RAF, stored Linton-on-Ouse	
XM379	Hunting Jet Provost T3	Army Apprentice College, Arborfield	
XM383	Hunting Jet Provost T3A [90]	Privately owned, Crowland, Lincs	
XM386	Hunting Jet Provost T3 (8076M) [08]	RAF St Athan	
XM387	Hunting Jet Provost T3A [I]	RAF, stored Shawbury	
XM401	Hunting Jet Provost T3A [17]		
XM402	Hunting Jet Provost T3 (8055AM)	Privately owned, Narborough, Norfolk [J]	
XM403	Hunting Jet Provost T3A (9048M) [V]	RAF No 2 SoTT, Cosford	
XM404	Hunting Jet Provost T3 (8055BM)	Privately owned, Moreton-in-Marsh	
XM405	Hunting Jet Provost T3A (G-TORE) [42]	Privately owned, Cranfield	
XM408	Hunting Jet Provost T3 (8233M) [D]	Privately owned, Bruntingthorpe	
XM409	Hunting Jet Provost T3 (8082M) (rear fuselage only)	RAF, stored St Athan	
XM410	Hunting Jet Provost T3 (8054AM) [B]	RAF North Luffenham Training Area	
XM411	Hunting Jet Provost T3 (8434M) [L]	RAF Halton, dismantled	
XM412	Hunting Jet Provost T3A (9011M)	RAF CTTS, St Athan	
XM413	Hunting Jet Provost T3	Army Apprentice College, Arborfield	
XM414	Hunting Jet Provost T3A (8996M)		
XM417	Hunting Jet Provost T3 (8054BM)	RAF No 1 SoTT, Halton	
XM419	Hunting Jet Provost T3A (8990M) [102]	RAF CTTS, St Athan	
XM424	Hunting Jet Provost T3A	RAF, stored Shawbury	
XM425	Hunting Jet Provost T3A (8995M) [88]		
XM426	Hunting Jet Provost T3 [64] (cockpit)	Robertsbridge Aviation Museum	
XM455	Hunting Jet Provost T3A (8960M) [K]	RAF No 2 SoTT, Cosford	
XM459	Hunting Jet Provost T3A [F]	RAF, stored Shawbury	
XM461	Hunting Jet Provost T3A [11]	Sold to USA as N6204H, 1993	
XM463	Hunting Jet Provost T3A [38] (fuselage)	RAF Museum, Hendon	
XM464	Hunting Jet Provost T3A [23]		
XM465	Hunting Jet Provost T3A [55]		
XM466	Hunting Jet Provost T3A	Sold to USA as N7075U, 1993	
XM467	Hunting Jet Provost T3 (8085M)		
XM468	Hunting Jet Provost T3 (8081M)	Privately owned, Ipswich	
XM470	Hunting Jet Provost T3A [12]	RAF, stored Linton-on-Ouse	
XM471	Hunting Jet Provost T3A (8968M) [L,93]	RAF No 2 SoTT, Cosford	
XM472	Hunting Jet Provost T3A (9051M) (cockpit)	No 1005 Sqn ATC, Radcliffe, Manchester	
XM473	Hunting Jet Provost T3A (8974M/ G-TINY)	Privately owned, Norwich	
XM474	Hunting Jet Provost T3 (8121M)	No 1330 Sqn ATC, Warrington	
XM475	Hunting Jet Provost T3A (9112M) [44]	FSCTE, RAF Manston	

XM478 – XN258

Notes	Serial	Type	Owner or Operator
	XM478	Hunting Jet Provost T3A (8983M) [33]	RAF No 1 SoTT, Halton
	XM479	Hunting Jet Provost T3A (G-BVEZ) [54]	Privately owned, Sandtoft
	XM480	Hunting Jet Provost T3 (8080M)	RAF No 1 SoTT, Halton
	XM515	DH Vampire T11 (7998M/really XD515)	Solway Aviation Society, Carlisle
	XM529	Saro Skeeter AOP12 (7979M/ G-BDNS)	Privately owned, Handforth
	XM553	Saro Skeeter AOP12 (G-AWSV)	Privately owned, Middle Wallop
	XM555	Saro Skeeter AOP12 (8027M)	RAF Cosford Aerospace Museum, stored
	XM556	Saro Skeeter AOP12 (7870M/ G-HELI)	IHM, Weston-super-Mare
	XM561	Saro Skeeter AOP12 (7980M)	Lincs Aviation Heritage Centre, East Kirkby
	XM564	Saro Skeeter AOP12	Royal Armoured Corps Museum, Bovington
	XM569	Avro Vulcan B2	Wales Aircraft Museum, Cardiff
	XM575	Avro Vulcan B2A (G-BLMC)	East Midlands Airport Aero Park
	XM594	Avro Vulcan B2	Newark Air Museum, Winthorpe
	XM597	Avro Vulcan B2	Royal Scottish Museum of Flight, East Fortune
	XM598	Avro Vulcan B2 (8778M)	RAF Cosford Aerospace Museum
	XM602	Avro Vulcan B2 (cockpit)	Avro Aircraft Restoration Society, BAe Woodford
	XM603	Avro Vulcan B2	Avro Aircraft Restoration Society, BAe Woodford
	XM607	Avro Vulcan B2 (8779M)	RAF Waddington, on display
	XM612	Avro Vulcan B2	City of Norwich Aviation Museum
	XM652	Avro Vulcan B2 (cockpit)	Privately owned, Burntwood, Staffs
	XM655	Avro Vulcan B2 (G-VULC/N655AV)	Privately owned, Wellesbourne Mountford
	XM656	Avro Vulcan B2 (8757M) (cockpit)	Privately owned, Romford
	XM660	WS55 Whirlwind HAS7 [78]	North-East Aircraft Museum, Usworth
	XM665	WS55 Whirlwind HAS7	Booker Aircraft Museum
	XM685	WS55 Whirlwind HAS7 (G-AYZJ) [513/PO]	Newark Air Museum, Winthorpe
	XM693	HS Gnat T1 (7891M)	BAe Hamble on display
	XM693	HS Gnat T1 (8618M/XP504/ G-TIMM)	Kennet Aircraft, Cranfield
	XM694	HS Gnat T1	DRA Bedford Apprentice School
	XM697	HS Gnat T1 (G-NAAT) ●	Jet Heritage Ltd, Bournemouth
	XM706	HS Gnat T1 (8572M) [12]	RAF Swinderby Fire Section
	XM708	HS Gnat T1 (8573M)	RAF Locking, on display
	XM709	HS Gnat T1 (8617M) [67]	Privately owned
	XM715	HP Victor K2	Privately owned, Bruntingthorpe
	XM717	HP Victor K2 (cockpit)	RAF Museum, Hendon
	XM833	WS58 Wessex HAS3	Second World War Aircraft Preservation Society, Lasham
	XM838	WS58 Wessex HAS3 [05]	RN Predannack Fire School
	XM843	WS58 Wessex HAS1 (A2693) [527]	RN AES, Lee-on-Solent
	XM868	WS58 Wessex HAS1 (A2706) [517]	RN Predannack Fire School
	XM870	WS58 Wessex HAS3 [PO]	
	XM874	WS58 Wessex HAS1 (A2689) [521/CU]	RN Predannack Fire School
	XM923	WS58 Wessex HAS 3	RNAY Fleetlands, Fire Section
	XM927	WS58 Wessex HAS3 (8814M) [660/PO]	RAF Shawbury, Fire Section
	XM987	BAC Lightning T4	*Scrapped by February 1992*
	XN126	WS55 Whirlwind HAR10 (8655M) [S]	RAF Benson BDRT
	XN132	Sud Alouette AH2 (G-BUIV)	*Sold as PH-NSW*
	XN137	Hunting Jet Provost T3 (*XN493*) (cockpit)	Privately owned, Ottershaw
	XN185	Slingsby Sedbergh TX1 (8942M)	RAF ACCGS Syerston, preserved
	XN198	Slingsby Cadet TX3	Privately owned, Challock Lees
	XN238	Slingsby Cadet TX3 (front fuselage)	Robertsbridge Aviation Society, Mayfield
	XN239	Slingsby Cadet TX3 (8889M) [G]	Imperial War Museum, Duxford
	XN243	Slingsby Cadet TX3 (BGA 3145)	RAFGSA, Bicester
	XN246	Slingsby Cadet TX3	Southampton Hall of Aviation
	XN258	WS55 Whirlwind HAR9 [589/CU]	North-East Aircraft Museum, Usworth

Serial	Type	Owner or Operator	Notes
XN259	WS55 Whirlwind HAS7	London City Airport, Fire Section	
XN297	WS55 Whirlwind HAR9 [12] (really XN311/A2643)	Privately owned, Hull	
XN298	WS55 Whirlwind HAR9 [810/LS]	International Fire Training Centre, Chorley	
XN299	WS55 Whirlwind HAS7 [ZZ]	Royal Marines' Museum, Portsmouth	
XN302	WS55 Whirlwind HAS7 (A2654/9037M)	RAF Finningley, Fire Section	
XN304	WS55 Whirlwind HAS7 [64]	Norfolk & Suffolk Aviation Museum, Flixton	
XN308	WS55 Whirlwind HAS7 (A2605) [510]	RNAS Yeovilton Fire Section	
XN332	Saro P531 (G-APNV/A2579) [759]	FAA Museum, stored RNAS Yeovilton	
XN334	Saro P531 (A2525)	IHM, Crawley College of Technology	
XN341	Saro Skeeter AOP12 (8022M)	Privately owned, Luton Airport	
XN344	Saro Skeeter AOP12 (8018M)	Science Museum, South Kensington	
XN351	Saro Skeeter AOP12 (G-BKSC)	Privately owned, Shempston Farm, Lossiemouth	
XN359	WS55 Whirlwind HAR9 (A2712) [34/ED]	RNAS Lee-on-Solent, Fire Section	
XN380	WS55 Whirlwind HAS7 [67]	Lashenden Air Warfare Museum, Headcorn	
XN385	WS55 Whirlwind HAS7	*Sold to Cyprus 1992*	
XN386	WS55 Whirlwind HAR9 [435/ED]	Privately owned, Blackpool	
XN412	Auster AOP9	Cotswold Aircraft Restoration Grp, Innsworth	
XN435	Auster AOP9 (G-BGBU)	Privately owned, Egham	
XN437	Auster AOP9 (G-AXWA)	Privately owned, Welling, Kent	
XN441	Auster AOP9 (G-BGKT)	Privately owned, Reymerston Hall	
XN458	Hunting Jet Provost T3 (8234M)	Wales Aircraft Museum, Cardiff	
XN459	Hunting Jet Provost T3A [N]	RAF, stored Shawbury	
XN461	Hunting Jet Provost T3A (G-BVBE)	Privately owned, Sandtoft	
XN462	Hunting Jet Provost T3A [17]	RAF, stored Shawbury	
XN466	Hunting Jet Provost T3A [29] (front fuselage)	No 1005 Sqn ATC, Radcliffe, Greater Manchester	
XN467	Hunting Jet Provost T4 (8559M) [B]	RAF No 1 SoTT, Halton	
XN470	Hunting Jet Provost T3A [41]	RAF, stored Linton-on-Ouse	
XN471	Hunting Jet Provost T3A [24]	*Sold to USA as N471XN, 1993*	
XN472	Hunting Jet Provost T3A (8959M) [J,86]	RAF No 2 SoTT, Cosford	
XN473	Hunting Jet Provost T3A (8862M) [98] (cockpit)	RAF Church Fenton Fire Section	
XN492	Hunting Jet Provost T3 (8079M)	RAF No 2 SoTT, Cosford	
XN494	Hunting Jet Provost T3A (9012M)	AAC Middle Wallop, Fire Section	
XN495	Hunting Jet Provost T3A (8786M) [102]	RAF Finningley, Fire Section	
XN497	Hunting Jet Provost T3A [52]	RAF St Athan	
XN498	Hunting Jet Provost T3A [16]	RAF, stored Linton-on-Ouse	
XN499	Hunting Jet Provost T3A [L]	*Sold to USA as N7075X, 1993*	
XN500	Hunting Jet Provost T3A [48]	CSE Ltd, Oxford, ground instruction	
XN501	Hunting Jet Provost T3A (8958M) [G]	RAF No 2 SoTT, Cosford	
XN502	Hunting Jet Provost T3A [D]	RAF, stored Shawbury	
XN503	Hunting Jet Provost T3	Wiltshire Historic Aviation Group, Salisbury	
XN505	Hunting Jet Provost T3A [25]	RAF, stored Linton-on-Ouse	
XN506	Hunting Jet Provost T3A [19]	*Sold to USA, February 1993*	
XN508	Hunting Jet Provost T3A [47]	RAF St Athan	
XN509	Hunting Jet Provost T3A [50]	*Sold to USA, 1993*	
XN510	Hunting Jet Provost T3A [40]	RAF, stored Linton-on-Ouse	
XN511	Hunting Jet Provost T3 [64] (cockpit)	Robertsbridge Aviation Museum, Mayfield	
XN512	Hunting Jet Provost T3 (8435M)	Princess Alexandra Hospital, Wroughton	
XN548	Hunting Jet Provost T3 (8971M) [32]	*Sold to USA as N4421B*	
XN549	Hunting Jet Provost T3 (8235M) [32,P]	RAF Shawbury Fire Section	
XN551	Hunting Jet Provost T3A (8984M)	RAF CTTS, St Athan	
XN552	Hunting Jet Provost T3A [32]	RAF, stored Shawbury	
XN553	Hunting Jet Provost T3A	RAF, stored Shawbury	
XN554	Hunting Jet Provost T3 (8436M) [K]	RAF North Luffenham Training Area	
XN573	Hunting Jet Provost T3 [E] (cockpit)	Newark Air Museum	
XN577	Hunting Jet Provost T3A (8956M) [89,F]	RAF No 2 SoTT, Cosford	

Notes	Serial	Type	Owner or Operator
	XN579	Hunting Jet Provost T3A (9137M) [14]	RAF North Luffenham Training Area
	XN581	Hunting Jet Provost T3A [C]	RAF St Athan
	XN582	Hunting Jet Provost T3A (8957M) [95,H]	RAF No 2 SoTT, Cosford
	XN584	Hunting Jet Provost T3A (9014M) [E]	RAF No 1 SoTT, Halton
	XN586	Hunting Jet Provost T3A (9039M) [91,S]	RAF No 2 SoTT, Cosford
	XN589	Hunting Jet Provost T3A (9143M) [46]	RAF Linton-on-Ouse, on display
	XN592	Hunting Jet Provost T3 (cockpit)	No 1105 Sqn ATC, Winchester
	XN593	Hunting Jet Provost T3A (8988M) [97,Q]	RAF No 2 SoTT, Cosford
	XN594	Hunting Jet Provost T3 (8077M) [W]	RAF No 2 SoTT, Cosford
	XN595	Hunting Jet Provost T3A [43]	Privately owned, Peterborough
	XN597	Hunting Jet Provost T3 (7984M) (cockpit)	North East Aircraft Museum, Usworth
	XN600	Hunting Jet Provost T3A (cockpit)	Yorkshire Air Museum, Elvington
	XN602	Hunting Jet Provost T3 (8088M)	FSCTE, RAF Manston
	XN606	Hunting Jet Provost T3A (9121M) [51]	RAF Brawdy, BDRT
	XN607	Hunting Jet Provost T3 (cockpit)	N Yorks Aircraft Recovery Centre, Chop Gate
	XN629	Hunting Jet Provost T3A (G-BVEG) [49]	Privately owned, Sandtoft
	XN632	Hunting Jet Provost T3 (8352M)	RAF Chivenor, crash rescue training
	XN634	Hunting Jet Provost T3A [53]	RAF St Athan
	XN636	Hunting Jet Provost T3A (9045M) [15]	RAF No 2 SoTT, Cosford
	XN637	Hunting Jet Provost T3 (G-BKOU) [3]	Vintage Aircraft Team, Bruntingthorpe
	XN640	Hunting Jet Provost T3A (9016M) [99,R]	RAF No 2 SoTT, Cosford
	XN641	Hunting Jet Provost T3A (8865M) [47]	RAF Newton Fire Section
	XN643	Hunting Jet Provost T3A (8704M) (cockpit)	RAF Cranwell
	XN647	DH Sea Vixen FAW2 (A2610) [707/VL]	Flambards Village Theme Park, Helston
	XN649	DH Sea Vixen FAW2 [126]	MoD(PE), stored DRA Farnborough
	XN650	DH Sea Vixen FAW2 (A2612 /A2620/A2639) [VL]	Wales Aircraft Museum, Cardiff
	XN651	DH Sea Vixen FAW2 (A2616) (cockpit)	Privately owned, Portsmouth
	XN657	DH Sea Vixen D3 [TR-1]	T&EE Llanbedr Fire Section
	XN685	DH Sea Vixen FAW2 (8173M) [03/VL]	Midland Air Museum, Coventry
	XN688	DH Sea Vixen FAW2 (8141M) [511]	DRA Farnborough Fire Section
	XN691	DH Sea Vixen FAW2 (8143M) [247/H]	Aces High, North Weald
	XN692	DH Sea Vixen FAW2 (A2624) [125/E]	RNAS Yeovilton
	XN694	DH Sea Vixen FAW2	MoD(PE), T&EE Llanbedr
	XN696	DH Sea Vixen FAW2 (cockpit)	Blyth Valley Aviation Collection, Walpole
	XN714	Hunting H126	RAF Cosford Aerospace Museum
	XN724	EE Lightning F2A (8513M) [F]	Privately owned, Newcastle-upon-Tyne
	XN728	EE Lightning F2A (8546M) [V]	Privately owned, Balderton, Notts
	XN734	EE Lightning F3A (8346M/ G-27-239/G-BNCA)	Privately owned, Cranfield
	XN769	EE Lightning F2 (8402M) [Z]	London ATCC, West Drayton
	XN774	EE Lightning F2A (8551M) [F]	RAF Coningsby, Fire Section
	XN776	EE Lightning F2A (8535M) [C]	Royal Scottish Museum of Flight, East Fortune
	XN817	AW Argosy C1	MoD(PE), DRA West Freugh Fire Section
	XN819	AW Argosy C1 (8205M) (cockpit)	Newark Air Museum, Winthorpe
	XN855	AW Argosy E1 (8556M)	Burned at Manston, May 1992
	XN923	HS Buccaneer S1 [13]	Privately owned, Charlwood, Surrey
	XN928	HS Buccaneer S1 (8179M) [353]	Wales Aircraft Museum, Cardiff
	XN929	HS Buccaneer S1 (8051M) (cockpit)	RAF Cranwell Engineering Wing

Serial	Type	Owner or Operator	Notes
XN930	HS Buccaneer S1 (8180M) [632/LM] (cockpit)	Privately owned, Chelmsford	
XN934	HS Buccaneer S1 (A2600) (fuselage)	RN Predannack Fire School	
XN953	HS Buccaneer S1 (A2655/8182M)	RN Predannack Fire School	
XN957	HS Buccaneer S1 [630/LM]	FAA Museum, RNAS Yeovilton	
XN964	HS Buccaneer S1 [613/LM]	Newark Air Museum, Winthorpe	
XN967	HS Buccaneer S1 (A2627) [103/E]	Donington Park Museum	
XN972	HS Buccaneer S1 (8183M/XN962) (cockpit)	RAF Exhibition Flight, St Athan	
XN974	HS Buccaneer S2A	Yorkshire Air Museum, Elvington	
XN979	HS Buccaneer S2 (cockpit)	ATC, RAF Stanbridge	
XN981	HS Buccaneer S2B	RAF stored Lossiemouth	
XN982	HS Buccaneer S2A		
XN983	HS Buccaneer S2B	RAF, stored Shawbury	
XP110	WS58 Wessex HAS3 [55/FL]	RNAY Fleetlands Apprentice School	
XP116	WS58 Wessex HAS3 (A2618) [520]	RN AES, Lee-on-Solent	
XP137	WS58 Wessex HAS3 [CU]	RN, stored Culdrose	
XP140	WS58 Wessex HAS3 (8806M) [653/PO]	RAF Chilmark, BDRT	
XP142	WS58 Wessex HAS3	FAA Museum, RNAS Yeovilton	
XP150	WS58 Wessex HAS3 [LS]	RN AES, Lee-on-Solent	
XP151	WS58 Wessex HAS1 (A2684) [047/R]	RN, Lee-on-Solent Fire Section	
XP157	WS58 Wessex HAS1 (A2680) [AN]	RNAS Yeovilton, Fire Section	
XP158	WS58 Wessex HAS1 (A2688) [522/CU]	RNAS Culdrose, Fire Section	
XP159	WS58 Wessex HAS1 (8877M) [047/R]	Privately owned, Brands Hatch	
XP160	WS58 Wessex HAS1 (A2650) [521/CU]	RN Predannack Fire School	
XP165	WS Scout AH1	IHM, Weston-super-Mare	
XP166	WS Scout AH1 (G-APVL)	DRA Farnborough, Apprentice School	
XP190	WS Scout AH1	South Yorkshire Aviation Museum, Firbeck	
XP191	WS Scout AH1	AAC Middle Wallop, BDRT	
XP226	Fairey Gannet AEW3 (A2667) [073/E]	Newark Air Museum, Winthorpe	
XP241	Auster AOP9	Rebel Air Museum, Andrewsfield	
XP242	Auster AOP9 (G-BUCI)	AAC Historic Aircraft Flight, Middle Wallop	
XP244	Auster AOP9 (7864M) [M7922]	Army Apprentice College, Arborfield	
XP248	Auster AOP9 (7822M)	Privately owned, Little Gransden	
XP254	Auster AOP11 (G-ASCC)	Privately owned, Glatton	
XP279	Auster AOP9 (G-BWKK)	Privately owned, Popham	
XP280	Auster AOP9	Leicester Museum of Science & Technology, Coalville	
XP281	Auster AOP9	Imperial War Museum, Duxford	
XP282	Auster AOP9 (G-BGTC)	Privately owned, Widmerpoll	
XP283	Auster AOP9 (7859M)	Privately owned, Lichfield	
XP299	WS55 Whirlwind HAR10 (8726M)	RAF Cosford Aerospace Museum	
XP329	WS55 Whirlwind HAR10 (8791M) [V]	Privately owned, Tattershall Thorpe	
XP330	WS55 Whirlwind HAR10	CAA Fire School, Teesside Airport	
XP338	WS55 Whirlwind HAR10 (8647M) [N]	RAF No 2 SoTT, Cosford	
XP344	WS55 Whirlwind HAR10 (8764M) [X]	RAF North Luffenham	
XP345	WS55 Whirlwind HAR10 (8792M)	Privately owned, Storwood, East Yorks	
XP346	WS55 Whirlwind HAR10 (8793M)	Stratford Aircraft Collection, Long Marston	
XP350	WS55 Whirlwind HAR10	Flambards Village Theme Park, Helston	
XP351	WS55 Whirlwind HAR10 (8672M) [Z]	RAF Shawbury, on display	
XP353	WS55 Whirlwind HAR10 (8720M)	Privately owned, Brands Hatch	
XP354	WS55 Whirlwind HAR10 (8721M)	RAF No 1 SoTT, Halton	
XP355	WS55 Whirlwind HAR10 (8463M/ G-BEBC)	City of Norwich Aviation Museum	
XP359	WS55 Whirlwind HAR10 (8447M)	RAF Stafford, Fire Section	
XP360	WS55 Whirlwind HAR10 [V]	Privately owned, Upper Hill, Hereford	
XP361	WS55 Whirlwind HAR10 (8731M)	RAF Coltishall, Fire Section	
XP393	WS55 Whirlwind HAR10 [U]	DRA Farnborough, Fire Section	
XP395	WS55 Whirlwind HAR10 (8674M) [A]	Privately owned, Tattershall Thorpe	

Notes	Serial	Type	Owner or Operator
	XP398	WS55 Whirlwind HAR10 (8794M)	Privately owned, Charlwood, Surrey
	XP399	WS55 Whirlwind HAR10	Privately owned, Raunds, Northants
	XP404	WS55 Whirlwind HAR10 (8682M)	IHM, Weston-super-Mare
	XP405	WS55 Whirlwind HAR10 (8656M) [Y]	Junior Infantry Reg't, Shorncliffe, Kent
	XP411	AW Argosy C1 (8442M) [C]	RAF Cosford Aerospace Museum
	XP458	Slingsby Grasshopper TX1	City of Norwich Aviation Museum
	XP488	Slingsby Grasshopper TX1	Fenland Aircraft Preservation Society, Wisbech
	XP502	HS Gnat T1 (8576M)	RAF St Athan, CTTS
	XP503	HS Gnat T1 (8568M) [73]	Privately owned, Bruntingthorpe
	XP504	HS Gnat T1 (8618M/G-TIMM) [04]	Repainted as XM693, 1993
	XP505	HS Gnat T1	Science Museum, Wroughton
	XP516	HS Gnat T1 (8580M) [16]	MoD(PE), DRA Farnborough
	XP530	HS Gnat T1 (8606M) [60]	RAF No 1 SoTT, Halton
	XP532	HS Gnat T1 (8577M/8615M) [32]	Privately owned, Colchester
	XP534	HS Gnat T1 (8620M) [64]	Privately owned, Cranfield
	XP540	HS Gnat T1 (8608M) [62]	Privately owned, Bruntingthorpe
	XP542	HS Gnat T1 (8575M) [42]	RAF St Athan, CTTS
	XP547	Hunting Jet Provost T4 (8992M) [N,03]	RAF No 2 SoTT, Cosford
	XP556	Hunting Jet Provost T4 (9027M) [B]	
	XP557	Hunting Jet Provost T4 (8494M)	Privately owned, Bruntingthorpe
	XP558	Hunting Jet Provost T4 (8627M/A2628) [20]	RAF St Athan Fire Section
	XP563	Hunting Jet Provost T4 (9028M) [C]	
	XP567	Hunting Jet Provost T4 (8510M) [23]	Scrapped at Halton, 1992
	XP568	Hunting Jet Provost T4	Stratford Aircraft Collection, Long Marston
	XP573	Hunting Jet Provost T4 (8236M) [19]	
	XP585	Hunting Jet Provost T4 (8407M) [24]	NE Wales Institute, Wrexham
	XP627	Hunting Jet Provost T4	North-East Aircraft Museum, Usworth
	XP629	Hunting Jet Provost T4 (9026M)	RAF North Luffenham Training Area
	XP638	Hunting Jet Provost T4 (9034M)	
	XP640	Hunting Jet Provost T4 (8501M) [D]	Yorkshire Air Museum, Elvington
	XP672	Hunting Jet Provost T4 (8458M/G-RAFI) [27]	Privately owned, Jurby, Isle of Man
	XP677	Hunting Jet Provost T4 (8587M) (cockpit)	No 2530 Sqn ATC, Headley Court, Uckfield
	XP680	Hunting Jet Provost T4 (8460M)	RAF St Athan, Fire Section
	XP686	Hunting Jet Provost T4 (8401M/8502M) [G]	RAF North Luffenham Training Area
	XP688	Hunting Jet Provost T4 (9031M) [E]	
	XP693	BAC Lightning F6 (G-FSIX)	Privately owned, Exeter
	XP701	BAC Lightning F3 (8924M) (cockpit)	Robertsbridge Aviation Society, Mayfield
	XP703	BAC Lightning F3 (cockpit)	Lightning Preservation Group, Bruntingthorpe
	XP706	BAC Lightning F3 (8925M)	Lincolnshire Lightning Preservation Society, Strubby
	XP741	BAC Lightning F3 (8939M) [AR]	FSCTE, RAF Manston
	XP745	BAC Lightning F3 (8453M) [H]	Privately owned, Greenford, West London
	XP772	DHC Beaver AL1 (G-BUCJ)	The Aircraft Restoration Co, Duxford
	XP775	DHC Beaver AL1	Privately owned
	XP806	DHC Beaver AL1	Museum of Army Flying, stored, Middle Wallop
	XP820	DHC Beaver AL1	AAC Historic Aircraft Flight, Middle Wallop
	XP821	DHC Beaver AL1 [MCO]	Museum of Army Flying, Middle Wallop
	XP822	DHC Beaver AL1	Privately owned
	XP831	Hawker P1127 (8406M)	Science Museum, South Kensington
	XP841	Handley-Page HP115	FAA/Concorde Museum, RNAS Yeovilton
	XP846	WS Scout AH1 [B,H] (fuselage)	Army, No 39 Engineer Reg't, Waterbeach
	XP847	WS Scout AH1	Museum of Army Flying, Middle Wallop
	XP848	WS Scout AH1	AAC SAE, Middle Wallop
	XP849	WS Scout AH1	MoD(PE) ETPS, Boscombe Down
	XP850	WS Scout AH1 (fuselage)	AAC, stored Dishforth
	XP853	WS Scout AH1	AAC SAE, Middle Wallop

Serial	Type	Owner or Operator	Notes
XP854	WS Scout AH1 (7898M/TAD043)	AAC SAE, Middle Wallop	
XP855	WS Scout AH1	Army Apprentice College, Arborfield	
XP856	WS Scout AH1	AAC Middle Wallop, BDRT	
XP857	WS Scout AH1	AAC, Middle Wallop Fire Section	
XP883	WS Scout AH1	AAC No 658 Sqn, Netheravon	
XP884	WS Scout AH1	AAC SAE, Middle Wallop	
XP886	WS Scout AH1	Army Apprentice College, Arborfield	
XP888	WS Scout AH1	AAC SAE, Middle Wallop	
XP890	WS Scout AH1 [G] (fuselage)	AAC, stored RNAW Almondbank	
XP891	WS Scout AH1 [S]	AAC No 666 (TA) Sqn, Middle Wallop	
XP893	WS Scout AH1	AAC, stored Middle Wallop	
XP899	WS Scout AH1 [D]	Army Apprentice College, Arborfield	
XP902	WS Scout AH1	AAC, Middle Wallop	
XP905	WS Scout AH1	AAC SAE, Middle Wallop	
XP907	WS Scout AH1	AAC, stored Fleetlands	
XP908	WS Scout AH1 [Y]	AAC No 660 Sqn, Brunei	
XP910	WS Scout AH1	AAC SAE, Middle Wallop	
XP919	DH Sea Vixen FAW2 (8163M) [706/VL]	City of Norwich Aviation Museum	
XP924	DH Sea Vixen D3	MoD(PE) T&EE Llanbedr	
XP925	DH Sea Vixen FAW2 [752] (cockpit)	DRA Farnborough, Fire Section	
XP956	DH Sea Vixen FAW2	Privately owned, Dunsfold	
XP980	Hawker P.1127 (A2700)	FAA Museum, RNAS Yeovilton	
XP984	Hawker P.1127 (A2658)	RN, stored Lee-on-Solent	
XR137	AW Argosy E1	Caernarfon Air World	
XR140	AW Argosy E1 (8579M) (fuselage)	RAF Halton, Fire Section	
XR220	BAC TSR2 (7933M)	RAF Cosford Aerospace Museum	
XR222	BAC TSR2	Imperial War Museum, Duxford	
XR232	Sud Alouette AH2 (F-WEIP)	Museum of Army Flying, Middle Wallop	
XR240	Auster AOP9 (G-BDFH)	Privately owned, Cambridge (on rebuild)	
XR241	Auster AOP9 (G-AXRR)	The Aircraft Restoration Co, Duxford	
XR244	Auster AOP9	AAC Historic Aircraft Flight, Middle Wallop	
XR246	Auster AOP9 (7862M/G-AZBU)	Privately owned, Reymerston Hall	
XR267	Auster AOP9 (G-BJXR)	Cotswold Aircraft Restoration Grp, Innsworth	
XR271	Auster AOP9	Museum of Artillery, Woolwich	
XR363	SC5 Belfast C1 (G-OHCA)	*Reverted to G-OHCA*	
XR371	SC5 Belfast C1	RAF Cosford Aerospace Museum	
XR379	Sud Alouette AH2	AAC, stored RNAW Almondbank	
XR396	DH Comet 4C (8882M/G-BDIU)	RAF Kinloss, BDRT	
XR436	Saro Scout AH1	AAC Middle Wallop, BDRT	
XR443	DH Sea Heron C1 (G-ODLG)	*Sold as VH-NJP, August 1993*	
XR453	WS55 Whirlwind HAR10 (8873M) [A]	RAF Odiham, on gate	
XR458	WS55 Whirlwind HAR10 (8662M) [H]	Museum of Army Flying, Middle Wallop	
XR478	WS55 Whirlwind HAR10	*Scrapped by August 1993*	
XR482	WS55 Whirlwind HAR10 [G]	*Scrapped by August 1993*	
XR485	WS55 Whirlwind HAR10 [Q]	Norfolk & Suffolk Aviation Museum, Flixton	
XR486	WS55 Whirlwind HCC12 (8727M/ G-RWWW)	Privately owned, Tattershall Thorpe	
XR497	WS58 Wessex HC2 [F]	RAF No 72 Sqn, Aldergrove	
XR498	WS58 Wessex HC2 [X]	RAF No 72 Sqn, Aldergrove	
XR499	WS58 Wessex HC2 [W]	RAF No 72 Sqn, Aldergrove	
XR501	WS58 Wessex HC2	RAF No 22 Sqn, A Flt, Chivenor	
XR502	WS58 Wessex HC2 [Z]	RAF No 60 Sqn, Benson	
XR503	WS58 Wessex HC2	RAF SAREW, St Mawgan	
XR504	WS58 Wessex HC2	RAF No 22 Sqn, St Mawgan	
XR505	WS58 Wessex HC2 [WA]	RAF No 2 FTS, Shawbury	
XR506	WS58 Wessex HC2 [V]	RAF No 72 Sqn, Aldergrove	
XR507	WS58 Wessex HC2	RAF SARTU, Valley	
XR508	WS58 Wessex HC2 [D]	RAF No 28 Sqn, Sek Kong	
XR509	WS58 Wessex HC2 (8752M)	RAF Benson, BDRT	
XR511	WS58 Wessex HC2 [L]	RAF No 60 Sqn, Benson	
XR515	WS58 Wessex HC2 [B]	RAF No 28 Sqn, Sek Kong	
XR516	WS58 Wessex HC2 [WB]	RAF No 2 FTS, Shawbury	
XR517	WS58 Wessex HC2 [N]	RAF No 60 Sqn, Benson	
XR518	WS58 Wessex HC2	RAF No 22 Sqn, A Flt, Chivenor	
XR519	WS58 Wessex HC2 [WC] (wreck)	RAF Shawbury	
XR520	WS58 Wessex HC2	RAF No 22 Sqn, A Flt, Chivenor	
XR521	WS58 Wessex HC2 [WD]	RAF No 2 FTS, Shawbury	

Notes	Serial	Type	Owner or Operator
	XR522	WS58 Wessex HC2 [A]	RAF No 28 Sqn, Sek Kong
	XR523	WS58 Wessex HC2 [M]	RAF No 60 Sqn, Benson
	XR524	WS58 Wessex HC2	*Crashed, Llyn Padarn, Gwynedd, 12 Aug 1993*
	XR525	WS58 Wessex HC2 [G]	RAF No 60 Sqn, Benson
	XR527	WS58 Wessex HC2 [K]	RAF No 72 Sqn, Aldergrove
	XR528	WS58 Wessex HC2 [T]	RAF No 72 Sqn, Aldergrove
	XR529	WS58 Wessex HC2 [E]	RAF No 72 Sqn, Aldergrove
	XR534	HS Gnat T1 (8578M) [65]	RAF Valley on display
	XR535	HS Gnat T1 (8569M) [05]	RAF No 1 SoTT, Halton
	XR537	HS Gnat T1 (8642M/G-NATY) [T] ●	Jet Heritage Ltd, Bournemouth
	XR538	HS Gnat T1 (8621M) (G-RORI) [69]	Privately owned, Cranfield
	XR569	HS Gnat T1 (8560M) [08]	Privately owned, Bruntingthorpe
	XR571	HS Gnat T1 (8493M)	RAF *Red Arrows*, Scampton, on display
	XR574	HS Gnat T1 (8631M) [72]	RAF No 1 SoTT, Halton
	XR588	WS58 Wessex HC2	RAF SARTU, Valley
	XR595	WS Scout AH1 [M]	AAC, stored RNAY Fleetlands
	XR597	WS Scout AH1	AAC SAE, Middle Wallop
	XR600	WS Scout AH1 (fuselage)	AAC Netheravon, BDRT
	XR601	WS Scout AH1	Army Apprentice College, Arborfield
	XR602	WS Scout AH1	*Sold in Cyprus, December 1992*
	XR627	WS Scout AH1	AAC Dishforth, derelict
	XR628	WS Scout AH1	AAC, stored RNAW Almondbank
	XR629	WS Scout AH1 (fuselage)	AAC, stored RNAW Almondbank
	XR630	WS Scout AH1 [U]	AAC Middle Wallop, BDRT
	XR632	WS Scout AH1	AAC No 658 Sqn, Netheravon
	XR635	WS Scout AH1	AAC SAE, Middle Wallop
	XR639	WS Scout AH1 [X] (fuselage)	AAC, stored RNAW Almondbank
	XR643	Hunting Jet Provost T4 (8516M) [26]	*Sold to Australia, 1992*
	XR650	Hunting Jet Provost T4 (8459M) [28]	
	XR651	Hunting Jet Provost T4 (8431M) [A]	
	XR653	Hunting Jet Provost T4 (9035M) [H]	*Sold to Australia, 1992*
	XR654	Hunting Jet Provost T4	Macclesfield Historical Aviation Society, Marthall
	XR658	Hunting Jet Provost T4 (8192M)	North Wales Institute of Higher Education Connah's Quay
	XR662	Hunting Jet Provost T4 (8410M) [25]	
	XR669	Hunting Jet Provost T4 (8062M) (cockpit) [02]	RAF No 1 SoTT, Halton
	XR670	Hunting Jet Provost T4 (8498M)	RAF Odiham, instructional use
	XR672	Hunting Jet Provost T4 (8495M) [50]	RAF Halton, Fire Section
	XR673	Hunting Jet Provost T4 (9032M) [L]	RAF No 1 SoTT, Halton
	XR674	Hunting Jet Provost T4 (9030M) [D]	Privately owned, North Weald
	XR679	Hunting Jet Provost T4 (8991M) [M,04]	RAF No 2 SoTT, Cosford
	XR681	Hunting Jet Provost T4 (8588M) (cockpit)	No 1349 Sqn ATC, Odiham
	XR700	Hunting Jet Provost T4 (8589M) (cockpit)	RAF Exhibition Flight, Aldergrove
	XR701	Hunting Jet Provost T4 (9025M) [K,21]	*Scrapped at Halton, 1992*
	XR704	Hunting Jet Provost T4 (8506M) [30]	*Scrapped at Halton, 1992*
	XR713	BAC Lightning F3 (8935M) [C]	RAF Leuchars
	XR716	BAC Lightning F3 (8940M)	RAF Cottesmore, Fire Section
	XR718	BAC Lightning F6 (8932M)	Blyth Valley Aviation Collection, Walpole
	XR724	BAC Lightning F6 (G-BTSY)	Privately owned, Binbrook
	XR725	BAC Lightning F6	Privately owned, Binbrook
	XR726	BAC Lightning F6 (cockpit)	Privately owned, Harrogate
	XR728	BAC Lightning F6 [JS]	Lightning Preservation Group, Bruntingthorpe
	XR747	BAC Lightning F6 (cockpit)	Privately owned, Plymouth
	XR749	BAC Lightning F3 (8934M) (cockpit)	S Yorkshire Aircraft Preservation Society, Firbeck
	XR751	BAC Lightning F3	Privately owned, Lower Tremar, Cornwall
	XR753	BAC Lightning F6 (8969M) [BP]	RAF Leeming on display
	XR754	BAC Lightning F6 (8972M) [BC]	*Scrapped by February 1992*
	XR755	BAC Lightning F6	Privately owned, Callington, Cornwall

Serial	Type	Owner or Operator	Notes
XR757	BAC Lightning F6 (cockpit)	Privately owned, New Waltham, Humberside	
XR759	BAC Lightning F6	*Scrapped at Rossington by July 1993*	
XR770	BAC Lightning F6 [JS]	Privately owned, New Waltham, Humberside	
XR771	BAC Lightning F6 [BM]	Midland Air Museum, Coventry	
XR773	BAC Lightning F6 (G-OPIB)	Privately owned, Exeter	
XR777	WS Scout AH1 (really XT625)	St George's Barracks, Sutton Coldfield	
XR806	BAC VC10 C1	RAF No 10 Sqn, Brize Norton	
XR807	BAC VC10 C1	RAF No 10 Sqn, Brize Norton	
XR808	BAC VC10 C1	RAF No 10 Sqn, Brize Norton	
XR810	BAC VC10 C1	RAF No 10 Sqn, Brize Norton	
XR944	Wallis WA116 (G-ATTB)	RAF Museum, Hendon	
XR953	HS Gnat T1 (8609M) [63]	RAF No 1 SoTT, Halton	
XR954	HS Gnat T1 (8570M) [30]	RAF No 1 SoTT, Halton	
XR955	HS Gnat T1 (A2678) [SAH-2]	Privately owned, Leavesden	
XR977	HS Gnat T1 (8640M)	RAF Cosford Aerospace Museum	
XR980	HS Gnat T1 (8622M) [70]	RAF No 1 SoTT, Halton	
XR985	HS Gnat T1 (7886M)	Vintage Aircraft Team, Cranfield	
XR991	HS Gnat T1 (8624M/XS102/ G-MOUR)	Intrepid Aviation Co, North Weald	
XR998	HS Gnat T1 (8623M) [71]	RAF No 1 SoTT, Halton	
XS101	HS Gnat T1 (8638M) (G-GNAT)	Privately owned, Cranfield	
XS122	WS58 Wessex HAS3 (A2707) [655/PO]	RNEC Manadon, for instruction	
XS128	WS58 Wessex HAS1 (A2670) [37]	RNAS Yeovilton, Fire Section	
XS149	WS58 Wessex HAS3 [661/GL]	IHM, Weston-super-Mare	
XS153	WS58 Wessex HAS3 [662/PO]	RN, Lee-on-Solent, BDRT	
XS176	Hunting Jet Provost T4 (8514M) [N]	University of Salford, Manchester	
XS177	Hunting Jet Provost T4 (9044M) [N]	RAF Valley Fire Section	
XS178	Hunting Jet Provost T4 (8994M) [P,05]	RAF No 2 SoTT, Cosford	
XS179	Hunting Jet Provost T4 (8237M) [20]	University of Salford, Manchester	
XS180	Hunting Jet Provost T4 (8238M) [21]	RAF St Athan (dismantled)	
XS181	Hunting Jet Provost T4 (9033M) [F]	RAF No 1 SoTT, Halton	
XS186	Hunting Jet Provost T4 (8408M) [M]	RAF North Luffenham Training Area	
XS209	Hunting Jet Provost T4 (8409M)	RAF Halton	
XS210	Hunting Jet Provost T4 (8239M) [22]	*Sold to Australia*	
XS215	Hunting Jet Provost T4 (8507M) [17]	RAF Halton, dismantled	
XS216	Hunting Jet Provost T4 (cockpit)	RAF Finningley Fire Section	
XS217	Hunting Jet Provost T4 (9029M) [O]	RAF Halton	
XS218	Hunting Jet Provost T4 (8508M) [18]	Museum of Berkshire Aviation, Woodley	
XS219	Hunting Jet Provost T4 (8993M) [O,06]	RAF No 2 SoTT, Cosford	
XS230	BAC Jet Provost T5P	MoD(PE) ETPS, Boscombe Down	
XS231	BAC Jet Provost T5 (G-ATAJ)	Privately owned, Bruntingthorpe	
XS235	DH Comet 4C	MoD(PE) A&AEE Boscombe Down	
XS241	WS58 Wessex HU5 (9102M)	RAF Benson, Fire Section	
XS416	BAC Lightning T5	Privately owned, New Waltham, Humberside	
XS417	BAC Lightning T5	Newark Air Museum, Winthorpe	
XS419	BAC Lightning T5	*Scrapped at Rossington by July 1993*	
XS420	BAC Lightning T5	Privately owned, Narborough, Norfolk	
XS422	BAC Lightning T5	Privately owned, Southampton Docks	
XS451	BAC Lightning T5 (8503M/ G-LTNG)	Privately owned, Plymouth	
XS452	BAC Lightning T5 (G-BPFE) [BT]	Privately owned, Cranfield	
XS456	BAC Lightning T5	Privately owned, Wainfleet	
XS457	BAC Lightning T5 (cockpit)	Privately owned, New Waltham	
XS458	BAC Lightning T5 [DY]	Privately owned, Cranfield	
XS459	BAC Lightning T5	Privately owned, Narborough, Norfolk	
XS463	WS Wasp HAS1 (really XT431)	IHM, Weston-super-Mare	
XS463	WS Wasp HAS1 (A2647)	RN Predannack Fire School	
XS479	WS58 Wessex HU5 (8819M) [XF]	JATE, RAF Brize Norton	

Notes	Serial	Type	Owner or Operator
	XS481	WS58 Wessex HU5	AAC 9 Regt Dishforth, BDRT
	XS482	WS58 Wessex HU5 [A-D]	DRA Farnborough Apprentice School
	XS483	WS58 Wessex HU5 [T/VL]	RN Lee-on-Solent, Fire Section
	XS484	WS58 Wessex HU5 [821/CU]	RAF Finningley, Fire Section
	XS485	WS58 Wessex HC5C (Hearts)	RAF No 84 Sqn, Akrotiri
	XS486	WS58 Wessex HU5 [524]	RN Recruiting Team, Lee-on-Solent
	XS488	WS58 Wessex HU5 (9056M) [XK]	RAF No 1 SoTT, Halton
	XS489	WS58 Wessex HU5 [R]	RAF Odiham, instructional use
	XS491	WS58 Wessex HU5 [XM]	RAF No 16 MU Stafford, Fire Section
	XS492	WS58 Wessex HU5 [623]	RN, stored
	XS493	WS58 Wessex HU5	RN, stored Fleetlands
	XS496	WS58 Wessex HU5 [625/PO]	RN AES, Lee-on-Solent
	XS498	WS58 Wessex HC5C (Joker)	RAF No 84 Sqn, Akrotiri
	XS506	WS58 Wessex HU5	RAF, stored Shawbury
	XS507	WS58 Wessex HU5 [627/PO]	RN AES, Lee-on-Solent
	XS508	WS58 Wessex HU5	FAA Museum, RNAS Yeovilton
	XS509	WS58 Wessex HU5 (A2597)	MoD(PE) ETPS, Boscombe Down
	XS510	WS58 Wessex HU5 [626/PO]	RN AES, Lee-on-Solent
	XS511	WS58 Wessex HU5 [M]	RN AES, Lee-on-Solent
	XS513	WS58 Wessex HU5 [419/PO]	RN, Lee-on-Solent, BDRT
	XS514	WS58 Wessex HU5 [L]	RN AES, Lee-on-Solent
	XS515	WS58 Wessex HU5 [N]	RN AES, Lee-on-Solent
	XS516	WS58 Wessex HU5 [Q]	RN AES, Lee-on-Solent
	XS517	WS58 Wessex HC5C (Diamonds)	RAF No 84 Sqn, Akrotiri
	XS520	WS58 Wessex HU5 [F]	RN AES, Lee-on-Solent
	XS522	WS58 Wessex HU5 [ZL]	RN, Lee-on-Solent, BDRT
	XS523	WS58 Wessex HU5 [824/CU]	RNAY Fleetlands
	XS527	WS Wasp HAS1	FAA Museum, RNAS Yeovilton
	XS529	WS Wasp HAS1 [461]	RN AES, Lee-on-Solent
	XS535	WS Wasp HAS1 [432]	RAOC, West Moors, Dorset
	XS538	WS Wasp HAS1 (A2725) [451]	RN, Culdrose, Fire Section
	XS539	WS Wasp HAS1 [435]	RN, stored Fleetlands
	XS541	WS Wasp HAS1 [602]	RN, stored Fleetlands
	XS545	WS Wasp HAS1 (A2702) [635]	RN AES, Lee-on-Solent
	XS562	WS Wasp HAS1 [605]	RN, stored Fleetlands
	XS567	WS Wasp HAS1 [434/E]	Imperial War Museum, Duxford
	XS568	WS Wasp HAS1 [441]	RNAY Fleetlands Apprentice School
	XS569	WS Wasp HAS1	RNAY Fleetlands Apprentice School
	XS570	WS Wasp HAS1 (A2699) [445/P]	Warship Preservation Trust, Birkenhead
	XS572	WS Wasp HAS1 (8845M) [414]	RAF No 16 MU Stafford, Fire Section
	XS576	DH Sea Vixen FAW2 [125/E]	Imperial War Museum, Duxford
	XS577	DH Sea Vixen D3	MoD(PE), stored T&EE Llanbedr
	XS587	DH Sea Vixen FAW(TT)2 (8828M/ G-VIXN)	Privately owned, Charlwood, Surrey
	XS590	DH Sea Vixen FAW2 [131/E]	FAA Museum, stored RNAS Yeovilton
	XS596	HS Andover C1(PR)	MoD(PE), A&AEE Boscombe Down
	XS597	HS Andover C1	Privately owned, Southend
	XS598	HS Andover C1 (fuselage)	RAF AMS, Brize Norton
	XS603	HS Andover E3	Hunting Air Services, East Midlands Airport
	XS605	HS Andover E3	Hunting Air Services, East Midlands Airport
	XS606	HS Andover C1	MoD(PE) ETPS, Boscombe Down
	XS607	HS Andover C1	MoD(PE) DRA Farnborough
	XS610	HS Andover E3	Hunting Air Services, East Midlands Airport
	XS637	HS Andover C1	Privately owned, Southend
	XS639	HS Andover E3A	RAF No 32 Sqn, Northolt
	XS640	HS Andover E3	Hunting Air Services, East Midlands Airport
	XS641	HS Andover C1(PR) (91. .M)	RAF No 2 SoTT, Cosford
	XS642	HS Andover C1 [C] (8785M)	RAF Benson Fire Section
	XS643	HS Andover E3A	RAF No 32 Sqn, Northolt
	XS644	HS Andover E3A	RAF No 32 Sqn, Northolt
	XS646	HS Andover C1(mod)	MoD(PE) DRA Farnborough
	XS674	WS58 Wessex HC2 [R]	RAF No 60 Sqn, Benson
	XS675	WS58 Wessex HC2	RAF No 22 Sqn, St Mawgan
	XS676	WS58 Wessex HC2 [WJ]	RAF No 2 FTS, Shawbury
	XS677	WS58 Wessex HC2 [WK]	RAF No 2 FTS, Shawbury
	XS679	WS58 Wessex HC2 [WG]	RAF No 2 FTS, Shawbury
	XS695	HS Kestrel FGA1 (A2619) [SAH-6]	RN, stored Lee-on-Solent
	XS709	HS Dominie T1 [M]	RAF No 6 FTS, Finningley
	XS710	HS Dominie T1 [O]	RAF No 6 FTS, Finningley
	XS711	HS Dominie T1 [L]	RAF No 6 FTS, Finningley
	XS712	HS Dominie T1 [A]	RAF No 6 FTS, Finningley
	XS713	HS Dominie T1 [C]	RAF No 6 FTS, Finningley
	XS714	HS Dominie T1 [P]	RAF No 6 FTS, Finningley

Serial	Type	Owner or Operator	Notes
XS726	HS Dominie T1 [T]	RAF No 6 FTS, Finningley	
XS727	HS Dominie T1 [D]	RAF No 6 FTS, Finningley	
XS728	HS Dominie T1 [E]	RAF No 6 FTS, Finningley	
XS729	HS Dominie T1 [G]	RAF No 6 FTS, Finningley	
XS730	HS Dominie T1 [H]	RAF No 6 FTS, Finningley	
XS731	HS Dominie T1 [J]	RAF No 6 FTS, Finningley	
XS732	HS Dominie T1 [B] (fuselage)	DRA, Fort Halstead, Kent	
XS733	HS Dominie T1 [Q]	RAF No 6 FTS, Finningley	
XS734	HS Dominie T1 [N]	RAF No 6 FTS, Finningley	
XS735	HS Dominie T1 [R]	RAF No 6 FTS, Finningley	
XS736	HS Dominie T1 [S]	RAF No 6 FTS, Finningley	
XS737	HS Dominie T1 [K]	RAF No 6 FTS, Finningley	
XS738	HS Dominie T1 [U]	RAF No 6 FTS, Finningley	
XS739	HS Dominie T1 [F]	RAF No 6 FTS, Finningley	
XS743	Beagle Basset CC1	MoD(PE) ETPS, Boscombe Down	
XS770	Beagle Basset CC1 (G-HRHI)	Privately owned, Cranfield	
XS789	HS Andover CC2	RAF No 32 Sqn, Northolt	
XS790	HS Andover CC2	MoD(PE) DRA Farnborough	
XS791	HS Andover CC2	RAF No 32 Sqn, Northolt	
XS792	HS Andover CC2	RAF No 32 Sqn, Northolt	
XS793	HS Andover CC2 (9178M)	RAF No 2 SoTT, Cosford	
XS794	HS Andover CC2	RAF No 32 Sqn, Northolt	
XS862	WS58 Wessex HAS3	NB&C Defence Centre, Winterbourne Gunner	
XS863	WS58 Wessex HAS1	Imperial War Museum, Duxford	
XS865	WS58 Wessex HAS1 (A2694) [529/CU]	RNAS Lee-on-Solent Fire Section	
XS866	WS58 Wessex HAS1 (A2705) [520/CU]	RN SAH, Culdrose	
XS868	WS58 Wessex HAS1 (A2691)	RNAY Fleetlands, on gate	
XS870	WS58 Wessex HAS1 (A2697)	RN Portland, Fire Section	
XS871	WS58 Wessex HAS1 (8457M) [AI]	RAF Odiham, Fire Section	
XS872	WS58 Wessex HAS1 (A2666) [572/CU]	RNAY Fleetlands Apprentice School	
XS873	WS58 Wessex HAS1 (A2686)	RN Predannack Fire School	
XS876	WS58 Wessex HAS1 (A2695) [523]	RN SAH, Culdrose	
XS877	WS58 Wessex HAS1 (A2687) [516/PO]	RN Culdrose, Fire Section	
XS878	WS58 Wessex HAS1 (A2683)	RN, Lee-on-Solent, Fire Section	
XS881	WS58 Wessex HAS1 (A2675) [046/R]	RNAS Yeovilton, Fire Section	
XS885	WS58 Wessex HAS1 (A2668) [12/CU]	RN, SAH Culdrose	
XS886	WS58 Wessex HAS1 (A2685) [527/CU]	Sea Scouts, Evesham, Worcs	
XS887	WS58 Wessex HAS1 (A2690) [403/FI]	Flambards Village Theme Park, Helston	
XS888	WS58 Wessex HAS1 [521]	Guernsey Airport, Fire Section	
XS897	BAC Lightning F6	South Yorkshire Aviation Museum, Firbeck	
XS898	BAC Lightning F6 [BD]	Privately owned, Cranfield	
XS899	BAC Lightning F6 [BL]	Privately owned, Cranfield	
XS903	BAC Lightning F6 [BA]	Yorkshire Air Museum, Elvington	
XS904	BAC Lightning F6	Sold to Germany	
XS919	BAC Lightning F6	Privately owned, Liskeard, Cornwall	
XS922	BAC Lightning F6 (8973M) [BJ]	Scrapped at Wattisham by June 1993	
XS923	BAC Lightning F6 [BE]	Privately owned, Cranfield	
XS925	BAC Lightning F6 (8961M) [BA]	RAF Museum, Hendon	
XS928	BAC Lightning F6	BAe, Warton, stored	
XS932	BAC Lightning F6 (cockpit)	Privately owned, Bruntingthorpe	
XS933	BAC Lightning F6 (cockpit)	Privately owned, Narborough, Norfolk	
XS935	BAC Lightning F6	Scrapped at Rossington by July 1993	
XS936	BAC Lightning F6	Privately owned, Liskeard, Cornwall	
XT108	Agusta-Bell Sioux AH1 [U]	Museum of Army Flying, Middle Wallop	
XT131	Agusta-Bell Sioux AH1 [B]	AAC Historic Aircraft Flight, Middle Wallop	
XT133	Agusta-Bell Sioux AH1 (7923M)	Royal Engineers' Museum, Chatham, stored	
XT140	Agusta-Bell Sioux AH1	Air Service Training, Perth	
XT148	Agusta-Bell Sioux AH1	Privately owned, Panshanger	
XT150	Agusta-Bell Sioux AH1 (7883M) [R]	AAC Netheravon, on display	
XT151	WS Sioux AH1 [W]	Museum of Army Flying, stored Middle Wallop	

Notes	Serial	Type	Owner or Operator
	XT175	WS Sioux AH1 (TAD175)	CSE Oxford for ground instruction
	XT176	WS Sioux AH1 [U]	FAA Museum, RNAS Yeovilton
	XT190	WS Sioux AH1	AAC Wattisham, on display
	XT200	WS Sioux AH1 [F]	Newark Air Museum, Winthorpe
	XT236	WS Sioux AH1 (frame only)	North-East Aircraft Museum, Usworth
	XT242	WS Sioux AH1 (composite)	The Aeroplane Collection, Warmingham, Cheshire
	XT255	WS58 Wessex HAS3 (8751M)	RAF No 14 MU, Carlisle, BDRT
	XT257	WS58 Wessex HAS3 (8719M)	RAF No 1 SoTT, Halton
	XT272	HS Buccaneer S2	DRA Farnborough Fire Section
	XT277	HS Buccaneer S2A (8853M)	RAF Cosford
	XT280	HS Buccaneer S2B	RAF stored Lossiemouth
	XT281	HS Buccaneer S2B (8705M) [ET]	Scrapped, 1992
	XT283	HS Buccaneer S2A	Scrapped, 1992
	XT284	HS Buccaneer S2A (8855M)	RAF St Athan, BDRT
	XT286	HS Buccaneer S2A	Scrapped at Shawbury, August 1993
	XT288	HS Buccaneer S2B (9134M)	RAF Lossiemouth, WLT
	XT415	WS Wasp HAS1 [FIR3]	Airwork Ltd, Bournemouth
	XT420	WS Wasp HAS1 [606]	RN, stored Fleetlands
	XT422	WS Wasp HAS1 [324]	Privately owned, Burgess Hill
	XT427	WS Wasp HAS1 [606]	Flambards Village Theme Park, Helston
	XT430	WS Wasp HAS1 [444]	Scrapped by August 1993
	XT434	WS Wasp HAS1 [455]	RNAY Fleetlands Apprentice School
	XT437	WS Wasp HAS1 [423]	RN AES, Lee-on-Solent
	XT439	WS Wasp HAS1 [605]	Cranfield Institute of Technology
	XT449	WS58 Wessex HU5 [C]	RN, Lee-on-Solent, Fire Section
	XT450	WS58 Wessex HU5 [V]	RN, Predannack Fire School
	XT451	WS58 Wessex HU5 [XN]	RAF, stored Shawbury
	XT453	WS58 Wessex HU5 [A]	RN AES, Lee-on-Solent
	XT455	WS58 Wessex HU5 [U]	RN AES, Lee-on-Solent
	XT456	WS58 Wessex HU5 (8941M) [XZ]	RAF Aldergrove, BDRT
	XT458	WS58 Wessex HU5 [622]	RN AES, Lee-on-Solent
	XT459	WS58 Wessex HU5 [D]	Privately owned, Faygate
	XT460	WS58 Wessex HU5 [K]	RN AES, Lee-on-Solent
	XT463	WS58 Wessex HC5C [Clubs]	RAF No 84 Sqn, Akrotiri
	XT466	WS58 Wessex HU5 (8921M) [XV]	RAF No 2 SoTT, Cosford
	XT468	WS58 Wessex HU5 [628]	RN AES, Lee-on-Solent
	XT469	WS58 Wessex HU5 (8920M)	RAF No 16 MU, Stafford, ground instruction
	XT470	WS58 Wessex HU5 [A]	AAC, Netheravon, Fire Section
	XT471	WS58 Wessex HU5	AAC, 9 Regt Dishforth, BDRT
	XT472	WS58 Wessex HU5 [XC]	IHM, Weston-super-Mare
	XT475	WS58 Wessex HU5 (9108M) [624]	FSCTE, RAF Manston
	XT479	WS58 Wessex HC5C (Spades)	RAF No 84 Sqn, Akrotiri
	XT480	WS58 Wessex HU5 [XQ]	RN Fleetlands
	XT481	WS58 Wessex HU5 [F]	RN Predannack Fire School
	XT482	WS58 Wessex HU5 [ZM/VL]	RN AES, Lee-on-Solent
	XT484	WS58 Wessex HU5 [H]	RN AES, Lee-on-Solent
	XT485	WS58 Wessex HU5 [621/PO]	RN AES, Lee-on-Solent
	XT486	WS58 Wessex HU5 (8919M) [XR]	RAF JATE, preserved Brize Norton
	XT487	WS58 Wessex HU5 (A2723) [815/LS]	RNAS Lee-on-Solent Fire Section
	XT575	Vickers Viscount 837 (OE-LAG) (cockpit)	Privately owned, Essex
	XT595	McD Phantom FG1 (8550M)	Scrapped at Wattisham by June 1993
	XT595	McD Phantom FG1 (8851M) (cockpit)	RAF Exhibition Flight, St Athan
	XT596	McD Phantom FG1	FAA Museum, RNAS Yeovilton
	XT597	McD Phantom FG1	MoD(PE) A&AEE Boscombe Down
	XT601	WS58 Wessex HC2	RAF No 22 Sqn, E Flt, Coltishall
	XT602	WS58 Wessex HC2	RAF No 22 Sqn, E Flt, Coltishall
	XT603	WS58 Wessex HC2 [WF]	RAF No 2 FTS, Shawbury
	XT604	WS58 Wessex HC2	RAF SARTU, Valley
	XT605	WS58 Wessex HC2 [E]	RAF No 28 Sqn, Sek Kong
	XT606	WS58 Wessex HC2 [WL]	RAF No 2 FTS, Shawbury
	XT607	WS58 Wessex HC2 [P]	RAF No 72 Sqn, Aldergrove
	XT614	WS Scout AH1 [C]	AAC No 660 Sqn, Sek Kong
	XT616	WS Scout AH1 (fuselage)	AAC, stored RNAW Almondbank
	XT617	WS Scout AH1	AAC, stored RNAW Almondbank
	XT620	WS Scout AH1	AAC Aldergrove, BDRT
	XT621	WS Scout AH1	Royal Military College of Science, Shrivenham
	XT623	WS Scout AH1	Army Apprentice College, Arborfield

Serial	Type	Owner or Operator	Notes
XT624	WS Scout AH1 [D]	AAC No 660 Sqn, Sek Kong	
XT626	WS Scout AH1 [Q]	AAC No 666(TA) Sqn, Middle Wallop	
XT628	WS Scout AH1 [E]	AAC No 660 Sqn, Sek Kong	
XT630	WS Scout AH1 [X]	AAC No 660 Sqn, Brunei	
XT631	WS Scout AH1 [D]	MoD(PE) A&AEE Boscombe Down	
XT632	WS Scout AH1	AAC No 658 Sqn, Netheravon	
XT633	WS Scout AH1	Army Apprentice College, Arborfield	
XT634	WS Scout AH1 [T]	AAC No 666(TA) Sqn, Middle Wallop	
XT636	WS Scout AH1 [F]	AAC No 660 Sqn, Sek Kong	
XT637	WS Scout AH1 (fuselage)	RNAS Yeovilton, Fire Section	
XT638	WS Scout AH1 [N]	AAC, stored RNAY Fleetlands	
XT639	WS Scout AH1 [Y] (fuselage)	AAC, stored RNAW Almondbank	
XT640	WS Scout AH1	AAC SAE, Middle Wallop	
XT642	WS Scout AH1 (fuselage)	AAC, stored RNAW Almondbank	
XT643	WS Scout AH1 [Z]	Army, No 39 Engineer Regt, Waterbeach	
XT644	WS Scout AH1 [Y]	AAC No 666(TA) Sqn, Middle Wallop	
XT645	WS Scout AH1 (fuselage)	RN, Lee-on-Solent	
XT646	WS Scout AH1 [Z]	AAC No 666(TA) Sqn, Middle Wallop	
XT648	WS Scout AH1	*Sold to Cyprus, November 1992*	
XT649	WS Scout AH1	AAC No 658 Sqn, Netheravon	
XT661	Vickers Viscount 838 (9G-AAV) (cockpit)	Privately owned, Essex	
XT667	WS58 Wessex HC2 [F]	RAF No 28 Sqn, Sek Kong	
XT668	WS58 Wessex HC2 [S]	RAF No 72 Sqn, Aldergrove	
XT669	WS58 Wessex HC2 (8894M) [T]	RAF Aldergrove, Fire Section	
XT670	WS58 Wessex HC2	RAF SAREW, St Mawgan	
XT671	WS58 Wessex HC2 [D]	RAF No 60 Sqn, Benson	
XT672	WS58 Wessex HC2 [WE]	RAF No 2 FTS, Shawbury	
XT673	WS58 Wessex HC2 [G]	RAF No 28 Sqn, Sek Kong	
XT675	WS58 Wessex HC2 [C]	RAF No 28 Sqn, Sek Kong	
XT676	WS58 Wessex HC2 [I]	RAF No 60 Sqn, Benson	
XT677	WS58 Wessex HC2 (8016M)	RAF Brize Norton Fire Section	
XT678	WS58 Wessex HC2 [H]	RAF No 28 Sqn, Sek Kong	
XT680	WS58 Wessex HC2	RAF No 22 Sqn, St Mawgan	
XT681	WS58 Wessex HC2 [U]	RAF No 72 Sqn, Aldergrove	
XT752	Fairey Gannet T5 (WN365/ G-APYO)	RN, stored Lee-on-Solent	
XT755	WS58 Wessex HU5 (9053M) [V]	RAF No 1 SoTT, Halton	
XT756	WS58 Wessex HU5 [ZJ]	RN, Lee-on-Solent, Fire Section	
XT759	WS58 Wessex HU5 [XY]	RN Fleetlands, derelict	
XT760	WS58 Wessex HU5 [418]	RN ETS, Culdrose	
XT761	WS58 Wessex HU5	RN AES, Lee-on-Solent	
XT762	WS58 Wessex HU5	RNAS Culdrose, SAH	
XT765	WS58 Wessex HU5 [J]	RN AES, Lee-on-Solent	
XT766	WS58 Wessex HU5 (9054M) [822/CU]	RAF No 1 SoTT, Halton	
XT768	WS58 Wessex HU5	RAF	
XT769	WS58 Wessex HU5 [823/CU]	FAA Museum, Yeovilton	
XT770	WS58 Wessex HU5 (9055M)	RAF No 1 SoTT, Halton	
XT771	WS58 Wessex HU5 [620/PO]	RN AES, Lee-on-Solent	
XT772	WS58 Wessex HU5 (8805M)	RAF Valley, ground instruction	
XT773	WS58 Wessex HU5 (9123M)	RAF St Athan, BDRT	
XT778	WS Wasp HAS1 [430]	RN AES, Lee-on-Solent	
XT780	WS Wasp HAS1 [636]	RNAY Fleetlands Apprentice School	
XT788	WS Wasp HAS1 [442] (G-BMIR)	Privately owned, Charlwood, Surrey	
XT793	WS Wasp HAS1 [456]	RN, stored Fleetlands	
XT795	WS Wasp HAS1 [476/LE]	*To The Netherlands, 19 April 1993*	
XT803	WS Sioux AH1 [Y]	Privately owned, Panshanger	
XT827	WS Sioux AH1 [D] (spares)	AAC Historic Flight, Middle Wallop	
XT852	McD Phantom FGR2	MoD(PE) DRA West Freugh, Fire Section	
XT853	McD Phantom FGR2 (9071M)	RAF Scampton Fire Section	
XT857	McD Phantom FG1 (8913M) [MP]	*Scrapped at Leuchars, April 1992*	
XT858	McD Phantom FG1	MoD(PE) Aston Down	
XT864	McD Phantom FG1 (8998M) [BJ]	RAF Leuchars on display	
XT867	McD Phantom FG1 (9064M) [BH]	RAF Leuchars BDRT	
XT874	McD Phantom FG1 (9068M) [BE]	*Scrapped at Wattisham by June 1993*	
XT891	McD Phantom FGR2 (9136M)	RAF Coningsby, on display	
XT892	McD Phantom FGR2 [J]	*Scrapped at Wattisham, April 1993*	
XT894	McD Phantom FGR2 [Y]	*Scrapped at Wattisham, September 1992*	
XT895	McD Phantom FGR2 (9171M) [Q]	RAF Valley, Fire Section	
XT896	McD Phantom FGR2 [V]	RAF, stored Shawbury	
XT897	McD Phantom FGR2 [N]	RAF, stored Shawbury	
XT898	McD Phantom FGR2 [CE]	*Scrapped at St Athan, 1993*	

Notes	Serial	Type	Owner or Operator
	XT900	McD Phantom FGR2 (9099M) [CO]	RAF Honington, BDRT
	XT903	McD Phantom FGR2 [X]	RAF Leuchars
	XT905	McD Phantom FGR2 [P]	RAF Coningsby, stored
	XT906	McD Phantom FGR2 [P]	*Scrapped at Wattisham by June 1993*
	XT907	McD Phantom FGR2 (9151M) [W]	Defence School, Chattenden, at gate
	XT910	McD Phantom FGR2 [O]	RAF, stored Shawbury
	XT911	McD Phantom FGR2 [T]	*Scrapped at St Athan, 1993*
	XT914	McD Phantom FGR2 [Z]	RAF Leeming
	XV101	BAC VC10 C1K	RAF No 10 Sqn, Brize Norton
	XV102	BAC VC10 C1K	RAF No 10 Sqn, Brize Norton
	XV103	BAC VC10 C1K	RAF No 10 Sqn, Brize Norton
	XV104	BAC VC10 C1K	RAF No 10 Sqn, Brize Norton
	XV105	BAC VC10 C1	RAF No 10 Sqn, Brize Norton
	XV106	BAC VC10 C1K	RAF No 10 Sqn, Brize Norton
	XV107	BAC VC10 C1K	RAF No 10 Sqn, Brize Norton
	XV108	BAC VC10 C1	RAF No 10 Sqn, Brize Norton
	XV109	BAC VC10 C1K	RAF No 10 Sqn, Brize Norton
	XV118	WS Scout AH1 (9141M)	RAF Air Movements School, Brize Norton
	XV119	WS Scout AH1 [T]	AAC, Netheravon, BDRT
	XV121	WS Scout AH1	AAC, stored RNAY Fleetlands
	XV122	WS Scout AH1 [D]	AAC, stored RNAW Almondbank
	XV123	WS Scout AH1	AAC, stored RNAY Fleetlands
	XV124	WS Scout AH1	AAC SAE, Middle Wallop
	XV126	WS Scout AH1 [X]	AAC No 666(TA) Sqn, Middle Wallop
	XV127	WS Scout AH1	AAC, stored RNAY Fleetlands
	XV128	WS Scout AH1	AAC No 658 Sqn, Netheravon
	XV129	WS Scout AH1 [V]	AAC No 666(TA) Sqn, Middle Wallop
	XV130	WS Scout AH1 [R]	AAC No 666(TA) Sqn, Middle Wallop
	XV131	WS Scout AH1 [Y]	AAC Middle Wallop
	XV134	WS Scout AH1 [P]	AAC, stored RNAY Fleetlands
	XV135	WS Scout AH1	AAC
	XV136	WS Scout AH1 [X]	AAC Netheravon, on display
	XV137	WS Scout AH1	AAC No 658 Sqn, Netheravon
	XV138	WS Scout AH1	AAC, stored RNAW Almondbank
	XV139	WS Scout AH1	Army Apprentice College, Arborfield
	XV140	WS Scout AH1 [K]	AAC No 666(TA) Sqn, Middle Wallop
	XV141	WS Scout AH1	Army Apprentice College, Arborfield
	XV147	HS Nimrod MR1(mod)	MoD(PE), BAe Warton
	XV148	HS Nimrod MR1(mod)	MoD(PE), BAe Woodford
	XV154	HS Buccaneer S2A (8854M)	*Scrapped at Lossiemouth, 1992*
	XV155	HS Buccaneer S2B (8716M)	*Scrapped*
	XV161	HS Buccaneer S2B (9117M)	RAF, stored Lossiemouth
	XV163	HS Buccaneer S2A	*Scrapped at Shawbury, August 1993*
	XV165	HS Buccaneer S2B	RAF, stored Shawbury
	XV168	HS Buccaneer S2B	BAe Brough, on display
	XV176	Lockheed Hercules C3P	RAF Lyneham Transport Wing
	XV177	Lockheed Hercules C3P	RAF Lyneham Transport Wing
	XV178	Lockheed Hercules C1P	RAF Lyneham Transport Wing
	XV179	Lockheed Hercules C1P	RAF Lyneham Transport Wing
	XV181	Lockheed Hercules C1P	RAF Lyneham Transport Wing
	XV182	Lockheed Hercules C1P	MoD(PE), A&AEE Boscombe Down
	XV183	Lockheed Hercules C3P	RAF Lyneham Transport Wing
	XV184	Lockheed Hercules C3P	RAF Lyneham Transport Wing
	XV185	Lockheed Hercules C1P	RAF Lyneham Transport Wing
	XV186	Lockheed Hercules C1P	MoD(PE), A&AEE Boscombe Down
	XV187	Lockheed Hercules C1P	RAF Lyneham Transport Wing
	XV188	Lockheed Hercules C3P	RAF Lyneham Transport Wing
	XV189	Lockheed Hercules C3P	RAF Lyneham Transport Wing
	XV190	Lockheed Hercules C3P	RAF Lyneham Transport Wing
	XV191	Lockheed Hercules C1P	RAF Lyneham Transport Wing
	XV192	Lockheed Hercules C1K	RAF Lyneham Transport Wing
	XV193	Lockheed Hercules C3P	*Written off, Blair Atholl, 20 May 1993*
	XV195	Lockheed Hercules C1P	RAF Lyneham Transport Wing
	XV196	Lockheed Hercules C1P	RAF Lyneham Transport Wing
	XV197	Lockheed Hercules C3P	RAF Lyneham Transport Wing
	XV199	Lockheed Hercules C3P	RAF Lyneham Transport Wing
	XV200	Lockheed Hercules C1P	RAF Lyneham Transport Wing
	XV201	Lockheed Hercules C1K	RAF No 1312 Flt, Mount Pleasant, Fl
	XV202	Lockheed Hercules C3P	RAF Lyneham Transport Wing
	XV203	Lockheed Hercules C1K	RAF Lyneham Transport Wing
	XV204	Lockheed Hercules C1K	RAF No 1312 Flt, Mount Pleasant, Fl
	XV205	Lockheed Hercules C1P	RAF Lyneham Transport Wing

Serial	Type	Owner or Operator	Notes
XV206	Lockheed Hercules C1P	RAF Lyneham Transport Wing	
XV207	Lockheed Hercules C3P	RAF Lyneham Transport Wing	
XV208	Lockheed Hercules W2	MoD(PE) MRF Farnborough	
XV209	Lockheed Hercules C3P	RAF Lyneham Transport Wing	
XV210	Lockheed Hercules C1P	RAF Lyneham Transport Wing	
XV211	Lockheed Hercules C1P	RAF Lyneham Transport Wing	
XV212	Lockheed Hercules C3P	RAF Lyneham Transport Wing	
XV213	Lockheed Hercules C1K	RAF No 1312 Flt, Mount Pleasant, FI	
XV214	Lockheed Hercules C3P	RAF Lyneham Transport Wing	
XV215	Lockheed Hercules C1P	RAF Lyneham Transport Wing	
XV217	Lockheed Hercules C3P	RAF Lyneham Transport Wing	
XV218	Lockheed Hercules C1P	RAF Lyneham Transport Wing	
XV219	Lockheed Hercules C3P	MoD(PE), A&AEE Boscombe Down	
XV220	Lockheed Hercules C3P	RAF Lyneham Transport Wing	
XV221	Lockheed Hercules C3P	RAF Lyneham Transport Wing	
XV222	Lockheed Hercules C3P	RAF Lyneham Transport Wing	
XV223	Lockheed Hercules C3P	RAF Lyneham Transport Wing	
XV226	HS Nimrod MR2P	RAF No 120 Sqn, Kinloss	
XV227	HS Nimrod MR2P	RAF No 120 Sqn, Kinloss	
XV228	HS Nimrod MR2P	RAF Kinloss MR Wing	
XV229	HS Nimrod MR2P	RAF No 206 Sqn, Kinloss	
XV230	HS Nimrod MR2P	RAF No 201 Sqn, Kinloss	
XV231	HS Nimrod MR2P	RAF No 206 Sqn, Kinloss	
XV232	HS Nimrod MR2P	RAF No 201 Sqn, Kinloss	
XV233	HS Nimrod MR2P	RAF No 206 Sqn, Kinloss	
XV234	HS Nimrod MR2P	RAF, stored Kinloss	
XV235	HS Nimrod MR2P	RAF No 120 Sqn, Kinloss	
XV236	HS Nimrod MR2P	RAF No 42 Sqn, Kinloss	
XV238	HS Nimrod Replica (parts G-ALYW)	RAF Exhibition Flight, St Athan	
XV239	HS Nimrod MR2P	RAF Kinloss MR Wing	
XV240	HS Nimrod MR2P	RAF No 120 Sqn, Kinloss	
XV241	HS Nimrod MR2P	RAF No 201 Sqn, Kinloss	
XV242	HS Nimrod MR2P	RAF, stored Kinloss	
XV243	HS Nimrod MR2P	RAF No 120 Sqn, Kinloss	
XV244	HS Nimrod MR2P	RAF No 201 Sqn, Kinloss	
XV245	HS Nimrod MR2P	RAF Kinloss MR Wing	
XV246	HS Nimrod MR2P	RAF Kinloss MR Wing	
XV247	HS Nimrod MR2P	RAF, stored Kinloss	
XV248	HS Nimrod MR2P	RAF Kinloss MR Wing	
XV249	HS Nimrod MR2P	RAF, stored Kinloss	
XV250	HS Nimrod MR2P	RAF No 120 Sqn, Kinloss	
XV251	HS Nimrod MR2P	RAF No 206 Sqn, Kinloss	
XV252	HS Nimrod MR2P	RAF No 206 Sqn, Kinloss	
XV253	HS Nimrod MR2P (9118M)	RAF Kinloss, instructional use	
XV254	HS Nimrod MR2P	RAF No 201 Sqn, Kinloss	
XV255	HS Nimrod MR2P	RAF Kinloss MR Wing	
XV258	HS Nimrod MR2P	RAF No 206 Sqn, Kinloss	
XV260	HS Nimrod MR2P	RAF No 120 Sqn, Kinloss	
XV263	BAe Nimrod AEW3P (8967M)	RAF Air Engineer Sqn, Finningley	
XV268	DHC Beaver AL1 (G-BVER)	Privately owned, Leavesden	
XV269	DHC Beaver AL1 (8011M)	AAC SAE, Middle Wallop	
XV277	HS Harrier GR3	RN ETS, Yeovilton	
XV279	HS Harrier GR1 (8566M) [44]	RAF Wittering WLT	
XV280	HS Harrier GR1 (cockpit)	RNAS Yeovilton, Fire Section	
XV281	HS Harrier GR3	BAe Kingston	
XV290	Lockheed Hercules C3P	RAF Lyneham Transport Wing	
XV291	Lockheed Hercules C1P	RAF Lyneham Transport Wing	
XV292	Lockheed Hercules C1P	RAF Lyneham Transport Wing	
XV293	Lockheed Hercules C1P	RAF Lyneham Transport Wing	
XV294	Lockheed Hercules C3P	RAF Lyneham Transport Wing	
XV295	Lockheed Hercules C1P	RAF Lyneham Transport Wing	
XV296	Lockheed Hercules C1K	RAF No 1312 Flt, Mount Pleasant, FI	
XV297	Lockheed Hercules C1P	RAF Lyneham Transport Wing	
XV298	Lockheed Hercules C1P	RAF Lyneham Transport Wing	
XV299	Lockheed Hercules C3P	RAF Lyneham Transport Wing	
XV300	Lockheed Hercules C1P	RAF Lyneham Transport Wing	
XV301	Lockheed Hercules C3P	RAF Lyneham Transport Wing	
XV302	Lockheed Hercules C3P	RAF Lyneham Transport Wing	
XV303	Lockheed Hercules C3P	RAF Lyneham Transport Wing	
XV304	Lockheed Hercules C3P	RAF Lyneham Transport Wing	
XV305	Lockheed Hercules C3P	RAF Lyneham Transport Wing	
XV306	Lockheed Hercules C1P	RAF Lyneham Transport Wing	
XV307	Lockheed Hercules C3P	RAF Lyneham Transport Wing	

Notes	Serial	Type	Owner or Operator
	XV328	BAC Lightning T5 [BZ]	Privately owned, Cranfield
	XV332	HS Buccaneer S2B	RAF No 208 Sqn, Lossiemouth
	XV333	HS Buccaneer S2B	RAF, stored Lossiemouth
	XV337	HS Buccaneer S2C (8852M)	RAF St Athan, BDRT
	XV344	HS Buccaneer S2C	MoD(PE), DRA Farnborough
	XV350	HS Buccaneer S2B	MoD(PE), stored Shawbury
	XV352	HS Buccaneer S2B	RAF No 208 Sqn, Lossiemouth
	XV353	HS Buccaneer S2B (9144M)	RAF, stored Lossiemouth
	XV359	HS Buccaneer S2B	RAF, stored Lossiemouth
	XV361	HS Buccaneer S2B	RAF No 208 Sqn, Lossiemouth
	XV370	Sikorsky SH-3D (G-ATYU)	RN AES, Lee-on-Solent
	XV371	WS61 Sea King HAS1	MoD(PE), DRA Farnborough
	XV372	WS61 Sea King HAS1	Privately owned, Trowbridge, Wilts
	XV393	McD Phantom FGR2 [Q]	RAF Marham, WLT
	XV398	McD Phantom FGR2 [CI]	*Scrapped at Wattisham by June 1993*
	XV399	McD Phantom FGR2 [L]	*Scrapped at St Athan, September 1992*
	XV401	McD Phantom FGR2 [I]	RAF, stored Wattisham
	XV404	McD Phantom FGR2	MoD(PE) Boscombe Down, GI use
	XV406	McD Phantom FGR2 (9098M) [CK]	RAF Carlisle, on display
	XV408	McD Phantom FGR2 (9165M) [Z]	RAF Cranwell, on display
	XV410	McD Phantom FGR2 [E]	*Scrapped at Wattisham by June 1993*
	XV411	McD Phantom FGR2 (9103M) [L]	FSCTE, RAF Manston
	XV415	McD Phantom FGR2 (9163M) [E]	RAF Boulmer, on display
	XV419	McD Phantom FGR2 [AA]	*Scrapped by June 1993*
	XV420	McD Phantom FGR2 [O]	AAC Wattisham, preserved
	XV422	McD Phantom FGR2 (9157M) [T]	Stornoway Airport, on display
	XV423	McD Phantom FGR2 [Y]	RAF Leeming
	XV424	McD Phantom FGR2 (9152M) [I]	RAF Museum, Hendon
	XV426	McD Phantom FGR2 [P]	RAF Coningsby, BDRT
	XV433	McD Phantom FGR2 [E]	RAF, stored Shawbury
	XV435	McD Phantom FGR2 [R]	T&EE Llanbedr, Fire Section
	XV460	McD Phantom FGR2 [R]	AAC Wattisham, on display
	XV465	McD Phantom FGR2 [S]	RAF Leeming
	XV467	McD Phantom FGR2 (9158M) [F]	Benbecula Airport, on display
	XV468	McD Phantom FGR2 (9159M) [H]	RAF Woodvale, on display
	XV469	McD Phantom FGR2	RAF, stored Shawbury
	XV473	McD Phantom FGR2 [N]	*Scrapped at Waddington, May 1993*
	XV474	McD Phantom FGR2 [T]	The Old Flying Machine Company, Duxford
	XV482	McD Phantom FGR2 (9107M) [T]	RAF Leuchars, Fire Section
	XV486	McD Phantom FGR2 [N]	*Scrapped at St Athan, 1993*
	XV487	McD Phantom FGR2 [G]	RAF, stored Shawbury
	XV488	McD Phantom FGR2 [O]	*Scrapped at Wattisham, September 1992*
	XV489	McD Phantom FGR2 (cockpit)	Privately owned, Bruntingthorpe
	XV490	McD Phantom FGR2 (cockpit)	Privately owned, Bruntingthorpe
	XV494	McD Phantom FGR2 [O]	*Scrapped at Wattisham by June 1993*
	XV495	McD Phantom FGR2	*Scrapped at St Athan, 1993*
	XV496	McD Phantom FGR2 [A]	*Scrapped at Wattisham by June 1993*
	XV497	McD Phantom FGR2 [W]	RAF Coningsby, BDRT
	XV499	McD Phantom FGR2 [I]	RAF Leeming, WLT
	XV500	McD Phantom FGR2 (9113M)	RAF St Athan, on display
	XV570	McD Phantom FG1 (9069M) [BN]	*Scrapped at Wattisham, September 1992*
	XV577	McD Phantom FG1 (9065M) [AM]	RAF Leuchars, BDRT
	XV581	McD Phantom FG1 (9070M) [AE]	RAF Buchan, on display
	XV582	McD Phantom FG1 (9066M) [M]	RAF Leuchars on display
	XV585	McD Phantom FG1 [AP]	RAF Leuchars
	XV586	McD Phantom FG1 (9067M) [AJ]	RAF Leuchars BDRT
	XV587	McD Phantom FG1 (9088M) [BR]	*Scrapped by April 1993*
	XV588	McD Phantom FG1 [007] (cockpit)	RN Predannack Fire School
	XV591	McD Phantom FG1 (cockpit)	RAF St Athan
	XV615	BHC SR.N6 Winchester 2	*Reclassified as ship*
	XV623	WS Wasp HAS1 (A2724) [601]	RN Portland, BDRT
	XV625	WS Wasp HAS1 [471]	RNEC Manadon, for instruction
	XV629	WS Wasp HAS1	AAC Middle Wallop, BDRT
	XV631	WS Wasp HAS1	DRA Farnborough, ground instruction
	XV638	WS Wasp HAS1 (8826M) [430/A]	RAF High Wycombe
	XV639	WS Wasp HAS1 [612]	RN, stored Fleetlands
	XV642	WS61 Sea King HAS2A	RN AES, Lee-on-Solent
	XV643	WS61 Sea King HAS6 [703/PW]	RN No 819 Sqn, Prestwick
	XV644	WS61 Sea King HAS1 (A2664) [664]	RN Predannack Fire School
	XV647	WS61 Sea King HAR5 [820]	RN AMG, Culdrose
	XV648	WS61 Sea King HAS6 [582]	RN No 706 Sqn, Culdrose

Serial	Type	Owner or Operator	Notes
XV649	WS61 Sea King AEW2A [184/R]	RN No 849 Sqn, Culdrose	
XV650	WS61 Sea King AEW2A [182/R]	RN No 849 Sqn, Culdrose	
XV651	WS61 Sea King HAS6 [591]	RN No 706 Sqn, Culdrose	
XV653	WS61 Sea King HAS6 [500]	RN No 810 Sqn, Culdrose	
XV654	WS61 Sea King HAS6 [705/PW]	RN No 819 Sqn, Prestwick	
XV655	WS61 Sea King HAS6 [701/PW]	RN No 819 Sqn, Prestwick	
XV656	WS61 Sea King AEW2A [187/N]	RN No 849 Sqn, Culdrose	
XV657	WS61 Sea King HAS6 [132]	RNAY Fleetlands	
XV659	WS61 Sea King HAS6 [268/U]	RN No 814 Sqn, Culdrose	
XV660	WS61 Sea King HAS6 [503/CU]	RN No 810 Sqn, Culdrose	
XV661	WS61 Sea King HAR5 [824/CU]	RN No 771 Sqn, Culdrose	
XV663	WS61 Sea King HAS6 [501/CU]	RN No 810 Sqn, Culdrose	
XV664	WS61 Sea King AEW2A [181/CU]	RN No 849 Sqn, Culdrose	
XV665	WS61 Sea King HAS6 [017/R]	RN No 820 Sqn, Culdrose	
XV666	WS61 Sea King HAR5 [823/CU]	RN No 771 Sqn, Culdrose	
XV669	WS61 Sea King HAS1 (A2659) [10]	RN ETS, Culdrose	
XV670	WS61 Sea King HAS6 [592]	RNAY Fleetlands	
XV671	WS61 Sea King AEW2A [186/N]	RN No 849 Sqn, Culdrose	
XV672	WS61 Sea King AEW2A [183/R]	RN No 849 Sqn, Culdrose	
XV673	WS61 Sea King HAS6 [588]	RN No 706 Sqn, Culdrose	
XV674	WS61 Sea King HAS6 [135/CL]	RN No 819 Sqn, Prestwick	
XV675	WS61 Sea King HAS6 [594]	RNAY Fleetlands	
XV676	WS61 Sea King HAS6 [707/PW]	RN No 819 Sqn, Prestwick	
XV677	WS61 Sea King HAS6 [017/R]	RN No 820 Sqn, Culdrose	
XV696	WS61 Sea King HAS6 [699/PW]	RN No 819 Sqn, Prestwick	
XV697	WS61 Sea King AEW2A [185/R]	RN No 849 Sqn, Culdrose	
XV699	WS61 Sea King HAS5 [134]	MoD(PE)/Westland, Yeovil	
XV700	WS61 Sea King HAS6 [508/CU]	RN No 810 Sqn, Culdrose	
XV701	WS61 Sea King HAS6 [010/R]	RN No 820 Sqn, Culdrose	
XV703	WS61 Sea King HAS6 [702/PW]	RN No 819 Sqn, Prestwick	
XV704	WS61 Sea King AEW2A [184]	RNAY Fleetlands	
XV705	WS61 Sea King HAR5 [821/CU]	RN No 771 Sqn, Culdrose	
XV706	WS61 Sea King HAS6 [505/CU]	RN No 810 Sqn, Culdrose	
XV707	WS61 Sea King AEW2A [181/CU]	RN No 849 Sqn, Culdrose	
XV708	WS61 Sea King HAS6 [510/CU]	RN No 810 Sqn, Culdrose	
XV709	WS61 Sea King HAS6 [585]	RNAY Fleetlands	
XV710	WS61 Sea King HAS6 [270/N]	RN No 814 Sqn, Culdrose	
XV711	WS61 Sea King HAS6 [709/PW]	RN No 819 Sqn, Prestwick	
XV712	WS61 Sea King HAS6 [012]	RN No 820 Sqn, Culdrose	
XV713	WS61 Sea King HAS6 [018]	RN No 820 Sqn, Culdrose	
XV714	WS61 Sea King AEW2A [180/CU]	RN No 849 Sqn, Culdrose	
XV720	WS58 Wessex HC2	RAF No 60 Sqn, Benson	
XV721	WS58 Wessex HC2 [H]	RAF No 72 Sqn, Aldergrove	
XV722	WS58 Wessex HC2 [WH]	RAF No 2 FTS, Shawbury	
XV723	WS58 Wessex HC2 [Q]	RAF No 72 Sqn, Aldergrove	
XV724	WS58 Wessex HC2	RAF No 22 Sqn, C Flt, Valley	
XV725	WS58 Wessex HC2 [C]	RAF No 60 Sqn, Benson	
XV726	WS58 Wessex HC2 [J]	RAF No 72 Sqn, Aldergrove	
XV728	WS58 Wessex HC2 [A]	RAF No 60 Sqn, Benson	
XV729	WS58 Wessex HC2	RAF No 22 Sqn, A Flt, Chivenor	
XV730	WS58 Wessex HC2	RAF No 22 Sqn, St Mawgan	
XV731	WS58 Wessex HC2 [Y]	RAF No 72 Sqn, Aldergrove	
XV732	WS58 Wessex HCC4	RAF Queen's Flight, Benson	
XV733	WS58 Wessex HCC4	RAF Queen's Flight, Benson	
XV738	HS Harrier GR3 (9074M) [B]	RAF No 1 SoTT, Halton	
XV741	HS Harrier GR3	RN SAH, Culdrose	
XV744	HS Harrier GR3 (9167M) [3K]	Royal Military College of Science, Shrivenham	
XV747	HS Harrier GR3 (8979M) (fuselage)	Privately owned, Bruntingthorpe	
XV748	HS Harrier GR3 [3D]	MoD(PE), DRA Bedford	
XV751	HS Harrier GR3	RN AES, Lee-on-Solent	
XV752	HS Harrier GR3 (9078M) [B]	RAF No 2 SoTT, Cosford	
XV753	HS Harrier GR3 (9075M) [3F]	RAF No 1 SoTT, Halton	
XV755	HS Harrier GR3 [M]	RNAS Yeovilton, Fire Section	
XV759	HS Harrier GR3 [O]	RAF St Athan Fire Section	
XV760	HS Harrier GR3 [VL]	RNAS Yeovilton, gate guard	
XV778	HS Harrier GR3 (9001M)	RAF Valley Fire Section	
XV779	HS Harrier GR3 (8931M) [01/A]	RAF Wittering on display	
XV783	HS Harrier GR3 [N]	RN AES, Lee-on-Solent	
XV784	HS Harrier GR3 (8909M) (cockpit)	A&AEE, Boscombe Down	
XV786	HS Harrier GR3 [S]	RN Culdrose Fire Section	
XV806	HS Harrier GR3 [E]	RN SAH, Culdrose	

Notes	Serial	Type	Owner or Operator
	XV808	HS Harrier GR3 (9076M) [3J]	RAF No 1 SoTT, Halton
	XV810	HS Harrier GR3 (9038M) [K]	RAF St Athan
	XV814	DH Comet 4 (G-APDF)	A&AEE Boscombe Down, for spares
	XV859	BHC SR.N6 Winchester 6	Reclassified as ship
	XV863	HS Buccaneer S2B (9115M/ 9139M/9145M) [S]	RAF Lossiemouth, on display
	XV864	HS Buccaneer S2B	RAF Leeming
	XV865	HS Buccaneer S2B	RAF No 208 Sqn, Lossiemouth
	XV867	HS Buccaneer S2B	RAF No 208 Sqn, Lossiemouth
	XV869	HS Buccaneer S2B	RAF, stored Shawbury
	XW175	HS Harrier T4A(mod)	MoD(PE), DRA Bedford
	XW198	WS Puma HC1	RAF No 230 Sqn, Aldergrove
	XW199	WS Puma HC1	RAF No 33 Sqn, Odiham
	XW200	WS Puma HC1	RAF No 27(R) Sqn, Odiham
	XW201	WS Puma HC1 [FB]	RAF No 27(R) Sqn, Odiham
	XW202	WS Puma HC1	RAF No 1563 Flight, Belize
	XW204	WS Puma HC1 [DB]	RAF No 230 Sqn, Aldergrove
	XW206	WS Puma HC1	RAF No 33 Sqn, Odiham
	XW207	WS Puma HC1	RAF No 230 Sqn, Aldergrove
	XW208	WS Puma HC1 [C]	RAF No 33 Sqn, Aldergrove
	XW209	WS Puma HC1 [CF]	RAF No 230 Sqn, Aldergrove
	XW210	WS Puma HC1	RAF Odiham (on repair)
	XW211	WS Puma HC1 [CH]	MoD(PE), A&AEE Boscombe Down
	XW212	WS Puma HC1	RAF No 1563 Flight, Belize
	XW213	WS Puma HC1 [CJ]	RAF No 33 Sqn, Odiham
	XW214	WS Puma HC1 [CK]	RAF No 33 Sqn, Aldergrove
	XW215	WS Puma HC1 [R]	Westland, Yeovil (on rebuild)
	XW216	WS Puma HC1	RAF No 230 Sqn, Aldergrove
	XW217	WS Puma HC1 [CS]	RAF No 33 Sqn, Odiham
	XW218	WS Puma HC1 [BW]	RAF No 18 Sqn, Laarbruch
	XW219	WS Puma HC1 [DC]	RAF No 1563 Flight, Belize
	XW220	WS Puma HC1 [CZ]	RAF No 27(R) Sqn, Odiham
	XW221	WS Puma HC1 [CM]	RAF No 230 Sqn, Aldergrove
	XW222	WS Puma HC1 [BX]	RAF No 18 Sqn, Laarbruch
	XW223	WS Puma HC1 [CB]	RAF No 33 Sqn, Odiham
	XW224	WS Puma HC1 [DH]	RAF No 1563 Flight, Belize
	XW225	WS Puma HC1 [FE]	RAF No 27(R) Sqn, Odiham
	XW226	WS Puma HC1 [BY]	RAF No 18 Sqn, Laarbruch
	XW227	WS Puma HC1 [DN]	RAF No 230 Sqn, Aldergrove
	XW229	WS Puma HC1 [DB]	RAF No 33 Sqn, Odiham
	XW231	WS Puma HC1 [FD]	RAF No 27(R) Sqn, Odiham
	XW232	WS Puma HC1 [DJ]	RAF No 18 Sqn, Laarbruch
	XW233	WS Puma HC1 [CN]	Written off, 26 November 1992, Bessbrook
	XW234	WS Puma HC1 [CO]	RAF No 230 Sqn, Aldergrove
	XW235	WS Puma HC1 [CP]	RAF No 33 Sqn, Aldergrove
	XW236	WS Puma HC1 [BZ]	RAF No 18 Sqn, Laarbruch
	XW237	WS Puma HC1 [DL]	RAF No 230 Sqn, Aldergrove
	XW241	Sud SA330E Puma (F-ZJUX)	MoD(PE) Farnborough, Fire Section
	XW249	Cushioncraft CC7	Flambards Village Theme Park, Helston
	XW255	BHC BH-7 Wellington	Reclassified as ship
	XW264	HS Harrier T2 (front fuselage)	CARG store, RAF Innsworth
	XW265	HS Harrier T4A [W]	RAF HOCU/No 20(R) Sqn, Wittering
	XW266	HS Harrier T4N [719/VL]	RN No 899 Sqn, Yeovilton
	XW267	HS Harrier T4 [SA]	RAF SAOEU, Boscombe Down
	XW268	HS Harrier T8 [720/VL]	BAe, Dunsfold (conversion)
	XW269	HS Harrier T4 [BD]	RAF SAOEU, Boscombe Down
	XW270	HS Harrier T4 (fuselage)	RAF ASF, Wittering
	XW271	HS Harrier T4 [X]	RAF HOCU/No 20(R) Sqn, Wittering
	XW272	HS Harrier T4 (8783M) (cockpit)	BAe, Kingston-upon-Thames
	XW276	Aerospatiale SA341 (F-ZWRI)	North-East Aircraft Museum, Usworth
	XW280	WS Scout AH1 [Z]	AAC No 660 Sqn, Brunei
	XW281	WS Scout AH1 [U]	AAC No 666(TA) Sqn, Middle Wallop
	XW282	WS Scout AH1 [W]	AAC No 666(TA) Sqn, Middle Wallop
	XW283	WS Scout AH1	AAC, stored RNAY Fleetlands
	XW284	WS Scout AH1 [A] (fuselage)	AAC, stored RNAW Almondbank
	XW287	BAC Jet Provost T5 [P]	RAF, stored Shawbury
	XW289	BAC Jet Provost T5A [73]	RAF, stored Shawbury
	XW290	BAC Jet Provost T5A [41]	RAF, stored Shawbury
	XW291	BAC Jet Provost T5 [N]	RAF, stored Shawbury
	XW292	BAC Jet Provost T5 (9128M) [32]	RAF No 1 SoTT, Halton
	XW293	BAC Jet Provost T5 [Z]	RAF, stored Shawbury
	XW294	BAC Jet Provost T5A (9129M) [45]	RAF No 1 SoTT, Halton

Serial	Type	Owner or Operator	Notes
XW295	BAC Jet Provost T5A [29]	*Sold to Australia, 93*	
XW296	BAC Jet Provost T5 [Q]	RAF, stored Shawbury	
XW299	BAC Jet Provost T5A (9146M) [60]	RAF No 1 SoTT, Halton	
XW301	BAC Jet Provost T5A (9147M) [63]	RAF No 1 SoTT, Halton	
XW302	BAC Jet Provost T5 [T]	RAF, stored Shawbury	
XW303	BAC Jet Provost T5A (9119M) [127]	RAF No 1 SoTT, Halton	
XW304	BAC Jet Provost T5A (9172M) [MD]	RAF No 2 SoTT, Cosford	
XW305	BAC Jet Provost T5A [42]	RAF, stored Shawbury	
XW306	BAC Jet Provost T5 [O]	RAF, stored Shawbury	
XW307	BAC Jet Provost T5 [S]	RAF, stored Shawbury	
XW309	BAC Jet Provost T5 (91. .M) [V]	RAF No 2 SoTT, Cosford	
XW310	BAC Jet Provost T5A [37]	Privately owned	
XW311	BAC Jet Provost T5 [W]	RAF No 2 SoTT, Cosford	
XW312	BAC Jet Provost T5A (9109M) [64]	RAF No 1 SoTT, Halton	
XW313	BAC Jet Provost T5A [85]	RAF, stored Linton-on-Ouse	
XW315	BAC Jet Provost T5A	Stratford Aircraft Collection, Long Marston	
XW316	BAC Jet Provost T5A [28]	*Sold to the USA as N316HC*	
XW317	BAC Jet Provost T5A [79]	RAF, stored Shawbury	
XW318	BAC Jet Provost T5A (91. .M) [78]	RAF No 2 SoTT, Cosford	
XW319	BAC Jet Provost T5A [76]	RAF, stored Linton-on-Ouse	
XW320	BAC Jet Provost T5A (9015M) [71]	RAF No 1 SoTT, Halton	
XW321	BAC Jet Provost T5A (9154M) [62]	RAF No 2 SoTT, Cosford	
XW322	BAC Jet Provost T5B [D]	RAF, stored Shawbury	
XW323	BAC Jet Provost T5A (9166M) [86]	RAF Museum, Hendon	
XW324	BAC Jet Provost T5 [U]	RAF, stored Shawbury	
XW325	BAC Jet Provost T5B [E]	RAF, stored Shawbury	
XW326	BAC Jet Provost T5A [62]	Privately owned	
XW327	BAC Jet Provost T5A (9130M) [62]	RAF No 1 SoTT, Halton	
XW328	BAC Jet Provost T5A (9177M) [MI]	RAF No 2 SoTT, Cosford	
XW330	BAC Jet Provost T5A (91. .M) [82]	RAF No 2 SoTT, Cosford	
XW332	BAC Jet Provost T5A [34]	*Sold to the USA as N332RC*	
XW333	BAC Jet Provost T5A [79]	RAF, stored Shawbury	
XW334	BAC Jet Provost T5A [18]	*Sold to the USA as N334XW*	
XW335	BAC Jet Provost T5A (9061M) [74]	RAF No 1 SoTT, Halton	
XW336	BAC Jet Provost T5A [67]	RAF, stored Shawbury	
XW351	BAC Jet Provost T5A (9062M) [31]	RAF No 1 SoTT, Halton	
XW352	BAC Jet Provost T5 [R]	*Sold to the USA as N352XW*	
XW353	BAC Jet Provost T5A (9090M) [3]	RAF Cranwell, on display	
XW354	BAC Jet Provost T5A [70]	RAF, stored Shawbury	
XW355	BAC Jet Provost T5A [20]	Privately owned	
XW357	BAC Jet Provost T5A [5]	*Sold to Australia, 93*	
XW358	BAC Jet Provost T5A (91. .M) [59]	RAF No 2 SoTT, Cosford	
XW359	BAC Jet Provost T5B [65]	RAF, stored Shawbury	
XW360	BAC Jet Provost T5A (9153M) [61]	RAF No 2 SoTT, Cosford	
XW361	BAC Jet Provost T5A (91. .M) [81]	RAF No 2 SoTT, Cosford	
XW362	BAC Jet Provost T5A (91. .M) [17]	*Sold to Australia, 93*	
XW363	BAC Jet Provost T5A [36]	*Sold to the USA as N363XW, Jun 1993*	
XW364	BAC Jet Provost T5A (91. .M) [35]	RAF No 2 SoTT, Cosford	
XW365	BAC Jet Provost T5A (9018M) [73]	RAF No 1 SoTT, Halton	
XW366	BAC Jet Provost T5A (9097M) [75]	RAF No 1 SoTT, Halton	
XW367	BAC Jet Provost T5A (91. .M) [64]	RAF No 2 SoTT, Cosford	
XW368	BAC Jet Provost T5A [66]	RAF, stored Linton-on-Ouse	
XW369	BAC Jet Provost T5A [69]	RAF, stored Shawbury	
XW370	BAC Jet Provost T5A (91. .M) [72]	RAF No 2 SoTT, Cosford	
XW372	BAC Jet Provost T5A [M]	RAF, stored Shawbury	
XW373	BAC Jet Provost T5A [11]	*Sold to the USA as N373XW*	
XW374	BAC Jet Provost T5A [38]	*Sold to Australia, 93*	
XW375	BAC Jet Provost T5A (9149M) [52]	RAF No 1 SoTT, Halton	
XW404	BAC Jet Provost T5A (9049M)	RAF CTTS, St Athan	
XW405	BAC Jet Provost T5A (91. .M) [J]	RAF No 2 SoTT, Cosford	
XW406	BAC Jet Provost T5A [23]	Privately owned	
XW408	BAC Jet Provost T5A [24]	*Sold to Australia, 93*	
XW409	BAC Jet Provost T5A (9047M)	RAF CTTS, St Athan	
XW410	BAC Jet Provost T5A (9125M) [80]	RAF No 2 SoTT, Cosford	
XW412	BAC Jet Provost T5A [74]	RAF, stored Shawbury	
XW413	BAC Jet Provost T5A (9126M) [69]	RAF No 1 SoTT, Halton	
XW415	BAC Jet Provost T5A [80]	RAF, stored Linton-on-Ouse	
XW416	BAC Jet Provost T5A (91. .M) [84]	RAF No 2 SoTT, Cosford	
XW418	BAC Jet Provost T5A (9173M) [60]	RAF No 2 SoTT, Cosford	
XW419	BAC Jet Provost T5A (9120M) [125]	RAF No 1 SoTT, Halton	
XW420	BAC Jet Provost T5A (91. .M) [83]	RAF No 2 SoTT, Cosford	

Notes	Serial	Type	Owner or Operator
	XW421	BAC Jet Provost T5A (9111M) [60]	RAF No 1 SoTT, Halton
	XW422	BAC Jet Provost T5A [3]	RAF, stored Shawbury
	XW423	BAC Jet Provost T5A [14]	RAF, stored Shawbury
	XW425	BAC Jet Provost T5A [H]	*Scrapped at Shawbury, July 1993*
	XW427	BAC Jet Provost T5A (9124M) [67]	RAF No 1 SoTT, Halton
	XW428	BAC Jet Provost T5A [39]	DRA Farnborough Apprentice School
	XW429	BAC Jet Provost T5A [C]	RAF, stored Shawbury
	XW430	BAC Jet Provost T5A (9176M) [MW]	RAF No 2 SoTT, Cosford
	XW431	BAC Jet Provost T5B [A]	RAF, stored Shawbury
	XW432	BAC Jet Provost T5A (9127M) [76]	RAF No 2 SoTT, Cosford
	XW433	BAC Jet Provost T5A [63]	RAF, stored Shawbury
	XW434	BAC Jet Provost T5A (9091M) [78]	RAF No 1 SoTT, Halton
	XW435	BAC Jet Provost T5A [4]	*Sold to Australia, 93*
	XW436	BAC Jet Provost T5A (9148M) [68]	RAF No 1 SoTT, Halton
	XW437	BAC Jet Provost T5A [71]	RAF, stored Shawbury
	XW438	BAC Jet Provost T5B [B]	RAF, stored Shawbury
	XW527	HS Buccaneer S2B	RAF No 208 Sqn, Lossiemouth
	XW528	HS Buccaneer S2B (8861M) [C]	RAF Coningsby Fire Section
	XW529	HS Buccaneer S2B	*Scrapped at Lossiemouth 1992*
	XW530	HS Buccaneer S2B	RAF No 208 Sqn, Lossiemouth
	XW533	HS Buccaneer S2B	*Scrapped at Lossiemouth 1992*
	XW534	HS Buccaneer S2B	*Scrapped at Shawbury, August 1993*
	XW542	HS Buccaneer S2B	RAF, stored Lossiemouth
	XW544	HS Buccaneer S2B (8857M) [Y]	RAF No 2 SoTT, Cosford
	XW547	HS Buccaneer S2B (9169M) [R]	RAF Cosford Aerospace Museum
	XW549	HS Buccaneer S2B (8860M) (fuselage)	RAF Kinloss, BDRT
	XW566	SEPECAT Jaguar T2	MoD(PE), stored DRA Farnborough
	XW612	WS Scout AH1 [A]	AAC No 660 Sqn, Sek Kong
	XW613	WS Scout AH1 [B]	AAC No 660 Sqn, Sek Kong
	XW614	WS Scout AH1	AAC Historic Flight, Middle Wallop
	XW616	WS Scout AH1	AAC No 70 MU, Middle Wallop
	XW626	DH Comet 4AEW (G-APDS)	MoD(PE), DRA Bedford derelict
	XW630	HS Harrier GR3	RN AES, Lee-on-Solent
	XW635	Beagle D5/180 (G-AWSW)	Privately owned, Cranwell North
	XW664	HS Nimrod R1P	RAF No 51 Sqn, Wyton
	XW665	HS Nimrod R1P	RAF No 51 Sqn, Wyton
	XW666	HS Nimrod R1P	RAF No 51 Sqn, Wyton
	XW750	HS748 Series 107 (G-ASJT)	MoD(PE), DRA Bedford
	XW763	HS Harrier GR3 (9002M/9041M) [3F]	RAF St Athan, Fire Section
	XW764	HS Harrier GR3 (8981M)	RAF Leeming, Fire Section
	XW768	HS Harrier GR3 (9072M) [N]	RAF No 1 SoTT, Halton
	XW784	Mitchell-Procter Kittiwake I (G-BBRN)	Privately owned, Haverfordwest
	XW788	HS125 CC1	RAF No 32 Sqn, Northolt
	XW789	HS125 CC1	RAF No 32 Sqn, Northolt
	XW790	HS125 CC1	RAF No 32 Sqn, Northolt
	XW791	HS125 CC1	RAF No 32 Sqn, Northolt
	XW795	WS Scout AH1	AAC, stored RNAW Almondbank
	XW796	WS Scout AH1 [X]	AAC SAE, Middle Wallop
	XW797	WS Scout AH1 [G]	AAC No 660 Sqn, Sek Kong
	XW798	WS Scout AH1	AAC, Middle Wallop
	XW799	WS Scout AH1	AAC No 658 Sqn, Netheravon
	XW835	WS Lynx (G-BEAD)	AAC Dishforth, GI use
	XW836	WS Lynx	RNAS Lee-on-Solent, Fire Section
	XW837	WS Lynx (fuselage)	IHM, Weston-super-Mare
	XW838	WS Lynx [TAD 009]	AAC SAE, Middle Wallop
	XW839	WS Lynx	RNEC Manadon
	XW843	WS Gazelle AH1	AAC SAE, Middle Wallop
	XW844	WS Gazelle AH1	AAC No 3 Regiment, Wattisham
	XW845	WS Gazelle HT2 [47/CU]	RN No 705 Sqn, Culdrose
	XW846	WS Gazelle AH1 [M]	AAC No 670 Sqn, Middle Wallop
	XW847	WS Gazelle AH1	AAC No 665 Sqn, Aldergrove
	XW848	WS Gazelle AH1 [D]	AAC No 670 Sqn, Middle Wallop
	XW849	WS Gazelle AH1 [G]	RM 3 CBAS, Yeovilton
	XW851	WS Gazelle AH1 [H]	RM 3 CBAS, Yeovilton
	XW852	WS Gazelle HCC4	RAF No 32 Sqn, Northolt
	XW853	WS Gazelle HT2 [53/CU]	RN No 705 Sqn, Culdrose
	XW854	WS Gazelle HT2 [46/CU]	RN No 705 Sqn, Culdrose
	XW855	WS Gazelle HCC4	RAF No 32 Sqn, Northolt
	XW856	WS Gazelle HT2 [49/CU]	RN No 705 Sqn, Culdrose

Serial	Type	Owner or Operator	Notes
XW857	WS Gazelle HT2 [55/CU]	RN No 705 Sqn, Culdrose	
XW858	WS Gazelle HT3 [C]	RAF No 2 FTS, Shawbury	
XW860	WS Gazelle HT2	RNAY Fleetlands	
XW861	WS Gazelle HT2 [52/CU]	RN No 705 Sqn, Culdrose	
XW862	WS Gazelle HT3 [D]	RAF No 2 FTS, Shawbury	
XW863	WS Gazelle HT2 [42/CU]	AAC SAE, Middle Wallop	
XW864	WS Gazelle HT2 [54/CU]	RN No 705 Sqn, Culdrose	
XW865	WS Gazelle AH1 [C]	AAC No 670 Sqn, Middle Wallop	
XW866	WS Gazelle HT3 [E]	RAF No 2 FTS, Shawbury	
XW868	WS Gazelle HT2 [50/CU]	RN No 705 Sqn, Culdrose	
XW870	WS Gazelle HT3 [F]	RAF No 2 FTS, Shawbury	
XW871	WS Gazelle HT2 [44/CU]	RN No 705 Sqn, Culdrose	
XW884	WS Gazelle HT2 [41/CU]	RN No 705 Sqn, Culdrose	
XW885	WS Gazelle AH1 [B]	AAC No 670 Sqn, Middle Wallop	
XW887	WS Gazelle HT2	RNAY Fleetlands Station Flight	
XW888	WS Gazelle AH1	AAC SAE, Middle Wallop	
XW889	WS Gazelle AH1	AAC SAE, Middle Wallop	
XW890	WS Gazelle HT2 [53] (fuselage)	RNAY Fleetlands	
XW891	WS Gazelle HT2 [49] (fuselage)	RNAS Culdrose, Fire Section	
XW892	WS Gazelle AH1 [L]	AAC No 662 Sqn, Wattisham	
XW893	WS Gazelle AH1	Westland, Weston-super-Mare	
XW894	WS Gazelle HT2 [52/CU]	MoD(PE), DRA Farnborough	
XW895	WS Gazelle HT2 [51/CU]	RN No 705 Sqn, Culdrose	
XW897	WS Gazelle AH1 [Z]	AAC No 670 Sqn, Middle Wallop	
XW898	WS Gazelle HT3 [G]	RAF No 2 FTS, Shawbury	
XW899	WS Gazelle AH1 [K]	AAC No 662 Sqn, Wattisham	
XW900	WS Gazelle AH1 (TAD-900)	AAC SAE, Middle Wallop	
XW902	WS Gazelle HT3 [H]	RAF No 18 Sqn, Laarbruch	
XW903	WS Gazelle AH1	AAC No 3 (TA) Flt, Turnhouse	
XW904	WS Gazelle AH1	AAC No 7 Flight, Gatow	
XW906	WS Gazelle HT3 [J]	RAF No 2 FTS, Shawbury	
XW907	WS Gazelle HT2 [48/CU]	RN No 705 Sqn, Culdrose	
XW908	WS Gazelle AH1 [E]	AAC, Fleetlands	
XW909	WS Gazelle AH1	AAC 1 Regiment, Hildesheim	
XW910	WS Gazelle HT3 [K]	RAF No 2 FTS, Shawbury	
XW911	WS Gazelle AH1 [I]	AAC No 670 Sqn, Middle Wallop	
XW912	WS Gazelle AH1	AAC, stored RNAY Fleetlands	
XW913	WS Gazelle AH1 [U]	AAC No 657 Sqn, Dishforth	
XW916	HS Harrier GR3 [W]	RAF Wittering, Fire Section	
XW919	HS Harrier GR3 [W]	RN SAH, Culdrose	
XW923	HS Harrier GR3 (8724M) (cockpit)	RAF Wittering for rescue training	
XW924	HS Harrier GR3 (9073M) [G]	RAF No 1 SoTT, Halton	
XW927	HS Harrier T4 [02]	RAF Laarbruch	
XW930	HS125-1B (G-ATPC)	MoD(PE), stored Farnborough	
XW934	HS Harrier T4 [Y]	RAF HOCU/No 20(R) Sqn Wittering	
XW986	HS Buccaneer S2B	MoD(PE), A&AEE Boscombe Down	
XW987	HS Buccaneer S2B	MoD(PE), A&AEE Boscombe Down	
XW988	HS Buccaneer S2B	MoD(PE), A&AEE Boscombe Down	
XX101	Cushioncraft CC7	IHM, Weston-super-Mare	
XX102	Cushioncraft CC7	Museum of Army Transport, Beverley	
XX105	BAC 1-11/201 (G-ASJD)	MoD(PE), DRA Bedford	
XX108	SEPECAT Jaguar GR1 (G27-313)	MoD(PE), A&AEE Boscombe Down	
XX109	SEPECAT Jaguar GR1 (8918M) [US]	RAF Coltishall, ground instruction	
XX110	SEPECAT Jaguar GR1 Replica (BAPC169)	RAF No 1 SoTT, Halton	
XX110	SEPECAT Jaguar GR1 (8955M) [EP]	RAF No 2 SoTT, Cosford	
XX112	SEPECAT Jaguar GR1A [EC]	RAF stored Shawbury	
XX116	SEPECAT Jaguar GR1A (J1008) [02]	RAF No 16(R) Sqn, Lossiemouth	
XX117	SEPECAT Jaguar GR1A (J1004) [06]	MoD(PE), DRA Farnborough	
XX119	SEPECAT Jaguar GR1A (8898M) [01]	RAF No 16(R) Sqn, Lossiemouth	
XX139	SEPECAT Jaguar T2A [C]	RAF No 16(R) Sqn, Lossiemouth	
XX140	SEPECAT Jaguar T2 (9008M) [D]	RAF No 2 SoTT, Cosford	
XX141	SEPECAT Jaguar T2A [Z]	RAF No 16(R) Sqn, Lossiemouth	
XX143	SEPECAT Jaguar T2A (J1002) [GS]	RAF No 54 Sqn, Coltishall	
XX144	SEPECAT Jaguar T2A [I]	RAF No 16(R) Sqn, Lossiemouth	
XX145	SEPECAT Jaguar T2	MoD(PE) ETPS, Boscombe Down	

Notes	Serial	Type	Owner or Operator
	XX146	SEPECAT Jaguar T2A [J]	RAF No 16(R) Sqn, Lossiemouth
	XX150	SEPECAT Jaguar T2A [W]	RAF No 16(R) Sqn, Lossiemouth
	XX154	HS Hawk T1 [1]	MoD(PE), T&EE Llanbedr
	XX156	HS Hawk T1	MoD(PE), DRA Bedford
	XX157	HS Hawk T1A [B]	RAF No 7 FTS/92(R) Sqn, Chivenor
	XX158	HS Hawk T1A	RAF No 7 FTS/19(R) Sqn, Chivenor
	XX159	HS Hawk T1A [PA]	RAF CFS, Valley
	XX160	HS Hawk T1	MoD(PE), T&EE Llanbedr
	XX161	HS Hawk T1 [DQ]	RAF No 4 FTS/234(R) Sqn, Valley
	XX162	HS Hawk T1	MoD(PE) DRA, Farnborough
	XX163	HS Hawk T1 [PH]	*Written off, Valley 1 July 1993*
	XX164	HS Hawk T1 [CN]	RAF No 100 Sqn, Finningley
	XX165	HS Hawk T1 [TM]	RAF No 4 FTS/74(R) Sqn, Valley
	XX167	HS Hawk T1 [Q]	RAF No 7 FTS/92(R) Sqn, Chivenor
	XX168	HS Hawk T1	RAF No 6 FTS, Finningley
	XX169	HS Hawk T1	RAF No 6 FTS, Finningley
	XX170	HS Hawk T1 [DS]	MoD(PE), T&EE Llanbedr
	XX171	HS Hawk T1 [TK]	RAF No 4 FTS/74(R) Sqn, Valley
	XX172	HS Hawk T1	RAF St Athan Station Flight
	XX173	HS Hawk T1	RAF No 6 FTS, Finningley
	XX174	HS Hawk T1	RAF No 6 FTS, Finningley
	XX175	HS Hawk T1	RAF No 7 FTS/19(R) Sqn, Chivenor
	XX176	HS Hawk T1 [CO]	RAF No 100 Sqn, Finningley
	XX177	HS Hawk T1 [CP]	RAF No 100 Sqn, Finningley
	XX178	HS Hawk T1 [M]	RAF No 7 FTS/92(R) Sqn, Chivenor
	XX179	HS Hawk T1 [E]	RAF No 7 FTS/92(R) Sqn, Chivenor
	XX181	HS Hawk T1 [CB]	RAF No 100 Sqn, Finningley
	XX183	HS Hawk T1 [DU]	RAF No 4 FTS/234(R) Sqn, Valley
	XX184	HS Hawk T1	RAF St Athan Station Flight
	XX185	HS Hawk T1	RAF No 7 FTS/19(R) Sqn, Chivenor
	XX186	HS Hawk T1A	RAF No 7 FTS/19(R) Sqn, Chivenor
	XX187	HS Hawk T1A [PB]	RAF CFS, Valley
	XX188	HS Hawk T1A [CG]	RAF No 100 Sqn, Finningley
	XX189	HS Hawk T1A [TB]	RAF No 4 FTS/74(R) Sqn, Valley
	XX190	HS Hawk T1A [TA]	RAF No 4 FTS/74(R) Sqn, Valley
	XX191	HS Hawk T1A [DT]	RAF No 4 FTS/234(R) Sqn, Valley
	XX193	HS Hawk T1A [TT]	RAF No 4 FTS/74(R) Sqn, Valley
	XX194	HS Hawk T1A [TI]	RAF No 4 FTS/74(R) Sqn, Valley
	XX195	HS Hawk T1 [CA]	RAF No 100 Sqn, Finningley
	XX196	HS Hawk T1A [DB]	RAF No 4 FTS/234(R) Sqn, Valley
	XX198	HS Hawk T1A [DC]	RAF No 4 FTS/234(R) Sqn, Valley
	XX199	HS Hawk T1A [TG]	RAF No 4 FTS/74(R) Sqn, Valley
	XX200	HS Hawk T1A [DD]	RAF No 4 FTS/74(R) Sqn, Valley
	XX201	HS Hawk T1A [N]	RAF No 7 FTS/92(R) Sqn, Chivenor
	XX202	HS Hawk T1A [P]	RAF No 7 FTS/92(R) Sqn, Chivenor
	XX203	HS Hawk T1A [PC]	RAF CFS, Valley
	XX204	HS Hawk T1A [H]	RAF No 7 FTS/92(R) Sqn, Chivenor
	XX205	HS Hawk T1A [V]	RAF No 7 FTS/92(R) Sqn, Chivenor
	XX217	HS Hawk T1A	RAF No 7 FTS/19(R) Sqn, Chivenor
	XX218	HS Hawk T1A [TQ]	RAF No 4 FTS/74(R) Sqn, Valley
	XX219	HS Hawk T1A	RAF No 7 FTS/19(R) Sqn, Chivenor
	XX220	HS Hawk T1A [PD]	RAF CFS, Valley
	XX221	HS Hawk T1A [DG]	RAF No 4 FTS/234(R) Sqn, Valley
	XX222	HS Hawk T1A [TJ]	RAF No 4 FTS/74(R) Sqn, Valley
	XX223	HS Hawk T1 (fuselage)	Privately owned, Charlwood, Surrey
	XX224	HS Hawk T1 [PM]	RAF CFS, Valley
	XX225	HS Hawk T1	RAF No 7 FTS/19(R) Sqn, Chivenor
	XX226	HS Hawk T1	RAF CFS, Valley
	XX227	HS Hawk T1A	RAF *Red Arrows*, Scampton
	XX228	HS Hawk T1 [CC]	RAF No 100 Sqn, Finningley
	XX230	HS Hawk T1A	RAF No 7 FTS/19(R) Sqn, Chivenor
	XX231	HS Hawk T1	MoD(PE), A&AEE Boscombe Down
	XX232	HS Hawk T1	RAF No 6 FTS, Finningley
	XX233	HS Hawk T1	RAF *Red Arrows*, Scampton
	XX234	HS Hawk T1 [DV]	RAF No 4 FTS/234(R) Sqn, Valley
	XX235	HS Hawk T1 [PJ]	RAF CFS, Valley
	XX236	HS Hawk T1 [PK]	RAF CFS, Valley
	XX237	HS Hawk T1	RAF *Red Arrows*, Scampton
	XX238	HS Hawk T1	RAF No 6 FTS, Finningley
	XX239	HS Hawk T1 [PL]	RAF CFS, Valley
	XX240	HS Hawk T1	RAF No 6 FTS, Finningley
	XX242	HS Hawk T1 [Y]	RAF No 7 FTS/92(R) Sqn, Chivenor
	XX244	HS Hawk T1 [DW]	RAF No 4 FTS/234(R) Sqn, Valley

Serial	Type	Owner or Operator	Notes
XX245	HS Hawk T1	RAF No 7 FTS/19(R) Sqn, Chivenor	
XX246	HS Hawk T1A	RAF No 7 FTS/19(R) Sqn, Chivenor	
XX247	HS Hawk T1A [CM]	RAF No 100 Sqn, Finningley	
XX248	HS Hawk T1A [CJ]	RAF No 100 Sqn, Finningley	
XX249	HS Hawk T1 [DY]	RAF No 4 FTS/234(R) Sqn, Valley	
XX250	HS Hawk T1	RAF No 6 FTS, Finningley	
XX252	HS Hawk T1A	RAF Red Arrows, Scampton	
XX253	HS Hawk T1A	RAF Red Arrows, Scampton	
XX254	HS Hawk T1A	RAF No 7 FTS/19(R) Sqn, Chivenor	
XX255	HS Hawk T1A [TE]	RAF No 4 FTS/74(R) Sqn, Valley	
XX256	HS Hawk T1A	RAF No 7 FTS/19(R) Sqn, Chivenor	
XX257	HS Hawk T1	RAF Chivenor, BDRT	
XX258	HS Hawk T1A [PE]	RAF CFS, Valley	
XX260	HS Hawk T1A	RAF Red Arrows, Scampton	
XX261	HS Hawk T1A [DH]	RAF No 4 FTS/234(R) Sqn, Valley	
XX263	HS Hawk T1A	RAF No 7 FTS/19(R) Sqn, Chivenor	
XX263	HS Hawk T1 Replica (BAPC 152)	RAF Exhibition Flight, St Athan	
XX264	HS Hawk T1A	RAF Red Arrows, Scampton	
XX265	HS Hawk T1A [U]	RAF No 7 FTS/92(R) Sqn, Chivenor	
XX266	HS Hawk T1A	RAF Red Arrows, Scampton	
XX278	HS Hawk T1A	RAF No 7 FTS/19(R) Sqn, Chivenor	
XX280	HS Hawk T1A [DJ]	RAF No 4 FTS/234(R) Sqn, Valley	
XX281	HS Hawk T1A [O]	RAF No 7 FTS/92(R) Sqn, Chivenor	
XX282	HS Hawk T1A	RAF No 7 FTS/19(R) Sqn, Chivenor	
XX283	HS Hawk T1A [CD]	RAF No 100 Sqn, Finningley	
XX284	HS Hawk T1A [CL]	RAF No 100 Sqn, Finningley	
XX285	HS Hawk T1A [CH]	RAF No 100 Sqn, Finningley	
XX286	HS Hawk T1A [DK]	RAF No 4 FTS/234(R) Sqn, Valley	
XX287	HS Hawk T1A [S]	RAF No 7 FTS/92(R) Sqn, Chivenor	
XX288	HS Hawk T1 [DX]	RAF No 4 FTS/234(R) Sqn, Valley	
XX289	HS Hawk T1A	RAF No 7 FTS/19(R) Sqn, Chivenor	
XX290	HS Hawk T1 [CI]	RAF No 100 Sqn, Finningley	
XX292	HS Hawk T1 [R]	RAF No 7 FTS/92(R) Sqn, Chivenor	
XX294	HS Hawk T1	RAF Red Arrows, Scampton	
XX295	HS Hawk T1	RAF No 6 FTS, Finningley	
XX296	HS Hawk T1 [TR]	RAF No 4 FTS/74(R) Sqn, Valley	
XX297	HS Hawk T1A (8933M)	RAF Finningley Fire Section	
XX297	HS Hawk T1 Replica (BAPC 171)	RAF Exhibition Flight, St Athan	
XX299	HS Hawk T1 [J]	RAF No 7 FTS/92(R) Sqn, Chivenor	
XX301	HS Hawk T1A [L]	RAF No 7 FTS/92(R) Sqn, Chivenor	
XX302	HS Hawk T1A [TV]	RAF No 4 FTS/74(R) Sqn, Valley	
XX303	HS Hawk T1A [PF]	RAF CFS, Valley	
XX304	HS Hawk T1A (fuselage)	RAF, stored Shawbury	
XX306	HS Hawk T1A	RAF Red Arrows, Scampton	
XX307	HS Hawk T1	RAF Red Arrows, Scampton	
XX308	HS Hawk T1	RAF Red Arrows, Scampton	
XX309	HS Hawk T1	RAF No 6 FTS, Finningley	
XX310	HS Hawk T1 [TN]	RAF No 4 FTS/74(R) Sqn, Valley	
XX311	HS Hawk T1 [T]	RAF No 7 FTS/92(R) Sqn, Chivenor	
XX312	HS Hawk T1 [CF]	RAF No 100 Sqn, Finningley	
XX313	HS Hawk T1	RAF No 6 FTS, Finningley	
XX314	HS Hawk T1 [TP]	RAF No 4 FTS/74(R) Sqn, Valley	
XX315	HS Hawk T1A [DA]	RAF No 4 FTS/234(R) Sqn, Valley	
XX316	HS Hawk T1A [DF]	RAF No 4 FTS/234(R) Sqn, Valley	
XX317	HS Hawk T1A [DL]	RAF No 4 FTS/234(R) Sqn, Valley	
XX318	HS Hawk T1A [PG]	RAF CFS, Valley	
XX319	HS Hawk T1A [TF]	RAF No 4 FTS/74(R) Sqn, Valley	
XX320	HS Hawk T1A	RAF No 7 FTS/19(R) Sqn, Chivenor	
XX321	HS Hawk T1A	RAF No 7 FTS/19(R) Sqn, Chivenor	
XX322	HS Hawk T1A [W]	RAF No 7 FTS/92(R) Sqn, Chivenor	
XX323	HS Hawk T1A [TD]	RAF No 4 FTS/74(R) Sqn, Valley	
XX324	HS Hawk T1A [DM]	RAF No 4 FTS/234(R) Sqn, Valley	
XX325	HS Hawk T1A [CE]	RAF No 100 Sqn, Finningley	
XX326	HS Hawk T1A	RAF No 7 FTS/19(R) Sqn, Chivenor	
XX327	HS Hawk T1	RAF IAM, Farnborough	
XX329	HS Hawk T1A [C]	RAF No 7 FTS/92(R) Sqn, Chivenor	
XX330	HS Hawk T1A [D]	RAF No 7 FTS/92(R) Sqn, Chivenor	
XX331	HS Hawk T1A [CK]	RAF No 100 Sqn, Finningley	
XX332	HS Hawk T1A [F]	RAF No 7 FTS/92(R) Sqn, Chivenor	
XX335	HS Hawk T1A [I]	RAF No 7 FTS/92(R) Sqn, Chivenor	
XX337	HS Hawk T1A [K]	RAF No 7 FTS/92(R) Sqn, Chivenor	
XX338	HS Hawk T1	RAF No 7 FTS/19(R) Sqn, Chivenor	
XX339	HS Hawk T1A [TS]	RAF No 4 FTS/74(R) Sqn, Valley	

Notes	Serial	Type	Owner or Operator
	XX341	HS Hawk T1 ASTRA [1]	MoD(PE) ETPS, Boscombe Down
	XX342	HS Hawk T1 [2]	MoD(PE) ETPS, Boscombe Down
	XX343	HS Hawk T1 [3]	MoD(PE) ETPS, Boscombe Down
	XX344	HS Hawk T1 (8847M) (fuselage)	DRA Farnborough Fire Section
	XX345	HS Hawk T1A	RAF No 7 FTS/19(R) Sqn, Chivenor
	XX346	HS Hawk T1A	RAF No 7 FTS/19(R) Sqn, Chivenor
	XX348	HS Hawk T1A [DN]	RAF No 4 FTS/234(R) Sqn, Valley
	XX349	HS Hawk T1 [TL]	RAF No 4 FTS/74(R) Sqn, Valley
	XX350	HS Hawk T1A [TC]	RAF No 4 FTS/74(R) Sqn, Valley
	XX351	HS Hawk T1A [DP]	RAF No 4 FTS/234(R) Sqn, Valley
	XX352	HS Hawk T1A	RAF No 7 FTS/19(R) Sqn, Chivenor
	XX370	WS Gazelle AH1	AAC No 665 Sqn, Aldergrove
	XX371	WS Gazelle AH1	AAC No 12 Flt, Bruggen
	XX372	WS Gazelle AH1 [L]	AAC No 656 Sqn, Dishforth
	XX375	WS Gazelle AH1	AAC No 658 Sqn, Netheravon
	XX378	WS Gazelle AH1 [Q]	AAC No 670 Sqn, Middle Wallop
	XX379	WS Gazelle AH1	AAC No 658 Sqn, Netheravon
	XX380	WS Gazelle AH1 [A]	RM 3 CBAS, Yeovilton
	XX381	WS Gazelle AH1	AAC No 2 Flt, Netheravon
	XX382	WS Gazelle HT3 [M]	RAF No 2 FTS, Shawbury
	XX383	WS Gazelle AH1 [E]	AAC No 658 Sqn, Netheravon
	XX384	WS Gazelle AH1	AAC No 663 Sqn, Wattisham
	XX385	WS Gazelle AH1 [X]	AAC No 670 Sqn, Middle Wallop
	XX386	WS Gazelle AH1	AAC No 12 Flt, Bruggen
	XX387	WS Gazelle AH1	AAC, stored Fleetlands
	XX388	WS Gazelle AH1	AAC No 652 Sqn, Gütersloh
	XX389	WS Gazelle AH1 [C]	AAC
	XX391	WS Gazelle HT2 [56/CU]	RN No 705 Sqn, Culdrose
	XX392	WS Gazelle AH1 [A1]	AAC No 670 Sqn, Middle Wallop
	XX393	WS Gazelle AH1	AAC No 2 Flt, Netheravon
	XX394	WS Gazelle AH1	AAC No 2 Flt, Netheravon
	XX395	WS Gazelle AH1	AAC
	XX396	WS Gazelle HT3 (8718M) [N]	RAF Exhibition Flight, Henlow
	XX398	WS Gazelle AH1	AAC 4 Regiment, Detmold
	XX399	WS Gazelle AH1	AAC No 2 Flt, Netheravon
	XX403	WS Gazelle AH1 [Y]	Westland, Weston-super-Mare (on rebuild)
	XX405	WS Gazelle AH1 [C1]	AAC No 670 Sqn, Middle Wallop
	XX406	WS Gazelle HT3 [P]	RAF No 2 FTS, Shawbury
	XX407	WS Gazelle AH1 [D1]	AAC No 670 Sqn, Middle Wallop
	XX408	WS Gazelle AH1	AAC No 670 Sqn, Middle Wallop
	XX409	WS Gazelle AH1	AAC No 656 Sqn, Dishforth
	XX410	WS Gazelle HT2 [58/CU]	RN AES, Lee-on-Solent
	XX411	WS Gazelle AH1 [X]	AAC Middle Wallop, BDRT
	XX411	WS Gazelle AH1 (tail only)	FAA Museum, RNAS Yeovilton
	XX412	WS Gazelle AH1 [B]	RM 3 CBAS, Yeovilton
	XX413	WS Gazelle AH1 [C]	RM 3 CBAS, Yeovilton
	XX414	WS Gazelle AH1 [N]	AAC No 662 Sqn, Wattisham
	XX416	WS Gazelle AH1 [A]	AAC No 656 Sqn, Dishforth
	XX417	WS Gazelle AH1	AAC No 665 Sqn, Aldergrove
	XX418	WS Gazelle AH1	AAC No 651 Sqn, Gütersloh
	XX419	WS Gazelle AH1 [W]	AAC No 657 Sqn, Dishforth
	XX431	WS Gazelle HT2 [VL]	RN FONA, Yeovilton
	XX432	WS Gazelle AH1	AAC No 665 Sqn, Aldergrove
	XX433	WS Gazelle AH1	AAC No 670 Sqn, Middle Wallop
	XX435	WS Gazelle AH1 [B]	AAC No 653 Sqn, Wattisham
	XX436	WS Gazelle HT2 [39/CU]	RN No 705 Sqn, Culdrose
	XX437	WS Gazelle AH1 [G]	AAC
	XX438	WS Gazelle AH1 [B]	AAC No 664 Sqn, Dishforth
	XX439	WS Gazelle AH1	AAC No 651 Sqn, Gütersloh
	XX440	WS Gazelle AH1 (G-BCHN)	AAC No 665 Sqn, Aldergrove
	XX441	WS Gazelle HT2 [38/CU]	RN No 705 Sqn, Culdrose
	XX442	WS Gazelle AH1	AAC Fleetlands
	XX443	WS Gazelle AH1	AAC No 663 Sqn, Wattisham
	XX444	WS Gazelle AH1 [E]	AAC No 656 Sqn, Dishforth .
	XX445	WS Gazelle AH1	AAC No 664 Sqn, Dishforth
	XX446	WS Gazelle HT2 [57/CU]	RN No 705 Sqn, Culdrose
	XX447	WS Gazelle AH1 [U]	AAC No 663 Sqn, Wattisham
	XX448	WS Gazelle AH1 [A]	AAC No 669 Sqn, Detmold
	XX449	WS Gazelle AH1 [T]	AAC No 669 Sqn, Detmold
	XX450	WS Gazelle AH1 [D]	RM 3 CBAS, Yeovilton
	XX451	WS Gazelle HT2 [58/CU]	RN No 705 Sqn, Culdrose
	XX452	WS Gazelle AH1	AAC Middle Wallop Fire Section
	XX453	WS Gazelle AH1	AAC No 659 Sqn, Detmold

Serial	Type	Owner or Operator	Notes
XX454	WS Gazelle AH1	AAC No 659 Sqn, Detmold	
XX455	WS Gazelle AH1	AAC No 651 Sqn, Gütersloh	
XX456	WS Gazelle AH1	AAC No 7 Flt, Gatow	
XX457	WS Gazelle AH1	AAC No 2 Flt, Netheravon	
XX460	WS Gazelle AH1	AAC 4 Regiment, Detmold	
XX462	WS Gazelle AH1	AAC No 661 Sqn, Gütersloh	
XX466	HS Hunter T66B/T7 (830/DD)	RN Predannack Fire School	
XX467	HS Hunter T66B/T7	Air Service Training, Perth	
XX469	WS Lynx HAS2 (A2657/G-BNCL)	Lancashire Fire Brigade, Lancaster	
XX475	SA Jetstream T2 (G-AWVJ/ N1036S) [572/CU]	RN No 750 Sqn, Culdrose	
XX476	SA Jetstream T2 (G-AXGL/ N1037S) [561/CU]	RN No 750 Sqn, Culdrose	
XX477	SA Jetstream T1 (8462M/G-AXXS) (fuselage)	RAF Finningley for ground instruction	
XX478	SA Jetstream T2 (G-AXXT) [564/CU]	RN No 750 Sqn, Culdrose	
XX479	SA Jetstream T2 (G-AXUR) [563/CU]	RN No 750 Sqn, Culdrose	
XX480	SA Jetstream T2 (G-AXXU) [565/CU]	RN No 750 Sqn, Culdrose	
XX481	SA Jetstream T2 (G-AXUP) [560/CU]	RN No 750 Sqn, Culdrose	
XX482	SA Jetstream T1 [J]	RAF No 6 FTS/45(R) Sqn, Finningley	
XX483	SA Jetstream T2 [562/CU]	RN No 750 Sqn, Culdrose	
XX484	SA Jetstream T2 [566/CU]	RN No 750 Sqn, Culdrose	
XX485	SA Jetstream T2 [567/CU]	RN No 750 Sqn, Culdrose	
XX486	SA Jetstream T2 [569/CU]	RN No 750 Sqn, Culdrose	
XX487	SA Jetstream T2 [568/CU]	RN No 750 Sqn, Culdrose	
XX488	SA Jetstream T2 [571/CU]	RN No 750 Sqn, Culdrose	
XX490	SA Jetstream T2 [570/CU]	RN No 750 Sqn, Culdrose	
XX491	SA Jetstream T1 [K]	RAF No 6 FTS/45(R) Sqn, Finningley	
XX492	SA Jetstream T1 [A]	RAF No 6 FTS/45(R) Sqn, Finningley	
XX493	SA Jetstream T1 [L]	RAF No 6 FTS/45(R) Sqn, Finningley	
XX494	SA Jetstream T1 [B]	RAF No 6 FTS/45(R) Sqn, Finningley	
XX495	SA Jetstream T1 [C]	RAF No 6 FTS/45(R) Sqn, Finningley	
XX496	SA Jetstream T1 [D]	RAF No 6 FTS/45(R) Sqn, Finningley	
XX497	SA Jetstream T1 [E]	RAF No 6 FTS/45(R) Sqn, Finningley	
XX498	SA Jetstream T1 [F]	RAF No 6 FTS/45(R) Sqn, Finningley	
XX499	SA Jetstream T1 [G]	RAF No 6 FTS/45(R) Sqn, Finningley	
XX500	SA Jetstream T1 [H]	RAF No 6 FTS/45(R) Sqn, Finningley	
XX507	HS125 CC2	RAF No 32 Sqn, Northolt	
XX508	HS125 CC2	RAF No 32 Sqn, Northolt	
XX510	WS Lynx HAS2 [69/LS]	RN, Lee-on-Solent, BDRT	
XX513	SA Bulldog T1 [10]	RAF CFS, Scampton	
XX515	SA Bulldog T1 [A2]	RAF College Air Sqn, Cranwell	
XX516	SA Bulldog T1 [1]	RAF CFS, Scampton	
XX518	SA Bulldog T1 [Z]	RAF Cambridge UAS, Cambridge	
XX519	SA Bulldog T1 [A1]	RAF College Air Sqn, Cranwell	
XX520	SA Bulldog T1 [2]	RAF CFS, Scampton	
XX521	SA Bulldog T1 [01]	RAF East Lowlands UAS, Turnhouse	
XX522	SA Bulldog T1 [B2]	RAF College Air Sqn, Cranwell	
XX523	SA Bulldog T1 [X]	RAF Liverpool UAS, Woodvale	
XX524	SA Bulldog T1 [04]	RAF London UAS, Benson	
XX525	SA Bulldog T1 [03]	RAF East Lowlands UAS, Turnhouse	
XX526	SA Bulldog T1 [C]	RAF Oxford UAS, Benson	
XX527	SA Bulldog T1 [D]	RAF Queen's UAS, Sydenham	
XX528	SA Bulldog T1 [D]	RAF Oxford UAS, Benson	
XX529	SA Bulldog T1 [W]	RAF No 6 FTS, Finningley	
XX531	SA Bulldog T1 [06]	RAF Wales UAS, St Athan	
XX532	SA Bulldog T1 [D]	RAF Yorkshire UAS, Finningley	
XX533	SA Bulldog T1 [U]	RAF Northumbria UAS, Leeming	
XX534	SA Bulldog T1 [B]	RAF Birmingham UAS, Cosford	
XX535	SA Bulldog T1 [II]	RAF East Midlands UAS, Newton	
XX536	SA Bulldog T1 [6]	RAF Manchester UAS, Woodvale	
XX537	SA Bulldog T1 [02]	RAF East Lowlands UAS, Turnhouse	
XX538	SA Bulldog T1 [V]	RAF No 6 FTS, Finningley	
XX539	SA Bulldog T1 [L]	RAF Liverpool UAS, Woodvale	
XX540	SA Bulldog T1 [C2]	RAF College Air Sqn, Cranwell	
XX541	SA Bulldog T1 [L]	RAF, stored Linton-on-Ouse	
XX543	SA Bulldog T1 [F]	RAF Yorkshire UAS, Finningley	
XX544	SA Bulldog T1 [01]	RAF London UAS, Benson	
XX545	SA Bulldog T1 PAX [02]	RAF East Lowlands UAS, Turnhouse	

Notes	Serial	Type	Owner or Operator
	XX546	SA Bulldog T1 [03]	RAF London UAS, Benson
	XX547	SA Bulldog T1 [05]	RAF London UAS, Benson
	XX548	SA Bulldog T1 [06]	RAF London UAS, Benson
	XX549	SA Bulldog T1	RAF Southampton UAS, Boscombe Down
	XX550	SA Bulldog T1 [Z]	RAF Northumbria UAS, Leeming
	XX551	SA Bulldog T1	RAF London UAS, Benson
	XX552	SA Bulldog T1 [08]	RAF London UAS, Benson
	XX553	SA Bulldog T1	RAF London UAS, Benson
	XX554	SA Bulldog T1	RAF London UAS, Benson
	XX555	SA Bulldog T1 [10]	RAF CFS, Scampton
	XX556	SA Bulldog T1 [S]	RAF East Midlands UAS, Newton
	XX557	SA Bulldog T1 PAX	RAF Topcliffe, ground instruction
	XX558	SA Bulldog T1 [A]	RAF Birmingham UAS, Cosford
	XX559	SA Bulldog T1	RAF East Lowlands UAS, Turnhouse
	XX560	SA Bulldog T1 [r]	RAF Glasgow & Strathclyde UAS, Glasgow
	XX561	SA Bulldog T1 [A]	RAF Aberdeen, Dundee & St Andrews UAS, Leuchars
	XX562	SA Bulldog T1 [E]	RAF No 13 AEF, Sydenham
	XX611	SA Bulldog T1 [y]	RAF Glasgow & Strathclyde UAS, Glasgow
	XX612	SA Bulldog T1 [05]	RAF Wales UAS, St Athan
	XX614	SA Bulldog T1 [6]	RAF CFS, Scampton
	XX615	SA Bulldog T1 [2]	RAF Manchester UAS, Woodvale
	XX616	SA Bulldog T1 [3]	RAF Manchester UAS, Woodvale
	XX617	SA Bulldog T1 [4]	RAF Manchester UAS, Woodvale
	XX619	SA Bulldog T1 [B]	RAF Yorkshire UAS, Finningley
	XX620	SA Bulldog T1 [C]	RAF Yorkshire UAS, Finningley
	XX621	SA Bulldog T1 [X]	RAF No 6 FTS, Finningley
	XX622	SA Bulldog T1 [E]	RAF Yorkshire UAS, Finningley
	XX623	SA Bulldog T1 [M]	RAF East Midlands UAS, Newton
	XX624	SA Bulldog T1 [Y]	RAF No 6 FTS, Finningley
	XX625	SA Bulldog T1 [01]	RAF Wales UAS, St Athan
	XX626	SA Bulldog T1 [02]	RAF Wales UAS, St Athan
	XX627	SA Bulldog T1 [03]	RAF Wales UAS, St Athan
	XX628	SA Bulldog T1 [04]	RAF Wales UAS, St Athan
	XX629	SA Bulldog T1 [V]	RAF Northumbria UAS, Leeming
	XX630	SA Bulldog T1 [A]	RAF Liverpool UAS, Woodvale
	XX631	SA Bulldog T1 [W]	RAF Northumbria UAS, Leeming
	XX632	SA Bulldog T1 [D]	RAF Bristol UAS, Colerne
	XX633	SA Bulldog T1 [X]	RAF Northumbria UAS, Leeming
	XX634	SA Bulldog T1 [C]	RAF Cambridge UAS, Cambridge
	XX635	SA Bulldog T1 (8767M)	RAF St Athan, CTTS
	XX636	SA Bulldog T1 [Y]	RAF Northumbria UAS, Leeming
	XX637	SA Bulldog T1 [U]	RAF Northumbria UAS, Leeming
	XX638	SA Bulldog T1 [H]	RAF Yorkshire UAS, Finningley
	XX639	SA Bulldog T1 [02]	RAF London UAS, Benson
	XX640	SA Bulldog T1 [B]	RAF Queen's UAS, Sydenham
	XX653	SA Bulldog T1 [E]	RAF Bristol UAS, Colerne
	XX654	SA Bulldog T1 [A]	RAF Bristol UAS, Colerne
	XX655	SA Bulldog T1 [B]	RAF Bristol UAS, Colerne
	XX656	SA Bulldog T1 [C]	RAF Bristol UAS, Colerne
	XX657	SA Bulldog T1 [U]	RAF Cambridge UAS, Cambridge
	XX658	SA Bulldog T1 [A]	RAF Cambridge UAS, Cambridge
	XX659	SA Bulldog T1 [S]	RAF Cambridge UAS, Cambridge
	XX660	SA Bulldog T1 [A]	BAe Prestwick, spares recovery
	XX661	SA Bulldog T1 [B]	RAF Oxford UAS, Benson
	XX663	SA Bulldog T1 [B]	RAF Aberdeen, Dundee & St Andrews UAS, Leuchars
	XX664	SA Bulldog T1 [04]	RAF East Lowlands UAS, Turnhouse
	XX665	SA Bulldog T1 [E]	RAF Aberdeen, Dundee & St Andrews UAS, Leuchars
	XX666	SA Bulldog T1	RAF Glasgow & Strathclyde UAS, Glasgow
	XX667	SA Bulldog T1 [C1]	RAF College Air Sqn, Cranwell
	XX668	SA Bulldog T1 [1]	RAF Manchester UAS, Woodvale
	XX669	SA Bulldog T1 (8997M) [B]	Privately owned, Bruntingthorpe
	XX670	SA Bulldog T1 [C]	RAF Birmingham UAS, Cosford
	XX671	SA Bulldog T1 [D]	RAF Birmingham UAS, Cosford
	XX672	SA Bulldog T1 [E]	RAF Birmingham UAS, Cosford
	XX685	SA Bulldog T1 [C]	RAF Aberdeen, Dundee & St Andrews UAS, Leuchars

Serial	Type	Owner or Operator	Notes
XX686	SA Bulldog T1	RAF Glasgow & Strathclyde UAS, Glasgow	
XX687	SA Bulldog T1 [A]	RAF East Midlands UAS, Newton	
XX688	SA Bulldog T1 [S]	RAF Liverpool UAS, Woodvale	
XX689	SA Bulldog T1 [3]	RAF CFS, Scampton	
XX690	SA Bulldog T1 [A]	RAF Yorkshire UAS, Finningley	
XX691	SA Bulldog T1 [G]	RAF Yorkshire UAS, Finningley	
XX692	SA Bulldog T1 [5]	RAF CFS, Scampton	
XX693	SA Bulldog T1 [4]	RAF CFS, Scampton	
XX694	SA Bulldog T1 [E]	RAF East Midlands UAS, Newton	
XX695	SA Bulldog T1 [A]	RAF Oxford UAS, Benson	
XX696	SA Bulldog T1 [8]	RAF CFS, Scampton	
XX697	SA Bulldog T1 [C]	RAF Queen's UAS, Sydenham	
XX698	SA Bulldog T1	RAF CFS/*Red Arrows*, Scampton	
XX699	SA Bulldog T1 [F]	RAF Birmingham UAS, Cosford	
XX700	SA Bulldog T1 [B1]	RAF College Air Sqn, Cranwell	
XX701	SA Bulldog T1 [02]	RAF Southampton UAS, Boscombe Down	
XX702	SA Bulldog T1 [11]	RAF CFS, Scampton	
XX704	SA Bulldog T1 [U]	RAF East Midlands UAS, Newton	
XX705	SA Bulldog T1 [05]	RAF Southampton UAS, Boscombe Down	
XX706	SA Bulldog T1 [01]	RAF Southampton UAS, Boscombe Down	
XX707	SA Bulldog T1 [04]	RAF Southampton UAS, Boscombe Down	
XX708	SA Bulldog T1 [03]	RAF Southampton UAS, Boscombe Down	
XX709	SA Bulldog T1 [12]	RAF CFS, Scampton	
XX710	SA Bulldog T1 [5]	RAF Manchester UAS, Woodvale	
XX711	SA Bulldog T1 [D]	RAF Queen's UAS, Sydenham	
XX713	SA Bulldog T1 [Z]	RAF No 6 FTS, Finningley	
XX714	SA Bulldog T1 [7]	RAF CFS, Scampton	
XX718	SEPECAT Jaguar GR1 Replica (BAPC150) [GA]	RAF Exhibition Flight, St Athan	
XX719	SEPECAT Jaguar GR1A [EE]	RAF No 6 Sqn, Coltishall	
XX720	SEPECAT Jaguar GR1A (JI003) [EN]	RAF, stored Shawbury	
XX723	SEPECAT Jaguar GR1A [GQ]	RAF No 54 Sqn, Coltishall	
XX724	SEPECAT Jaguar GR1A [GA]	RAF, stored Shawbury	
XX725	SEPECAT Jaguar GR1A (JI010) [GT]	RAF No 54 Sqn, Coltishall	
XX726	SEPECAT Jaguar GR1 (8947M) [EB]	RAF No 1 SoTT, Halton	
XX727	SEPECAT Jaguar GR1 (8951M) [ER]	RAF No 2 SoTT, Cosford	
XX729	SEPECAT Jaguar GR1A (JI012) [GC]	RAF, stored Shawbury	
XX730	SEPECAT Jaguar GR1 (8952M) [EC]	RAF No 2 SoTT, Cosford	
XX733	SEPECAT Jaguar GR1A [ER]	RAF No 6 Sqn, Coltishall	
XX734	SEPECAT Jaguar GR1 (J1014/8816M)	*Scrapped 1992*	
XX736	SEPECAT Jaguar GR1 (J1013/9110M)	RAF Coltishall, BDRT	
XX737	SEPECAT Jaguar GR1A (JI015) [EG]	RAF, stored Shawbury	
XX738	SEPECAT Jaguar GR1A (JI016) [GJ]	RAF, stored Shawbury	
XX739	SEPECAT Jaguar GR1 (8902M)	RAF No 1 SoTT, Halton	
XX741	SEPECAT Jaguar GR1A [04]	RAF No 16(R) Sqn, Lossiemouth	
XX743	SEPECAT Jaguar GR1 (8949M) [EG]	RAF No 1 SoTT, Halton	
XX745	SEPECAT Jaguar GR1A [EG]	RAF No 6 Sqn, Coltishall	
XX746	SEPECAT Jaguar GR1A (8895M) [09]	RAF No 1 SoTT, Halton	
XX747	SEPECAT Jaguar GR1 (8903M)	RAF SIF, Cranwell	
XX748	SEPECAT Jaguar GR1A [GK]	RAF No 54 Sqn, Coltishall	
XX751	SEPECAT Jaguar GR1 (8937M) [10]	RAF No 2 SoTT, Cosford	
XX752	SEPECAT Jaguar GR1A [EQ]	RAF No 6 Sqn, Coltishall	
XX753	SEPECAT Jaguar GR1 (9087M) (cockpit)	RAF Exhibition Flight, St Athan	
XX756	SEPECAT Jaguar GR1 (8899M) [AM]	RAF No 2 SoTT, Cosford	
XX757	SEPECAT Jaguar GR1 (8948M) [CU]	RAF No 1 SoTT, Halton	
XX763	SEPECAT Jaguar GR1 (9009M)	RAF CTTS, St Athan	

Notes	Serial	Type	Owner or Operator
	XX764	SEPECAT Jaguar GR1 (9010M)	RAF CTTS, St Athan
	XX765	SEPECAT Jaguar ACT	Loughborough University
	XX766	SEPECAT Jaguar GR1A [EA]	RAF No 6 Sqn, Coltishall
	XX767	SEPECAT Jaguar GR1A [GE]	RAF No 54 Sqn, Coltishall
	XX818	SEPECAT Jaguar GR1 (8945M) [DE]	RAF No 1 SoTT, Halton
	XX819	SEPECAT Jaguar GR1 (8923M) [CE]	RAF No 2 SoTT, Cosford
	XX821	SEPECAT Jaguar GR1 (8896M) [P]	RAF SIF, Cranwell
	XX824	SEPECAT Jaguar GR1 (9019M) [AD]	RAF No 1 SoTT, Halton
	XX825	SEPECAT Jaguar GR1 (9020M) [BN]	RAF No 1 SoTT, Halton
	XX826	SEPECAT Jaguar GR1 (9021M) [34]	RAF No 2 SoTT, Cosford
	XX829	SEPECAT Jaguar T2A [ET]	RAF No 6 Sqn, Coltishall
	XX830	SEPECAT Jaguar T2	MoD(PE) ETPS, Boscombe Down
	XX832	SEPECAT Jaguar T2A [S]	RAF, stored Shawbury
	XX833	SEPECAT Jaguar T2A [N]	RAF SAOEU, Boscombe Down
	XX835	SEPECAT Jaguar T2	MoD(PE), DRA Farnborough
	XX836	SEPECAT Jaguar T2A	RAF, stored Shawbury
	XX837	SEPECAT Jaguar T2 (8978M) [Z]	RAF No 1 SoTT, Halton
	XX838	SEPECAT Jaguar T2A [X]	RAF, stored Shawbury
	XX839	SEPECAT Jaguar T2A	RAF No 41 Sqn, Coltishall
	XX840	SEPECAT Jaguar T2A [X]	RAF, stored Shawbury
	XX841	SEPECAT Jaguar T2A [ES]	RAF No 6 Sqn, Coltishall
	XX842	SEPECAT Jaguar T2A [EW]	RAF No 6 Sqn, Coltishall
	XX844	SEPECAT Jaguar T2 (9023M) [F]	RAF No 2 SoTT, Cosford
	XX845	SEPECAT Jaguar T2A [A]	RAF No 16(R) Sqn, Lossiemouth
	XX846	SEPECAT Jaguar T2A [Y]	RAF No 41 Sqn, Coltishall
	XX847	SEPECAT Jaguar T2A [X]	RAF No 41 Sqn, Coltishall
	XX885	HS Buccaneer S2B [L]	RAF, stored Lossiemouth
	XX886	HS Buccaneer S2B	RAF Honington, WLT use
	XX888	HS Buccaneer S2B (cockpit)	Privately owned, Ottershaw
	XX889	HS Buccaneer S2B [T]	RAF No 208 Sqn, Lossiemouth
	XX892	HS Buccaneer S2B	RAF, stored Lossiemouth
	XX893	HS Buccaneer S2B	RAF, stored Lossiemouth
	XX894	HS Buccaneer S2B	RAF No 208 Sqn, Lossiemouth
	XX895	HS Buccaneer S2B	RAF No 208 Sqn, Lossiemouth
	XX897	HS Buccaneer S2B	Privately owned, Bournemouth
	XX899	HS Buccaneer S2B	RAF No 208 Sqn, Lossiemouth
	XX900	HS Buccaneer S2B	RAF No 208 Sqn, Lossiemouth
	XX901	HS Buccaneer S2B	RAF, stored Lossiemouth
	XX910	WS Lynx HAS2	DRA, stored Farnborough
	XX914	BAC VC10 srs 1103 (8777M/ G-ATDJ) (rear fuselage only)	RAF AMS, Brize Norton
	XX919	BAC 1-11/402 (PI-C 1121)	MoD(PE), DRA Farnborough
	XX946	Panavia Tornado (P02) (8883M) [WT]	RAF Honington, WLT
	XX947	Panavia Tornado (P03) (8797M)	RAF Marham, GI use
	XX948	Panavia Tornado (P06) (8879M) [P]	RAF No 2 SoTT, Cosford
	XX955	SEPECAT Jaguar GR1A [GK]	RAF, stored Shawbury
	XX956	SEPECAT Jaguar GR1 (8950M) [BE]	RAF No 1 SoTT, Halton
	XX958	SEPECAT Jaguar GR1 (9022M) [BK]	RAF No 2 SoTT, Cosford
	XX959	SEPECAT Jaguar GR1 (8953M) [CJ]	RAF No 2 SoTT, Cosford
	XX962	SEPECAT Jaguar GR1A [EK]	RAF No 6 Sqn, Coltishall
	XX965	SEPECAT Jaguar GR1A [07]	RAF No 16(R) Sqn, Lossiemouth
	XX966	SEPECAT Jaguar GR1A (8904M)	RAF No 1 SoTT, Halton
	XX967	SEPECAT Jaguar GR1 (9006M) [AC]	RAF No 2 SoTT, Cosford
	XX968	SEPECAT Jaguar GR1 (9007M) [AJ]	RAF No 2 SoTT, Cosford
	XX969	SEPECAT Jaguar GR1A (8897M) [01]	RAF No 2 SoTT, Cosford
	XX970	SEPECAT Jaguar GR1A [EH]	RAF No 41 Sqn, Coltishall
	XX974	SEPECAT Jaguar GR1A [GH]	RAF No 54 Sqn, Coltishall
	XX975	SEPECAT Jaguar GR1 (8905M) [07]	RAF No 1 SoTT, Halton

Serial	Type	Owner or Operator	Notes
XX976	SEPECAT Jaguar GR1 (8906M) [BD]	RAF No 1 SoTT, Halton	
XX977	SEPECAT Jaguar GR1 (9132M) [DL,05]	RAF St Athan, BDRT	
XX979	SEPECAT Jaguar GR1A	MoD(PE), A&AEE Boscombe Down	
XZ101	SEPECAT Jaguar GR1A [06]	RAF No 16(R) Sqn, Lossiemouth	
XZ103	SEPECAT Jaguar GR1A [P]	RAF No 41 Sqn, Coltishall	
XZ104	SEPECAT Jaguar GR1A [FM]	RAF No 41 Sqn, Coltishall	
XZ106	SEPECAT Jaguar GR1A [R]	RAF No 41 Sqn, Coltishall	
XZ107	SEPECAT Jaguar GR1A [H]	RAF No 41 Sqn, Coltishall	
XZ108	SEPECAT Jaguar GR1A [GD]	RAF No 54 Sqn, Coltishall	
XZ109	SEPECAT Jaguar GR1A [EN]	RAF No 6 Sqn, Coltishall	
XZ111	SEPECAT Jaguar GR1A [GO]	RAF, stored Shawbury	
XZ112	SEPECAT Jaguar GR1A [GA]	RAF No 54 Sqn, Coltishall	
XZ113	SEPECAT Jaguar GR1A [FD]	RAF No 41 Sqn, Coltishall	
XZ114	SEPECAT Jaguar GR1A [FB]	RAF No 41 Sqn, Coltishall	
XZ115	SEPECAT Jaguar GR1A [FC]	RAF No 41 Sqn, Coltishall	
XZ117	SEPECAT Jaguar GR1A	RAF No 54 Sqn, Coltishall	
XZ118	SEPECAT Jaguar GR1A [FF]	RAF No 41 Sqn, Coltishall	
XZ119	SEPECAT Jaguar GR1A [G]	RAF No 41 Sqn, Coltishall	
XZ129	HS Harrier GR3 [ETS]	RN ETS, Yeovilton	
XZ130	HS Harrier GR3 (9079M) [A]	RAF No 2 SoTT, Cosford	
XZ131	HS Harrier GR3 (9174M) (cockpit)	RAF Exhibition Flight, St Athan	
XZ132	HS Harrier GR3 (9168M) [C]	RAF Cranwell, GI use	
XZ133	HS Harrier GR3 [10]	Imperial War Museum, Duxford	
XZ135	HS Harrier GR3 (8848M) (cockpit)	RAF Exhibition Flight, St Athan	
XZ138	HS Harrier GR3 (9040M) [14]	RAF Cranwell, for instructional use	
XZ145	HS Harrier T4 [14]	RAF No 1 Sqn, Wittering	
XZ146	HS Harrier T4	RAF ASF, Wittering	
XZ170	WS Lynx AH7(mod)	MoD(PE)/Westland, Yeovil	
XZ171	WS Lynx AH7	AAC 1 Regiment, Gütersloh	
XZ172	WS Lynx AH7	AAC No 655 Sqn, Aldergrove	
XZ173	WS Lynx AH7 [X]	AAC, Fleetlands	
XZ174	WS Lynx AH7	AAC No 655 Sqn, Aldergrove	
XZ175	WS Lynx AH7	AAC, Fleetlands	
XZ176	WS Lynx AH7	AAC, Fleetlands	
XZ177	WS Lynx AH7 [B]	AAC No 653 Sqn, Wattisham	
XZ178	WS Lynx AH7 [J]	AAC No 662 Sqn, Wattisham	
XZ179	WS Lynx AH7	AAC No 667 Sqn, Middle Wallop	
XZ180	WS Lynx AH7 [R]	RM 3 CBAS, Yeovilton	
XZ181	WS Lynx AH1	AAC No 656 Sqn, Dishforth	
XZ182	WS Lynx AH7 [M]	RM 3 CBAS, Yeovilton	
XZ183	WS Lynx AH7	AAC, Fleetlands	
XZ184	WS Lynx AH1 [W]	AAC No 656 Sqn, Dishforth	
XZ185	WS Lynx AH7 [L]	AAC, Fleetlands	
XZ186	WS Lynx AH7 (wreck)	AAC, Fleetlands	
XZ187	WS Lynx AH7	MoD(PE)/Westland, Yeovil	
XZ188	WS Lynx AH7	AAC, Fleetlands	
XZ190	WS Lynx AH7 [E]	AAC, Fleetlands	
XZ191	WS Lynx AH1 [X]	AAC No 663 Sqn, Wattisham	
XZ192	WS Lynx AH7 [G]	AAC No 671 Sqn, Middle Wallop	
XZ193	WS Lynx AH7 [I]	AAC No 662 Sqn, Wattisham	
XZ194	WS Lynx AH7 [T]	AAC No 663 Sqn, Wattisham	
XZ195	WS Lynx AH7	AAC No 655 Sqn, Aldergrove	
XZ196	WS Lynx AH1 [A]	AAC No 653 Sqn, Wattisham	
XZ197	WS Lynx AH7	AAC No 665 Sqn, Aldergrove	
XZ198	WS Lynx AH7	AAC No 655 Sqn, Aldergrove	
XZ199	WS Lynx AH7	AAC No 654 Sqn, Detmold	
XZ203	WS Lynx AH1 [C]	AAC No 653 Sqn, Wattisham	
XZ205	WS Lynx AH7	AAC No 665 Sqn, Aldergrove	
XZ206	WS Lynx AH1 [B]	AAC No 671 Sqn, Middle Wallop	
XZ207	WS Lynx AH7	AAC 4 Regiment, Detmold	
XZ208	WS Lynx AH7	AAC No 659 Sqn, Detmold	
XZ209	WS Lynx AH1 [T]	AAC No 656 Sqn, Dishforth	
XZ210	WS Lynx AH7 [N]	AAC No 662 Sqn, Wattisham	
XZ211	WS Lynx AH7	AAC, Fleetlands	
XZ212	WS Lynx AH1 [P]	AAC No 657 Sqn, Dishforth	
XZ213	WS Lynx AH1 [TAD213]	AAC SAE, Middle Wallop	
XZ214	WS Lynx AH7	AAC No 662 Sqn, Wattisham	
XZ215	WS Lynx AH7	AAC No 669 Sqn, Detmold	
XZ216	WS Lynx AH1 [V]	AAC, stored Fleetlands	
XZ217	WS Lynx AH7	AAC 4 Regiment, Detmold	

Notes	Serial	Type	Owner or Operator
	XZ218	WS Lynx AH7	AAC No 655 Sqn, Aldergrove
	XZ219	WS Lynx AH7	AAC 1 Regiment, Gütersloh
	XZ220	WS Lynx AH7	AAC No 657 Sqn, Dishforth
	XZ221	WS Lynx AH7	AAC No 669 Sqn, Detmold
	XZ222	WS Lynx AH7	AAC No 669 Sqn, Detmold
	XZ227	WS Lynx HAS3 [377]	RN, stored Fleetlands (for Portugal)
	XZ228	WS Lynx HAS3S [334/SN]	RN No 815 Sqn, Portland
	XZ229	WS Lynx HAS3S [338/CT]	RN No 815 Sqn, Portland
	XZ230	WS Lynx HAS3S [336/CV]	RN No 815 Sqn, Portland
	XZ231	WS Lynx HAS3 [342/BT]	RN No 815 Sqn, Portland
	XZ232	WS Lynx HAS3S	RN AMG, Portland
	XZ233	WS Lynx HAS3S [435/ED]	RN No 815 Sqn, Portland
	XZ234	WS Lynx HAS3S [361/NF]	RN No 815 Sqn, Portland
	XZ235	WS Lynx HAS3S [635]	RN No 702 Sqn, Portland
	XZ236	WS Lynx HAS8	MoD(PE), A&AEE Boscombe Down
	XZ237	WS Lynx HAS3S	RN AMG, Portland
	XZ238	WS Lynx HAS3S [645]	RN, Fleetlands
	XZ239	WS Lynx HAS3	RN No 815 Sqn, Portland
	XZ240	WS Lynx HAS3	RN, stored Fleetlands (for Portugal)
	XZ241	WS Lynx HAS3 [328/BA]	RN No 815 Sqn, Portland
	XZ243	WS Lynx HAS3 [635] (wreck)	RN Portland, GI use
	XZ245	WS Lynx HAS3S [352/SD]	RN No 815 Sqn, Portland
	XZ246	WS Lynx HAS3 [434/ED]	RN AMG, Portland
	XZ248	WS Lynx HAS3 [345/NC]	RN No 815 Sqn, Portland
	XZ249	WS Lynx HAS2	*Burned at Predannack by May 1993*
	XZ250	WS Lynx HAS3S [645]	RN No 702 Sqn, Portland
	XZ252	WS Lynx HAS3 [644]	RN No 702 Sqn, Portland
	XZ254	WS Lynx HAS3S [360/MC]	RN No 815 Sqn, Portland
	XZ255	WS Lynx HAS3S [335/CF]	RN No 815 Sqn, Portland
	XZ256	WS Lynx HAS8	MoD(PE)/Westland, Yeovil (conversion)
	XZ257	WS Lynx HAS3S [303]	RN No 815 Sqn, Portland
	XZ282	BAe Nimrod AEW3 (9000M)	*Scrapped at Kinloss 1992*
	XZ284	HS Nimrod MR2P	RAF No 206 Sqn, Kinloss
	XZ287	BAe Nimrod AEW3 (9140M) (fuselage)	RAF Stafford
	XZ290	WS Gazelle AH1 [F]	AAC No 670 Sqn, Middle Wallop
	XZ291	WS Gazelle AH1	AAC No 12 Flt, Bruggen
	XZ292	WS Gazelle AH1	AAC No 654 Sqn, Detmold
	XZ294	WS Gazelle AH1 [A]	AAC No 658 Sqn, Netheravon
	XZ295	WS Gazelle AH1	AAC No 6 (TA) Flt, Shawbury
	XZ296	WS Gazelle AH1	AAC No 664 Sqn, Dishforth
	XZ298	WS Gazelle AH1	AAC No 659 Sqn, Detmold
	XZ299	WS Gazelle AH1 [G1]	AAC, stored RNAY Fleetlands
	XZ300	WS Gazelle AH1 [L]	AAC No 670 Sqn, Middle Wallop
	XZ301	WS Gazelle AH1 [U]	AAC No 670 Sqn, Middle Wallop
	XZ302	WS Gazelle AH1	AAC, stored Fleetlands
	XZ303	WS Gazelle AH1	AAC No 663 Sqn, Wattisham
	XZ304	WS Gazelle AH1	AAC No 6 (TA) Flt, Shawbury
	XZ305	WS Gazelle AH1	AAC 3 Regiment, Wattisham
	XZ307	WS Gazelle AH1	AAC No 665 Sqn, Aldergrove
	XZ308	WS Gazelle AH1	AAC No 12 Flt, Bruggen
	XZ309	WS Gazelle AH1	AAC No 6 (TA) Flt, Shawbury
	XZ310	WS Gazelle AH1 [A]	AAC No 653 Sqn, Wattisham
	XZ311	WS Gazelle AH1	AAC No 6 (TA) Flt, Shawbury
	XZ312	WS Gazelle AH1	AAC, Fleetlands
	XZ313	WS Gazelle AH1 [S]	AAC No 670 Sqn, Middle Wallop
	XZ314	WS Gazelle AH1 [A]	AAC No 656 Sqn, Dishforth
	XZ315	WS Gazelle AH1	AAC No 665 Sqn, Aldergrove
	XZ316	WS Gazelle AH1 [R]	AAC No 670 Sqn, Middle Wallop
	XZ317	WS Gazelle AH1 [D1]	AAC No 670 Sqn, Middle Wallop
	XZ318	WS Gazelle AH1	AAC No 657 Sqn, Dishforth
	XZ320	WS Gazelle AH1	RM, stored Fleetlands
	XZ321	WS Gazelle AH1	AAC No 665 Sqn, Aldergrove
	XZ322	WS Gazelle AH1 [O]	AAC No 670 Sqn, Middle Wallop
	XZ323	WS Gazelle AH1	AAC, Fleetlands
	XZ324	WS Gazelle AH1	AAC No 3 (TA) Flt, Turnhouse
	XZ325	WS Gazelle AH1 [T]	AAC No 670 Sqn, Middle Wallop
	XZ326	WS Gazelle AH1	RM, Fleetlands
	XZ327	WS Gazelle AH1	AAC No 670 Sqn, Middle Wallop
	XZ328	WS Gazelle AH1 [C]	AAC 4 Regiment, Detmold
	XZ329	WS Gazelle AH1 [J]	AAC No 670 Sqn, Middle Wallop
	XZ330	WS Gazelle AH1	AAC No 7 Flt, Gatow
	XZ331	WS Gazelle AH1 [X]	AAC No 657 Sqn, Dishforth

Serial	Type	Owner or Operator	Notes
XZ332	WS Gazelle AH1 [O]	AAC No 670 Sqn, Middle Wallop	
XZ333	WS Gazelle AH1 [A]	AAC, Fleetlands	
XZ334	WS Gazelle AH1 [M]	AAC No 662 Sqn, Wattisham	
XZ335	WS Gazelle AH1	AAC, Fleetlands	
XZ337	WS Gazelle AH1	AAC No 658 Sqn, Netheravon	
XZ338	WS Gazelle AH1 [X]	AAC No 670 Sqn, Middle Wallop	
XZ339	WS Gazelle AH1	AAC No 667 Sqn, Middle Wallop	
XZ340	WS Gazelle AH1	AAC No 29 Flt, BATUS, Suffield, Canada	
XZ341	WS Gazelle AH1	AAC No 3 (TA) Flt, Turnhouse	
XZ342	WS Gazelle AH1	AAC No 653 Sqn, Wattisham	
XZ343	WS Gazelle AH1 [U]	AAC 4 Regiment, Detmold	
XZ344	WS Gazelle AH1 [F1]	AAC No 670 Sqn, Middle Wallop	
XZ345	WS Gazelle AH1	AAC	
XZ346	WS Gazelle AH1	AAC No 665 Sqn, Aldergrove	
XZ347	WS Gazelle AH1 [B]	AAC No 664 Sqn, Dishforth	
XZ348	WS Gazelle AH1 (wreck)	AAC, stored Fleetlands	
XZ349	WS Gazelle AH1	AAC No 3 (TA) Flt, Turnhouse	
XZ355	SEPECAT Jaguar GR1A [J]	RAF No 41 Sqn, Coltishall	
XZ356	SEPECAT Jaguar GR1A [EP]	RAF No 6 Sqn, Coltishall	
XZ357	SEPECAT Jaguar GR1A [FK]	RAF No 41 Sqn, Coltishall	
XZ358	SEPECAT Jaguar GR1A [L]	RAF No 41 Sqn, Coltishall	
XZ360	SEPECAT Jaguar GR1A [N]	RAF No 41 Sqn, Coltishall	
XZ361	SEPECAT Jaguar GR1A [T]	RAF No 41 Sqn, Coltishall	
XZ362	SEPECAT Jaguar GR1A [GC]	RAF No 54 Sqn, Coltishall	
XZ363	SEPECAT Jaguar GR1A	RAF No 41 Sqn, Coltishall	
XZ363	SEPECAT Jaguar GR1A Replica (BAPC 151)	RAF Exhibition Flight, St Athan	
XZ364	SEPECAT Jaguar GR1A [GJ]	RAF No 54 Sqn, Coltishall	
XZ366	SEPECAT Jaguar GR1A [S]	RAF No 41 Sqn, Coltishall	
XZ367	SEPECAT Jaguar GR1A [GP]	RAF No 54 Sqn, Coltishall	
XZ368	SEPECAT Jaguar GR1A [8900M] [AG]	RAF No 2 SoTT, Cosford	
XZ369	SEPECAT Jaguar GR1A [EF]	RAF No 6 Sqn, Coltishall	
XZ370	SEPECAT Jaguar GR1 (9004M) [JB]	RAF No 2 SoTT, Cosford	
XZ371	SEPECAT Jaguar GR1 (8907M) [AP]	RAF No 2 SoTT, Cosford	
XZ372	SEPECAT Jaguar GR1A [ED]	RAF No 6 Sqn, Coltishall	
XZ373	SEPECAT Jaguar GR1A [GF]	RAF No 54 Sqn, Coltishall	
XZ374	SEPECAT Jaguar GR1 (9005M) [JC]	RAF No 2 SoTT, Cosford	
XZ375	SEPECAT Jaguar GR1A [GR]	RAF No 54 Sqn, Coltishall	
XZ377	SEPECAT Jaguar GR1A [EB]	RAF No 6 Sqn, Coltishall	
XZ378	SEPECAT Jaguar GR1A [EP]	RAF, stored Shawbury	
XZ381	SEPECAT Jaguar GR1A [EC]	RAF No 6 Sqn, Coltishall	
XZ382	SEPECAT Jaguar GR1 (8908M) [AE]	RAF Coltishall BDRF	
XZ383	SEPECAT Jaguar GR1 (8901M) [AF]	RAF No 2 SoTT, Cosford	
XZ384	SEPECAT Jaguar GR1 (8954M) [BC]	RAF No 2 SoTT, Cosford	
XZ385	SEPECAT Jaguar GR1A [03]	RAF No 16(R) Sqn, Lossiemouth	
XZ389	SEPECAT Jaguar GR1 (8946M) [BL]	RAF No 1 SoTT, Halton	
XZ390	SEPECAT Jaguar GR1A (9003M) [35]	RAF No 2 SoTT, Cosford	
XZ391	SEPECAT Jaguar GR1A [GM]	RAF No 54 Sqn, Coltishall	
XZ392	SEPECAT Jaguar GR1A [GQ]	RAF, stored Shawbury	
XZ394	SEPECAT Jaguar GR1A [GN]	RAF No 54 Sqn, Coltishall	
XZ396	SEPECAT Jaguar GR1A [EM]	RAF No 6 Sqn, Coltishall	
XZ398	SEPECAT Jaguar GR1A (J1007) [A]	RAF No 41 Sqn, Coltishall	
XZ399	SEPECAT Jaguar GR1A [EJ]	RAF No 6 Sqn, Coltishall	
XZ400	SEPECAT Jaguar GR1A [EG]	RAF, stored Shawbury	
XZ431	HS Buccaneer S2B	RAF No 208 Sqn, Lossiemouth	
XZ439	BAe Sea Harrier FRS2 [2]	MoD(PE)/BAe Dunsfold	
XZ440	BAe Sea Harrier FRS1 [126/N]	RN, BAe Brough, on rebuild	
XZ445	BAe Harrier T4A [721]	RN No 899 Sqn, Yeovilton	
XZ455	BAe Sea Harrier FRS2	MoD(PE)/BAe Brough (conversion)	
XZ457	BAe Sea Harrier FRS2	MoD(PE)/BAe Brough (conversion)	
XZ459	BAe Sea Harrier FRS1 [001/R]	RN No 801 Sqn, Yeovilton	
XZ492	BAe Sea Harrier FRS1 [002/R]	RN No 801 Sqn, Yeovilton	
XZ493	BAe Sea Harrier FRS1 [714/VL]	RN AMG, Yeovilton	

Notes	Serial	Type	Owner or Operator
	XZ494	BAe Sea Harrier FRS1 [126]	RN No 800 Sqn, Yeovilton
	XZ495	BAe Sea Harrier FRS2 [713/OEU]	RN No 899 Sqn/OEU, Yeovilton
	XZ497	BAe Sea Harrier FRS2 [R]	MoD(PE) A&AEE Boscombe Down
	XZ498	BAe Sea Harrier FRS1 [124]	RN No 800 Sqn, Yeovilton
	XZ499	BAe Sea Harrier FRS1 [003/R]	RN No 801 Sqn, Yeovilton
	XZ557	Slingsby Venture T2 [7]	RAFGSA, stored Bicester
	XZ558	Slingsby Venture T2 [8]	*To G-BUXJ, May 1993*
	XZ570	WS61 Sea King HAS5 (mod)	MoD(PE)/Westland, Yeovil
	XZ571	WS61 Sea King HAS6 [136]	RNAY Fleetlands
	XZ574	WS61 Sea King HAS6 [704/PW]	RN No 819 Sqn, Prestwick
	XZ575	WS61 Sea King HAS6 [599]	RN No 706 Sqn, Culdrose
	XZ576	WS61 Sea King HAS6	MoD(PE), A&AEE Boscombe Down
	XZ577	WS61 Sea King HAS5 [138]	RN No 826 Sqn, Culdrose
	XZ578	WS61 Sea King HAS6 [581]	RN No 706 Sqn, Culdrose
	XZ579	WS61 Sea King HAS6 [011/R]	RN AMG, Culdrose
	XZ580	WS61 Sea King HAS6 [267/N]	RN No 814 Sqn, Culdrose
	XZ581	WS61 Sea King HAS6 [133/BD]	MoD(PE), A&AEE Boscombe Down
	XZ585	WS61 Sea King HAR3	RAF SAREW, St Mawgan
	XZ586	WS61 Sea King HAR3	RAF No 202 Sqn, St Mawgan
	XZ587	WS61 Sea King HAR3	RAF No 202 Sqn, B Flt, Brawdy
	XZ588	WS61 Sea King HAR3	RAF No 202 Sqn, C Flt, Manston
	XZ589	WS61 Sea King HAR3	RAF No 202 Sqn, St Mawgan
	XZ590	WS61 Sea King HAR3	RAF No 202 Sqn, E Flt, Leconfield
	XZ591	WS61 Sea King HAR3	RAF SAREW, St Mawgan
	XZ592	WS61 Sea King HAR3	RAF No 78 Sqn, Mount Pleasant, FI
	XZ593	WS61 Sea King HAR3	RAF, Fleetlands for repair
	XZ594	WS61 Sea King HAR3	RAF SAREW, St Mawgan
	XZ595	WS61 Sea King HAR3	RAF SAREW, St Mawgan
	XZ596	WS61 Sea King HAR3	RAF SAREW, St Mawgan
	XZ597	WS61 Sea King HAR3	RAF SKTU, St Mawgan
	XZ598	WS61 Sea King HAR3	RAF SKTU, St Mawgan
	XZ599	WS61 Sea King HAR3	RAF SKTU, St Mawgan
	XZ605	WS Lynx AH7 [Y]	RM 3 CBAS, Yeovilton
	XZ606	WS Lynx AH7	AAC, Fleetlands
	XZ607	WS Lynx AH7 [M]	AAC No 671 Sqn, Middle Wallop
	XZ608	WS Lynx AH7	AAC No 671 Sqn, Middle Wallop
	XZ609	WS Lynx AH7	AAC 1 Regiment, Hildesheim
	XZ610	WS Lynx AH7	AAC No 669 Sqn, Detmold
	XZ611	WS Lynx AH7	AAC, Fleetlands
	XZ612	WS Lynx AH7 [N]	RM 3 CBAS, Yeovilton
	XZ613	WS Lynx AH7	AAC No 655 Sqn, Aldergrove
	XZ614	WS Lynx AH7 [X]	RM 3 CBAS, Yeovilton
	XZ615	WS Lynx AH7	AAC No 655 Sqn, Aldergrove
	XZ616	WS Lynx AH7	AAC No 664 Sqn, Dishforth
	XZ617	WS Lynx AH7	AAC 4 Regiment, Detmold
	XZ631	Panavia Tornado GR4T	MoD(PE)/BAe, Warton
	XZ641	WS Lynx AH7	AAC SAE, Middle Wallop
	XZ642	WS Lynx AH7	AAC No 654 Sqn, Detmold
	XZ643	WS Lynx AH7 [N]	AAC No 662 Sqn, Wattisham
	XZ644	WS Lynx AH7 (wreck)	AAC, Detmold
	XZ645	WS Lynx AH7 [X]	AAC No 663 Sqn, Wattisham
	XZ646	WS Lynx AH7	AAC 1 Regiment, Gütersloh
	XZ647	WS Lynx AH7 [M]	AAC No 657 Sqn, Dishforth
	XZ648	WS Lynx AH7 [D]	AAC, Fleetlands
	XZ649	WS Lynx AH7	AAC No 665 Sqn, Aldergrove
	XZ650	WS Lynx AH7	AAC, Fleetlands
	XZ651	WS Lynx AH1 [P]	AAC No 664 Sqn, Dishforth
	XZ652	WS Lynx AH7	AAC, stored Fleetlands
	XZ653	WS Lynx AH7	AAC No 659 Sqn, Detmold
	XZ654	WS Lynx AH7	AAC No 654 Sqn, Detmold
	XZ655	WS Lynx AH7	AAC 4 Regiment, Detmold
	XZ661	WS Lynx AH1 [L]	AAC No 671 Sqn, Middle Wallop
	XZ662	WS Lynx AH7	AAC No 665 Sqn, Aldergrove
	XZ663	WS Lynx AH7	AAC No 665 Sqn, Aldergrove
	XZ664	WS Lynx AH7	AAC 4 Regiment, Detmold
	XZ665	WS Lynx AH7	AAC No 654 Sqn, Detmold
	XZ666	WS Lynx AH7	AAC 4 Regiment, Detmold
	XZ667	WS Lynx AH7	AAC No 665 Sqn, Aldergrove
	XZ668	WS Lynx AH7 [E]	MoD(PE)/Westland, Yeovil
	XZ669	WS Lynx AH7 [D]	AAC No 653 Sqn, Wattisham
	XZ670	WS Lynx AH7	AAC No 664 Sqn, Dishforth
	XZ671	WS Lynx AH9	Westland, Yeovil, test rig
	XZ672	WS Lynx AH7	AAC No 1 Regiment, Gütersloh

Serial	Type	Owner or Operator	Notes
XZ673	WS Lynx AH7 [P]	AAC No 671 Sqn, Middle Wallop	
XZ674	WS Lynx AH1 [Y]	AAC No 663 Sqn, Wattisham	
XZ675	WS Lynx AH7 [E]	AAC No 671 Sqn, Middle Wallop	
XZ676	WS Lynx AH7 [N]	AAC No 671 Sqn, Middle Wallop	
XZ677	WS Lynx AH7 [O]	AAC No 662 Sqn, Dishforth	
XZ678	WS Lynx AH7 [L]	AAC No 662 Sqn, Dishforth	
XZ679	WS Lynx AH7	AAC No 659 Sqn, Detmold	
XZ680	WS Lynx AH7	AAC 1 Regiment, Gütersloh	
XZ681	WS Lynx AH1	AAC Middle Wallop, BDRT	
XZ689	WS Lynx HAS3S [330/BZ]	RN No 815 Sqn, Portland	
XZ690	WS Lynx HAS3S [420/EX]	RN No 815 Sqn, Portland	
XZ691	WS Lynx HAS3S	RN AMG, Portland	
XZ692	WS Lynx HAS3S [322/AV]	RN No 815 Sqn, Portland	
XZ693	WS Lynx HAS3S [632]	RN No 702 Sqn, Portland	
XZ694	WS Lynx HAS3 [346/BW]	RN No 815 Sqn, Portland	
XZ695	WS Lynx HAS3S [411/EB]	RN No 815 Sqn, Portland	
XZ696	WS Lynx HAS3S [305]	RN No 815 Sqn, Portland	
XZ697	WS Lynx HAS3CTS [341/AG]	RN No 815 Sqn, Portland	
XZ698	WS Lynx HAS3 [479]	RN No 815 Sqn, Portland	
XZ699	WS Lynx HAS3 [301]	RN No 815 Sqn, Portland	
XZ719	WS Lynx HAS3S [638]	RN No 702 Sqn, Portland	
XZ720	WS Lynx HAS3S [332/LP]	RN No 815 Sqn, Portland	
XZ721	WS Lynx HAS3S [344/GW]	RN No 815 Sqn, Portland	
XZ722	WS Lynx HAS3S [304]	RN No 815 Sqn, Portland	
XZ723	WS Lynx HAS3S [374/VB]	RN No 815 Sqn, Portland	
XZ724	WS Lynx HAS3S [307]	RN No 815 Sqn, Portland	
XZ725	WS Lynx HAS3S [327/AL]	RN No 815 Sqn, Portland	
XZ726	WS Lynx HAS3S [306]	RN No 815 Sqn, Portland	
XZ727	WS Lynx HAS3 [636]	RN No 702 Sqn, Portland	
XZ728	WS Lynx HAS3 [641]	RN No 702 Sqn, Portland	
XZ729	WS Lynx HAS3S [642]	RN, Fleetlands	
XZ730	WS Lynx HAS3S [634]	RN No 702 Sqn, Portland	
XZ731	WS Lynx HAS3S [457]	RN No 815 Sqn, Portland	
XZ732	WS Lynx HAS8 [635]	MoD(PE)/Westland, Yeovil (conversion)	
XZ733	WS Lynx HAS3 [308]	RN No 815 Sqn, Portland	
XZ735	WS Lynx HAS3 [376/XB]	RN No 815 Sqn, Portland	
XZ736	WS Lynx HAS3S [333/BM]	RN No 815 Sqn, Portland	
XZ918	WS61 Sea King HAS6 [589]	RN No 706 Sqn, Culdrose	
XZ920	WS61 Sea King HAR5 [822/CU]	RN No 771 Sqn, Culdrose	
XZ921	WS61 Sea King HAS6 [593/CU]	RNAY Fleetlands	
XZ922	WS61 Sea King HAS6 [134/BD]	MoD(PE), A&AEE Boscombe Down	
XZ930	WS Gazelle HT3 [Q]	RAF No 2 FTS, Shawbury	
XZ931	WS Gazelle HT3 [R]	RAF No 2 FTS, Shawbury	
XZ932	WS Gazelle HT3 [S]	RAF No 2 FTS, Shawbury	
XZ933	WS Gazelle HT3 [T]	RAF No 2 FTS, Shawbury	
XZ934	WS Gazelle HT3 [U]	RAF No 2 FTS, Shawbury	
XZ935	WS Gazelle HCC4	RAF No 32 Sqn, Northolt	
XZ936	WS Gazelle HT2	MoD(PE) ETPS, Boscombe Down	
XZ937	WS Gazelle HT2 [Y]	RAF No 2 FTS, Shawbury	
XZ938	WS Gazelle HT2 [45/CU]	RN No 705 Sqn, Culdrose	
XZ939	WS Gazelle HT2 [Z]	MoD(PE) ETPS, Boscombe Down	
XZ940	WS Gazelle HT2 [O]	RAF No 2 FTS, Shawbury	
XZ941	WS Gazelle HT2 [B]	RAF No 2 FTS, Shawbury	
XZ942	WS Gazelle HT2 [42/CU]	RN No 705 Sqn, Culdrose	
XZ964	BAe Harrier GR3	RAF, stored St Athan	
XZ965	BAe Harrier GR3 [L]	RAF Stafford, GI use	
XZ966	BAe Harrier GR3 [D]	Preserved in Belize, 1993	
XZ967	BAe Harrier GR3 (9077M) [F]	RAF No 1 SoTT, Halton	
XZ968	BAe Harrier GR3	RAF, stored St Athan	
XZ969	BAe Harrier GR3 [D]	RNEC Manadon	
XZ970	BAe Harrier GR3	RAF, stored St Athan	
XZ971	BAe Harrier GR3 [G]	RAF Wittering	
XZ987	BAe Harrier GR3 [C]	RAF Stafford, at main gate	
XZ991	BAe Harrier GR3 (9162M) [3A]	RAF St Athan, BDRT	
XZ993	BAe Harrier GR3 [M]	RAF, stored St Athan	
XZ994	BAe Harrier GR3 (9170M) [U]	RAF Air Movements School, Brize Norton	
XZ995	BAe Harrier GR3 [3G]	RAF St Mawgan, Fire Section	
XZ996	BAe Harrier GR3 [F]	RN, SAH Culdrose	
XZ997	BAe Harrier GR3 (9122M) [V]	RAF Museum, Hendon	
XZ998	BAe Harrier GR3 (9161M) [D]	CSDE Swanton Morley, GI use	
ZA101	BAe Hawk 100 (G-HAWK/XX155)	BAe Warton	
ZA105	WS61 Sea King HAR3 [S]	RAF No 78 Sqn, Mount Pleasant, FI	

Notes	Serial	Type	Owner or Operator
	ZA110	BAe Jetstream T2 (G-AXUO) [573/CU]	RN No 750 Sqn, Culdrose
	ZA111	BAe Jetstream T2 (G-AXFV) [574/CU]	RN No 750 Sqn, Culdrose
	ZA126	WS61 Sea King HAS6 [509]	RN No 810 Sqn, Culdrose
	ZA127	WS61 Sea King HAS6	RNAY Fleetlands
	ZA128	WS61 Sea King HAS6 [598]	RNAY Fleetlands
	ZA129	WS61 Sea King HAS6 [502/CU]	RN No 810 Sqn, Culdrose
	ZA130	WS61 Sea King HAS6 [587]	RN No 706 Sqn, Culdrose
	ZA131	WS61 Sea King HAS6 [011]	RN No 820 Sqn, Culdrose
	ZA133	WS61 Sea King HAS6 [013]	RN No 820 Sqn, Culdrose
	ZA134	WS61 Sea King HAS6 [598]	RN No 706 Sqn, Culdrose
	ZA135	WS61 Sea King HAS6 [015]	RN AMG, Culdrose
	ZA136	WS61 Sea King HAS6 [015]	RN No 820 Sqn, Culdrose
	ZA137	WS61 Sea King HAS6 [597]	RN No 706 Sqn, Culdrose
	ZA140	BAe VC10 K2 (G-ARVL) [A]	RAF No 101 Sqn, Brize Norton
	ZA141	BAe VC10 K2 (G-ARVG) [B]	RAF No 101 Sqn, Brize Norton
	ZA142	BAe VC10 K2 (G-ARVI) [C]	RAF No 101 Sqn, Brize Norton
	ZA143	BAe VC10 K2 (G-ARVK) [D]	RAF No 101 Sqn, Brize Norton
	ZA144	BAe VC10 K2 (G-ARVC) [E]	RAF No 101 Sqn, Brize Norton
	ZA147	BAe VC10 K3 (5H-MMT) [F]	RAF No 101 Sqn, Brize Norton
	ZA148	BAe VC10 K3 (5Y-ADA) [G]	RAF No 101 Sqn, Brize Norton
	ZA149	BAe VC10 K3 (5X-UVJ) [H]	RAF No 101 Sqn, Brize Norton
	ZA150	BAe VC10 K3 (5H-MOG) [J]	RAF No 101 Sqn, Brize Norton
	ZA166	WS61 Sea King HAS6 [590]	RN No 706 Sqn, Culdrose
	ZA167	WS61 Sea King HAS6 [131]	RNAY Fleetlands
	ZA168	WS61 Sea King HAS6 [703]	RNAY Fleetlands
	ZA169	WS61 Sea King HAS6 [266/N]	RN No 814 Sqn, Culdrose
	ZA170	WS61 Sea King HAS6 [584]	RN AMG, Culdrose
	ZA175	BAe Sea Harrier FRS1 [717/VL]	RN No 899 Sqn, Yeovilton
	ZA176	BAe Sea Harrier FRS2	MoD(PE), BAe Dunsfold
	ZA195	BAe Sea Harrier FRS2	MoD(PE), A&AEE Boscombe Down
	ZA250	BAe Harrier T52 (G-VTOL)	Brooklands Aviation Museum, Weybridge
	ZA254	Panavia Tornado F2	MoD(PE), BAe Warton
	ZA267	Panavia Tornado F2T	MoD(PE), A&AEE Boscombe Down
	ZA283	Panavia Tornado F2	MoD(PE), BAe Warton
	ZA291	WS61 Sea King HC4 [VN]	RN No 846 Sqn, Yeovilton
	ZA292	WS61 Sea King HC4 [ZW]	RN, AMG Yeovilton
	ZA293	WS61 Sea King HC4 [VO]	RN No 846 Sqn, Yeovilton
	ZA295	WS61 Sea King HC4 [ZU]	RN No 707 Sqn, Yeovilton
	ZA296	WS61 Sea King HC4 [ZR]	RN No 707 Sqn, Yeovilton
	ZA297	WS61 Sea King HC4 [25]	RN No 772 Sqn, Portland
	ZA298	WS61 Sea King HC4 (G-BJNM)	RN No 846 Sqn, Yeovilton
	ZA299	WS61 Sea King HC4 [VJ]	RN No 846 Sqn, Yeovilton
	ZA310	WS61 Sea King HC4 [V]	RNAY Fleetlands
	ZA312	WS61 Sea King HC4 [B]	RNAY Fleetlands
	ZA313	WS61 Sea King HC4	RN No 845 Sqn, Yeovilton
	ZA314	WS61 Sea King HC4	RN, AMG Yeovilton
	ZA319	Panavia Tornado GR1T [B-11]	RAF TTTE, Cottesmore
	ZA320	Panavia Tornado GR1T [B-01]	RAF TTTE, Cottesmore
	ZA321	Panavia Tornado GR1 [B-58]	RAF TTTE, Cottesmore
	ZA322	Panavia Tornado GR1 [B-50]	RAF TTTE, Cottesmore
	ZA323	Panavia Tornado GR1T [B-14]	RAF TTTE, Cottesmore
	ZA324	Panavia Tornado GR1T [B-02]	RAF TTTE, Cottesmore
	ZA325	Panavia Tornado GR1T [B-03]	RAF TTTE, Cottesmore
	ZA326	Panavia Tornado GR1T	MoD(PE), DRA Bedford
	ZA327	Panavia Tornado GR1 [B-51]	RAF TTTE, Cottesmore
	ZA328	Panavia Tornado GR1	MoD(PE), BAe Warton
	ZA330	Panavia Tornado GR1T [B-08]	RAF TTTE, Cottesmore
	ZA352	Panavia Tornado GR1T [B-04]	RAF TTTE, Cottesmore
	ZA353	Panavia Tornado GR1T [B-53]	RAF TTTE, Cottesmore
	ZA354	Panavia Tornado GR1	MoD(PE), A&AEE Boscombe Down
	ZA355	Panavia Tornado GR1 [B-54]	RAF TTTE, Cottesmore
	ZA356	Panavia Tornado GR1T [B-07]	RAF TTTE, Cottesmore
	ZA357	Panavia Tornado GR1T [B-05]	RAF TTTE, Cottesmore
	ZA358	Panavia Tornado GR1T [B-06]	RAF TTTE, Cottesmore
	ZA359	Panavia Tornado GR1 [B-55]	RAF TTTE, Cottesmore
	ZA360	Panavia Tornado GR1 [B-56]	RAF TTTE, Cottesmore
	ZA361	Panavia Tornado GR1 [B-57]	RAF TTTE, Cottesmore
	ZA362	Panavia Tornado GR1T [B-09]	RAF TTTE, Cottesmore
	ZA365	Panavia Tornado GR1T	RAF No 12 Sqn, Lossiemouth
	ZA367	Panavia Tornado GR1T [AJ-Y]	RAF No 617 Sqn, Lossiemouth
	ZA368	Panavia Tornado GR1T [AJ-P]	RAF No 617 Sqn, Lossiemouth

Serial	Type	Owner or Operator	Notes
ZA369	Panavia Tornado GR1A [II]	RAF No 2 Sqn, Marham	
ZA370	Panavia Tornado GR1A [A]	RAF No 2 Sqn, Marham	
ZA371	Panavia Tornado GR1A [C]	RAF No 2 Sqn, Marham	
ZA372	Panavia Tornado GR1A [E]	RAF No 2 Sqn, Marham	
ZA373	Panavia Tornado GR1A [H]	RAF No 2 Sqn, Marham	
ZA374	Panavia Tornado GR1A [CN]	RAF No 17 Sqn, Bruggen	
ZA375	Panavia Tornado GR1	RAF No 12 Sqn, Lossiemouth	
ZA393	Panavia Tornado GR1 [BE]	RAF No 14 Sqn, Bruggen	
ZA395	Panavia Tornado GR1A [N]	RAF No 2 Sqn, Marham	
ZA397	Panavia Tornado GR1A [O]	RAF No 2 Sqn, Marham	
ZA398	Panavia Tornado GR1A [S]	RAF No 2 Sqn, Marham	
ZA399	Panavia Tornado GR1A [AJ-G]	RAF No 617 Sqn, Lossiemouth	
ZA400	Panavia Tornado GR1A [T]	RAF No 2 Sqn, Marham	
ZA401	Panavia Tornado GR1A [R]	RAF No 2 Sqn, Marham	
ZA402	Panavia Tornado GR1	MoD(PE), A&AEE Boscombe Down	
ZA404	Panavia Tornado GR1A [W]	RAF No 2 Sqn, Marham	
ZA405	Panavia Tornado GR1A [Y]	RAF No 2 Sqn, Marham	
ZA406	Panavia Tornado GR1A	RAF No 17 Sqn, Bruggen	
ZA407	Panavia Tornado GR1B [AJ-G]	MoD(PE)/BAe Warton (conversion)	
ZA409	Panavia Tornado GR1T [FQ]	RAF No 12 Sqn, Lossiemouth	
ZA410	Panavia Tornado GR1T [FZ]	RAF No 12 Sqn, Lossiemouth	
ZA411	Panavia Tornado GR1T [AJ-S]	RAF No 617 Sqn, Lossiemouth	
ZA412	Panavia Tornado GR1T [FX]	RAF, stored St Athan	
ZA446	Panavia Tornado GR1T [AJ-H]	RAF No 617 Sqn, Lossiemouth	
ZA446	Panavia Tornado GR1 Replica (BAPC155) [F]	RAF Exhibition Flight, St Athan	
ZA447	Panavia Tornado GR1	RAF No 12 Sqn, Lossiemouth	
ZA449	Panavia Tornado GR1	MoD(PE), DRA Bedford	
ZA450	Panavia Tornado GR1	RAF No 12 Sqn, Lossiemouth	
ZA452	Panavia Tornado GR1	RAF No 12 Sqn, Lossiemouth	
ZA453	Panavia Tornado GR1	RAF No 12 Sqn, Lossiemouth	
ZA455	Panavia Tornado GR1	RAF No 12 Sqn, Lossiemouth	
ZA456	Panavia Tornado GR1 [AJ-Q]	RAF No 617 Sqn, Lossiemouth	
ZA457	Panavia Tornado GR1 [AJ-J]	RAF No 617 Sqn, Lossiemouth	
ZA458	Panavia Tornado GR1	RAF No 14 Sqn, Bruggen	
ZA459	Panavia Tornado GR1 [AJ-B]	RAF No 617 Sqn, Lossiemouth	
ZA460	Panavia Tornado GR1 [AJ-A]	RAF No 617 Sqn, Lossiemouth	
ZA461	Panavia Tornado GR1 [AJ-M]	RAF No 617 Sqn, Lossiemouth	
ZA462	Panavia Tornado GR1	RAF No 14 Sqn, Bruggen	
ZA463	Panavia Tornado GR1	RAF No 14 Sqn, Bruggen	
ZA465	Panavia Tornado GR1 [AJ-F]	RAF No 617 Sqn, Lossiemouth	
ZA466	Panavia Tornado GR1 (cockpit)	RAF St Athan, BDRT	
ZA469	Panavia Tornado GR1 [AJ-O]	RAF No 617 Sqn, Lossiemouth	
ZA470	Panavia Tornado GR1	RAF No 14 Sqn, Bruggen	
ZA471	Panavia Tornado GR1 [AJ-K]	RAF No 617 Sqn, Lossiemouth	
ZA472	Panavia Tornado GR1	RAF No 14 Sqn, Bruggen	
ZA473	Panavia Tornado GR1 [FG]	RAF No 12 Sqn, Lossiemouth	
ZA474	Panavia Tornado GR1 [FF]	RAF No 12 Sqn, Lossiemouth	
ZA475	Panavia Tornado GR1 [FH]	RAF No 12 Sqn, Lossiemouth	
ZA490	Panavia Tornado GR1	RAF No 12 Sqn, Lossiemouth	
ZA491	Panavia Tornado GR1	RAF No 12 Sqn, Lossiemouth	
ZA492	Panavia Tornado GR1	RAF No 12 Sqn, Lossiemouth	
ZA541	Panavia Tornado GR1T [TO]	RAF No 15(R) Sqn, Lossiemouth	
ZA542	Panavia Tornado GR1 [JA]	RAF, stored St Athan	
ZA543	Panavia Tornado GR1	RAF, stored St Athan	
ZA544	Panavia Tornado GR1T [TP]	RAF No 15(R) Sqn, Lossiemouth	
ZA546	Panavia Tornado GR1 [AJ-C]	RAF No 617 Sqn, Lossiemouth	
ZA547	Panavia Tornado GR1 [JC]	RAF, stored St Athan	
ZA548	Panavia Tornado GR1T [TQ]	RAF No 15(R) Sqn, Lossiemouth	
ZA549	Panavia Tornado GR1T [TR]	RAF No 15(R) Sqn, Lossiemouth	
ZA550	Panavia Tornado GR1 [JD]	RAF, stored St Athan	
ZA551	Panavia Tornado GR1T [X]	RAF No 2 Sqn, Marham	
ZA552	Panavia Tornado GR1T [TS]	RAF No 15(R) Sqn, Lossiemouth	
ZA553	Panavia Tornado GR1 [JE]	RAF, stored St Athan	
ZA554	Panavia Tornado GR1 [DM]	RAF, stored St Athan	
ZA556	Panavia Tornado GR1 [TA]	RAF No 15(R) Sqn, Lossiemouth	
ZA557	Panavia Tornado GR1	RAF, stored St Athan	
ZA559	Panavia Tornado GR1 [TB]	RAF No 15(R) Sqn, Lossiemouth	
ZA560	Panavia Tornado GR1 [B-59]	RAF TTTE, Cottesmore	
ZA562	Panavia Tornado GR1T [TT]	RAF No 15(R) Sqn, Lossiemouth	
ZA563	Panavia Tornado GR1 [TC]	RAF No 15(R) Sqn, Lossiemouth	
ZA564	Panavia Tornado GR1 [JK]	RAF, stored St Athan	
ZA585	Panavia Tornado GR1	RAF, stored St Athan	

Notes	Serial	Type	Owner or Operator
	ZA587	Panavia Tornado GR1 [TD]	RAF No 15(R) Sqn, Lossiemouth
	ZA588	Panavia Tornado GR1 [B-52]	RAF, stored St Athan
	ZA589	Panavia Tornado GR1 [TE]	RAF No 15(R) Sqn, Lossiemouth
	ZA590	Panavia Tornado GR1	RAF, stored St Athan
	ZA591	Panavia Tornado GR1	RAF, stored St Athan
	ZA592	Panavia Tornado GR1 [B]	RAF, stored St Athan
	ZA594	Panavia Tornado GR1T [TU]	RAF No 15(R) Sqn, Lossiemouth
	ZA595	Panavia Tornado GR1T [TV]	RAF No 15(R) Sqn, Lossiemouth
	ZA596	Panavia Tornado GR1	RAF, stored St Athan
	ZA597	Panavia Tornado GR1 [M]	MoD(PE)/BAe Warton, on rebuild
	ZA598	Panavia Tornado GR1T [S]	RAF, stored St Athan
	ZA599	Panavia Tornado GR1T [TW]	RAF, stored St Athan
	ZA600	Panavia Tornado GR1 [F]	RAF No 15(R) Sqn, Lossiemouth
	ZA601	Panavia Tornado GR1 [TI]	RAF No 15(R) Sqn, Lossiemouth
	ZA602	Panavia Tornado GR1T [TX]	RAF No 15(R) Sqn, Lossiemouth
	ZA604	Panavia Tornado GR1T [TY]	RAF No 15(R) Sqn, Lossiemouth
	ZA606	Panavia Tornado GR1	RAF, stored St Athan
	ZA607	Panavia Tornado GR1 [TJ]	RAF No 15(R) Sqn, Lossiemouth
	ZA608	Panavia Tornado GR1 [TK]	RAF No 15(R) Sqn, Lossiemouth
	ZA609	Panavia Tornado GR1 [J]	RAF, stored St Athan
	ZA611	Panavia Tornado GR1 [A]	RAF, stored St Athan
	ZA612	Panavia Tornado GR1T [TZ]	RAF No 15(R) Sqn, Lossiemouth
	ZA613	Panavia Tornado GR1 [N]	RAF No 617 Sqn, Lossiemouth
	ZA614	Panavia Tornado GR1 [F]	RAF, ASF Honington
	ZA654	Slingsby Venture T2 [4]	RAFGSA, stored Bicester
	ZA665	Slingsby Venture T2	RAFGSA, stored Bicester
	ZA670	B-V Chinook HC1 [BG]	RAF No 18 Sqn, Laarbruch
	ZA671	B-V Chinook HC1 [EO]	RAF No 7 Sqn, Odiham
	ZA673	B-V Chinook HC2 [BF]	Boeing, Philadelphia (conversion)
	ZA674	B-V Chinook HC2 [BA]	Boeing, Philadelphia (conversion)
	ZA675	B-V Chinook HC1 [BB]	RAF, Fleetlands
	ZA676	B-V Chinook HC1 [FG] (wreck)	RAF, stored Fleetlands
	ZA677	B-V Chinook HC1 [EU]	RAF No 7 Sqn, Odiham
	ZA678	B-V Chinook HC1 [EZ] (wreck)	RAF, stored Fleetlands
	ZA679	B-V Chinook HC1 [EZ]	RAF No 7 Sqn, Odiham
	ZA680	B-V Chinook HC1 [EM]	RAF No 7 Sqn, Odiham
	ZA681	B-V Chinook HC2	RAF No 7 Sqn/27(R) Sqn, Odiham
	ZA682	B-V Chinook HC1 [EM]	RAF No 7 Sqn, Odiham
	ZA683	B-V Chinook HC1 [EW]	RAF No 7 Sqn, Odiham
	ZA684	B-V Chinook HC1 [BE]	RAF No 18 Sqn, Laarbruch
	ZA704	B-V Chinook HC1 [EJ]	RAF No 7 Sqn, Odiham
	ZA705	B-V Chinook HC1 [EO]	RAF No 7 Sqn, Odiham
	ZA707	B-V Chinook HC1 [EV]	RAF No 7 Sqn, Odiham
	ZA708	B-V Chinook HC2 [EK]	Boeing, Philadelphia (conversion)
	ZA709	B-V Chinook HC1	RAF No 78 Sqn, Mount Pleasant, FI
	ZA710	B-V Chinook HC2	RAF No 7/27 (R) Sqn, Odiham
	ZA711	B-V Chinook HC1 [ET]	RAF No 7 Sqn, Odiham
	ZA712	B-V Chinook HC1 [ER]	RAF No 7 Sqn, Odiham
	ZA713	B-V Chinook HC1 [EN]	RAF No 72 Sqn, Aldergrove
	ZA714	B-V Chinook HC2 [EX]	Boeing, Philadelphia (conversion)
	ZA717	B-V Chinook HC1 [C] (wreck)	RAF, stored Fleetlands
	ZA718	B-V Chinook HC2 [BN]	MoD(PE) A&AEE, Boscombe Down
	ZA720	B-V Chinook HC1 [EP]	RAF No 7 Sqn, Odiham
	ZA726	WS Gazelle AH1	AAC No 663 Sqn, Wattisham
	ZA728	WS Gazelle AH1 [E]	RM 3 CBAS, Yeovilton
	ZA729	WS Gazelle AH1	AAC 1 Regiment, Gütersloh
	ZA730	WS Gazelle AH1	AAC No 665 Sqn, Aldergrove
	ZA731	WS Gazelle AH1 [A]	AAC No 29 Flt, BATUS, Suffield, Canada
	ZA733	WS Gazelle AH1	AAC No 665 Sqn, Aldergrove
	ZA734	WS Gazelle AH1	AAC, stored Fleetlands
	ZA735	WS Gazelle AH1	AAC No 25 Flt, Belize
	ZA736	WS Gazelle AH1 [S]	AAC No 29 Flt, BATUS, Suffield, Canada
	ZA737	WS Gazelle AH1 [V]	AAC No 670 Sqn, Middle Wallop
	ZA765	WS Gazelle AH1	AAC No 25 Flt, Belize
	ZA766	WS Gazelle AH1	AAC 1 Regiment, Gütersloh
	ZA767	WS Gazelle AH1	AAC No 25 Flt, Belize
	ZA768	WS Gazelle AH1 [F] (wreck)	AAC, stored Fleetlands
	ZA769	WS Gazelle AH1 [K]	AAC No 670 Sqn, Middle Wallop
	ZA771	WS Gazelle AH1 [D]	AAC No 664 Sqn, Dishforth
	ZA772	WS Gazelle AH1 [F]	AAC No 656 Sqn, Dishforth
	ZA773	WS Gazelle AH1	AAC No 665 Sqn, Aldergrove
	ZA774	WS Gazelle AH1	AAC No 665 Sqn, Aldergrove
	ZA775	WS Gazelle AH1 [E1]	AAC, stored Fleetlands

Serial	Type	Owner or Operator	Notes
ZA776	WS Gazelle AH1 [F]	RM 3 CBAS, Yeovilton	
ZA777	WS Gazelle AH1	AAC, Fleetlands	
ZA802	WS Gazelle HT3 [W]	RAF No 2 FTS, Shawbury	
ZA803	WS Gazelle HT3 [X]	RAF No 2 FTS, Shawbury	
ZA804	WS Gazelle HT3 [I]	RAF No 2 FTS, Shawbury	
ZA934	WS Puma HC1 [FC]	RAF No 230 Sqn, Aldergrove	
ZA935	WS Puma HC1	RAF No 230 Sqn, Aldergrove	
ZA936	WS Puma HC1	RAF No 33 Sqn, Odiham	
ZA937	WS Puma HC1	RAF No 33 Sqn, Aldergrove	
ZA938	WS Puma HC1 [CW]	RAF No 33 Sqn, Aldergrove	
ZA939	WS Puma HC1 [DN]	RAF No 230 Sqn, Aldergrove	
ZA940	WS Puma HC1 [CY]	RAF No 230 Sqn, Algergrove	
ZA947	Douglas Dakota C3 [YS-DM]	RAF BBMF, Coningsby	
ZB506	WS61 Sea King Mk 4X	MoD(PE), DRA Bedford	
ZB507	WS61 Sea King Mk 4X	MoD(PE), ETPS Boscombe Down	
ZB600	BAe Harrier T4 [Z]	RAF Wittering	
ZB601	BAe Harrier T4	RAF, stored St Athan	
ZB602	BAe Harrier T4 [R]	RAF HOCU/No 20(R) Sqn, Wittering	
ZB603	BAe Harrier T4 [718/VL]	RN No 899 Sqn, Yeovilton	
ZB604	BAe Harrier T4N [722]	RN No 899 Sqn, Yeovilton	
ZB605	BAe Harrier T8 [721]	MoD(PE), BAe Dunsfold (conversion)	
ZB615	SEPECAT Jaguar T2A	MoD(PE), IAM, Farnborough	
ZB625	WS Gazelle HT3 [N]	RAF No 2 FTS, Shawbury	
ZB626	WS Gazelle HT3 [L]	RAF No 2 FTS, Shawbury	
ZB627	WS Gazelle HT3 [A]	RAF No 7 Sqn, Odiham	
ZB628	WS Gazelle HT3 [V]	Written off, near Monaco, 9 Sept 1993	
ZB629	WS Gazelle HCC4	RAF No 32 Sqn, Northolt	
ZB646	WS Gazelle HT2	MoD(PE), DRA Farnborough	
ZB647	WS Gazelle HT2 [59/CU]	RN No 705 Sqn, Culdrose	
ZB648	WS Gazelle HT2 [40/CU] (wreck)	RN, Culdrose	
ZB649	WS Gazelle HT2 [43/CU]	RN No 705 Sqn, Culdrose	
ZB665	WS Gazelle AH1	AAC No 16 Flt, Dhekelia, Cyprus	
ZB666	WS Gazelle AH1 [G]	AAC No 670 Sqn, Middle Wallop	
ZB667	WS Gazelle AH1	AAC, UNFICYP, Nicosia	
ZB668	WS Gazelle AH1 [UN]	AAC, stored Fleetlands	
ZB669	WS Gazelle AH1	AAC, Fleetlands	
ZB670	WS Gazelle AH1	AAC No 665 Sqn, Aldergrove	
ZB671	WS Gazelle AH1	AAC No 29 Flt, BATUS, Suffield, Canada	
ZB672	WS Gazelle AH1 [V]	AAC No 657 Sqn, Dishforth	
ZB673	WS Gazelle AH1 [P]	AAC No 670 Sqn, Middle Wallop	
ZB674	WS Gazelle AH1	AAC No 665 Sqn, Aldergrove	
ZB676	WS Gazelle AH1 [E1]	AAC, stored Fleetlands	
ZB677	WS Gazelle AH1	AAC No 29 Flt, BATUS, Suffield, Canada	
ZB678	WS Gazelle AH1	AAC No 16 Flt, Dhekelia, Cyprus	
ZB679	WS Gazelle AH1	AAC No 16 Flt, Dhekelia, Cyprus	
ZB680	WS Gazelle AH1 [B]	Written off, Suffield, Canada, 12 Sept 1990	
ZB681	WS Gazelle AH1	Written off, Bessbrook, 27 November 1992	
ZB682	WS Gazelle AH1	AAC No 665 Sqn, Aldergrove	
ZB683	WS Gazelle AH1	Westland, Weston-super-Mare (rebuild)	
ZB684	WS Gazelle AH1	AAC No 655 Sqn, Ballykelly	
ZB685	WS Gazelle AH1	AAC No 665 Sqn, Aldergrove	
ZB686	WS Gazelle AH1	AAC No 655 Sqn, Ballykelly	
ZB688	WS Gazelle AH1 [H]	AAC No 670 Sqn, Middle Wallop	
ZB689	WS Gazelle AH1 [W]	AAC No 670 Sqn, Middle Wallop	
ZB690	WS Gazelle AH1	AAC No 16 Flt, Dhekelia, Cyprus	
ZB691	WS Gazelle AH1 [C]	AAC No 664 Sqn, Dishforth	
ZB692	WS Gazelle AH1 [E]	AAC No 664 Sqn, Dishforth	
ZB693	WS Gazelle AH1	AAC No 670 Sqn, Middle Wallop	
ZD230	BAC Super VC10 K4 (G-ASGA)	MoD(PE), BAe Filton	
ZD232	BAC Super VC10 (8699M/ G-ASGD)	RAF Brize Norton Fire Section	
ZD234	BAC Super VC10 (G-ASGF)	RAF Brize Norton, tanker simulator	
ZD235	BAC Super VC10 K4 (G-ASGG)	MoD(PE), BAe Filton	
ZD239	BAC Super VC10 (G-ASGK)	FSCTE, RAF Manston	
ZD240	BAC Super VC10 K4 (G-ASGL)	MoD(PE), BAe Filton	
ZD241	BAC Super VC10 K4 (G-ASGM)	MoD(PE), BAe Filton	
ZD242	BAC Super VC10 K4 (G-ASGP)	MoD(PE), BAe Filton	
ZD243	BAC Super VC10 (G-ASGR)	BAe, Filton (spares use)	
ZD249	WS Lynx HAS3	MoD(PE), A&AEE Boscombe Down	
ZD250	WS Lynx HAS3S [417]	RN No 815 Sqn, Portland	
ZD251	WS Lynx HAS3S	RN, Fleetlands	

Notes	Serial	Type	Owner or Operator
	ZD252	WS Lynx HAS3S [302]	RN No 815 Sqn, Portland
	ZD253	WS Lynx HAS3S [472/AM]	RN No 815 Sqn, Portland
	ZD254	WS Lynx HAS3 [631]	RN No 702 Sqn, Portland
	ZD255	WS Lynx HAS3S [348/CW]	RN No 815 Sqn, Portland
	ZD256	WS Lynx HAS3S [605]	RN, Fleetlands
	ZD257	WS Lynx HAS3S [363/MA]	RN No 815 Sqn, Portland
	ZD258	WS Lynx HAS3S [330]	RN AMG, Portland
	ZD259	WS Lynx HAS3S [405/LO]	RN No 815 Sqn, Portland
	ZD260	WS Lynx HAS3S [352]	RN AMG, Portland
	ZD261	WS Lynx HAS8 [636]	MoD(PE), Westland Yeovil
	ZD262	WS Lynx HAS3S [632]	RN AMG, Portland
	ZD263	WS Lynx HAS3S [630/PO]	RN No 702 Sqn, Portland
	ZD264	WS Lynx HAS3S	RN, Fleetlands
	ZD265	WS Lynx HAS3S [407/YK]	RN No 815 Sqn, Portland
	ZD266	WS Lynx HAS8	MoD(PE), Westland Yeovil (conversion)
	ZD267	WS Lynx HAS8	MoD(PE), Westland Yeovil
	ZD268	WS Lynx HAS3S [432/SC]	RN No 815 Sqn, Portland
	ZD272	WS Lynx AH7 [H]	AAC No 671 Sqn, Middle Wallop
	ZD273	WS Lynx AH7	AAC No 655 Sqn, Aldergrove
	ZD274	WS Lynx AH7 [M]	AAC No 662 Sqn, Wattisham
	ZD275	WS Lynx AH7	AAC No 665 Sqn, Aldergrove
	ZD276	WS Lynx AH7 [F]	AAC No 653 Sqn, Wattisham
	ZD277	WS Lynx AH7 [P]	AAC No 662 Sqn, Wattisham
	ZD278	WS Lynx AH7 [A]	AAC No 671 Sqn, Middle Wallop
	ZD279	WS Lynx AH7 [C]	AAC No 671 Sqn, Middle Wallop
	ZD280	WS Lynx AH1 [Y]	AAC No 656 Sqn, Dishforth
	ZD281	WS Lynx AH7 [K]	AAC No 671 Sqn, Middle Wallop
	ZD282	WS Lynx AH7 [L]	RM 3 CBAS, Yeovilton
	ZD283	WS Lynx AH1 [Z]	AAC No 656 Sqn, Dishforth
	ZD284	WS Lynx AH7 [H]	AAC
	ZD285	WS Lynx AH7	MoD(PE), DRA Farnborough
	ZD318	BAe Harrier GR7	MoD(PE), A&AEE Boscombe Down
	ZD319	BAe Harrier GR7	MoD(PE), A&AEE Boscombe Down
	ZD320	BAe Harrier GR5A	MoD(PE), BAe Dunsfold
	ZD321	BAe Harrier GR5	MoD(PE), A&AEE Boscombe Down
	ZD322	BAe Harrier GR7	MoD(PE)/BAe Dunsfold (conversion)
	ZD323	BAe Harrier GR7	MoD(PE)/BAe Dunsfold (conversion)
	ZD324	BAe Harrier GR7	MoD(PE)/BAe Dunsfold (conversion)
	ZD326	BAe Harrier GR7	MoD(PE)/BAe Dunsfold (conversion)
	ZD327	BAe Harrier GR5 [L]	RAF, stored Shawbury
	ZD328	BAe Harrier GR7	RAF, ASF Wittering
	ZD329	BAe Harrier GR7	MoD(PE)/BAe Dunsfold (conversion)
	ZD330	BAe Harrier GR7	MoD(PE)/BAe Dunsfold (conversion)
	ZD345	BAe Harrier GR7 [J]	RAF HOCU/No 20(R) Sqn, Wittering
	ZD346	BAe Harrier GR5 [5E]	RAF, stored Shawbury
	ZD347	BAe Harrier GR5 [K]	RAF HOCU/No 20(R) Sqn, Wittering
	ZD348	BAe Harrier GR7	RAF, ASF Laarbruch
	ZD349	BAe Harrier GR7 [AJ]	RAF No 3 Sqn, Laarbruch
	ZD350	BAe Harrier GR7 [A]	RAF HOCU/No 20(R) Sqn, Wittering
	ZD351	BAe Harrier GR5	RAF, ASF Wittering
	ZD352	BAe Harrier GR7	MoD(PE)/BAe Dunsfold (under conversion)
	ZD353	BAe Harrier GR5	RAF, ASF Wittering
	ZD354	BAe Harrier GR5 [5C]	RAF HOCU/No 20(R) Sqn, Wittering
	ZD375	BAe Harrier GR5 [5D]	RAF HOCU/No 20(R) Sqn, Wittering
	ZD376	BAe Harrier GR5 [F]	RAF Wittering (repair)
	ZD377	BAe Harrier GR7	MoD(PE)/BAe Dunsfold (conversion)
	ZD378	BAe Harrier GR7	MoD(PE)/BAe Dunsfold (conversion)
	ZD379	BAe Harrier GR7	MoD(PE)/BAe Dunsfold (conversion)
	ZD380	BAe Harrier GR7 [06]	RAF No 1 Sqn, Wittering
	ZD400	BAe Harrier GR7	MoD(PE)/BAe Dunsfold (conversion)
	ZD401	BAe Harrier GR7	MoD(PE)/BAe Dunsfold (conversion)
	ZD402	BAe Harrier GR7 [E]	RAF HOCU/No 20(R) Sqn, Wittering
	ZD403	BAe Harrier GR7 [G]	RAF HOCU/No 20(R) Sqn, Wittering
	ZD404	BAe Harrier GR7 [H]	RAF HOCU/No 20(R) Sqn, Wittering
	ZD405	BAe Harrier GR7 [N]	RAF HOCU/No 20(R) Sqn, Wittering
	ZD406	BAe Harrier GR7 [WB]	RAF No 1 Sqn, Wittering
	ZD407	BAe Harrier GR7 [AK]	RAF No 3 Sqn, Laarbruch
	ZD408	BAe Harrier GR7 [O]	RAF HOCU/No 20(R) Sqn, Wittering
	ZD409	BAe Harrier GR7 [B]	RAF HOCU/No 20(R) Sqn, Wittering
	ZD410	BAe Harrier GR7 [AJ]	RAF No 3 Sqn, Laarbruch
	ZD411	BAe Harrier GR7 [L]	RAF HOCU/No 20(R) Sqn, Wittering
	ZD412	BAe Harrier GR5 [AH] (wreck)	RAF St Athan

Serial	Type	Owner or Operator	Notes
ZD430	BAe Harrier GR7 [AO]	*Written off, 13 June 1993, Heckington, Lincs*	
ZD431	BAe Harrier GR7 [02]	RAF No 1 Sqn, Wittering	
ZD432	BAe Harrier GR7 [N]	RAF HOCU/No 20(R) Sqn, Wittering	
ZD433	BAe Harrier GR7 [AD]	RAF No 3 Sqn, Laarbruch	
ZD434	BAe Harrier GR7 [WE]	RAF No 4 Sqn, Incirlik	
ZD435	BAe Harrier GR7 [04]	RAF No 1 Sqn, Wittering	
ZD436	BAe Harrier GR7	MoD(PE), BAe Dunsfold	
ZD437	BAe Harrier GR7 [05]	RAF No 1 Sqn, Wittering	
ZD438	BAe Harrier GR7 [03]	RAF No 1 Sqn, Wittering	
ZD461	BAe Harrier GR7 [WH]	RAF No 1 Sqn, Wittering	
ZD462	BAe Harrier GR7 [07]	RAF No 1 Sqn, Wittering	
ZD463	BAe Harrier GR7 [09]	RAF No 1 Sqn, Wittering	
ZD464	BAe Harrier GR7 [10]	RAF No 1 Sqn, Wittering	
ZD465	BAe Harrier GR7 [11]	RAF No 1 Sqn, Wittering	
ZD466	BAe Harrier GR7 [I]	RAF HOCU/No 20(R) Sqn, Wittering	
ZD467	BAe Harrier GR7 [WA]	RAF No 4 Sqn, Incirlik	
ZD468	BAe Harrier GR7 [12]	RAF No 1 Sqn, Wittering	
ZD469	BAe Harrier GR7 [08]	RAF No 1 Sqn, Wittering	
ZD470	BAe Harrier GR7 [01]	RAF No 1 Sqn, Wittering	
ZD472	Harrier GR5 Replica [01] (BAPC191)	RAF Exhibition Flight, St Athan	
ZD477	WS61 Sea King HC4	RN No 845 Sqn, Yeovilton	
ZD478	WS61 Sea King HC4 [VM]	RN No 846 Sqn, Yeovilton	
ZD479	WS61 Sea King HC4 [ZV]	RN No 846 Sqn, Yeovilton	
ZD480	WS61 Sea King HC4 [C]	RN No 845 Sqn, Yeovilton	
ZD559	WS Lynx AH5	MoD(PE), DRA Bedford	
ZD560	WS Lynx AH7	MoD(PE), ETPS, Boscombe Down	
ZD565	WS Lynx HAS3S [633]	RN No 702 Sqn, Portland	
ZD566	WS Lynx HAS3S [637]	RN No 702 Sqn, Portland	
ZD567	WS Lynx HAS3S [365/AY]	RN No 815 Sqn, Portland	
ZD574	B-V Chinook HC1 [EH]	RAF No 7 Sqn, Odiham	
ZD575	B-V Chinook HC1 [BL]	RAF No 18 Sqn, Laarbruch	
ZD576	B-V Chinook HC1 [BC]	RAF No 18 Sqn, Laarbruch	
ZD578	BAe Sea Harrier FRS1 [715/VL]	RN No 899 Sqn, Yeovilton	
ZD579	BAe Sea Harrier FRS2	MoD(PE)/BAe Brough (conversion)	
ZD580	BAe Sea Harrier FRS1	RN, St Athan	
ZD581	BAe Sea Harrier FRS1 [000/R]	RN No 801 Sqn, Yeovilton	
ZD582	BAe Sea Harrier FRS2	MoD(PE)/BAe Dunsfold	
ZD607	BAe Sea Harrier FRS1 [001/R]	RN No 801 Sqn, Yeovilton	
ZD608	BAe Sea Harrier FRS2	MoD(PE)/BAe Brough (conversion)	
ZD610	BAe Sea Harrier FRS1 [710]	RN AMG, Yeovilton	
ZD611	BAe Sea Harrier FRS2	MoD(PE)/BAe Brough (conversion)	
ZD612	BAe Sea Harrier FRS2	MoD(PE)/BAe Dunsfold (conversion)	
ZD613	BAe Sea Harrier FRS2	MoD(PE)/BAe Dunsfold (conversion)	
ZD614	BAe Sea Harrier FRS2 [004/R]	RN No 801 Sqn, Yeovilton	
ZD615	BAe Sea Harrier FRS2 [712/OEU]	RN No 899 Sqn OEU, Yeovilton	
ZD620	BAe 125 CC3	RAF No 32 Sqn, Northolt	
ZD621	BAe 125 CC3	RAF No 32 Sqn, Northolt	
ZD625	WS61 Sea King HC4 [ZZ]	RN No 707 Sqn, Yeovilton	
ZD626	WS61 Sea King HC4 [ZY]	RN No 707 Sqn, Yeovilton	
ZD627	WS61 Sea King HC4 [ZW]	RN No 707 Sqn, Yeovilton	
ZD630	WS61 Sea King HAS6 [265/N]	RN AMG, Culdrose	
ZD631	WS61 Sea King HAS6 [66] (fuselage)	RN, ETS Yeovilton	
ZD633	WS61 Sea King HAS6 [507]	RN No 810 Sqn, Culdrose	
ZD634	WS61 Sea King HAS6 [506]	RN No 810 Sqn, Culdrose	
ZD636	WS61 Sea King HAS5 [825]	RN No 771 Sqn, Culdrose	
ZD637	WS61 Sea King HAS6 [700/PW]	RN No 819 Sqn, Prestwick	
ZD657	Schleicher Valiant TX1 (BGA2893)	RAF ACCGS, Syerston	
ZD658	Schleicher Valiant TX1 (BGA2894)	RAF No 618 VGS, West Malling	
ZD659	Schleicher Valiant TX1 (BGA2895)	RAF ACCGS, Syerston	
ZD660	Schleicher Valiant TX1 (BGA2896)	RAF ACCGS, Syerston	
ZD667	BAe Harrier GR3 [3B]	RN, SAH Culdrose	
ZD668	BAe Harrier GR3 [3E]	RAF	
ZD669	BAe Harrier GR3 [3B]	RAF	
ZD670	BAe Harrier GR3 [3A]	RAF	
ZD703	BAe 125 CC3	RAF No 32 Sqn, Northolt	
ZD704	BAe 125 CC3	RAF No 32 Sqn, Northolt	
ZD707	Panavia Tornado GR1 [BK]	RAF No 14 Sqn, Bruggen	
ZD708	Panavia Tornado GR4	MoD(PE), BAe Warton	
ZD709	Panavia Tornado GR1 [BR]	RAF No 14 Sqn, Bruggen	
ZD711	Panavia Tornado GR1T [DY]	RAF No 31 Sqn, Bruggen	

Notes	Serial	Type	Owner or Operator
	ZD712	Panavia Tornado GR1T [BY]	RAF No 14 Sqn, Bruggen
	ZD713	Panavia Tornado GR1T [BX]	RAF No 14 Sqn, Bruggen
ZD713	Hunting Jet Provost T3 (XM381/ 8232M) [A]	RAF Marham Fire Section
	ZD714	Panavia Tornado GR1 [AP]	RAF No 9 Sqn, Bruggen
	ZD715	Panavia Tornado GR1 [DB]	RAF No 31 Sqn, Bruggen
	ZD716	Panavia Tornado GR1 [O]	RAF SAOEU, Boscombe Down
	ZD719	Panavia Tornado GR1	RAF No 9 Sqn, Bruggen
	ZD720	Panavia Tornado GR1 [AG]	RAF No 9 Sqn, Bruggen
	ZD739	Panavia Tornado GR1 [AC]	RAF No 9 Sqn, Bruggen
	ZD740	Panavia Tornado GR1 [DA]	RAF No 31 Sqn, Bruggen
	ZD741	Panavia Tornado GR1T [DZ]	RAF No 31 Sqn, Bruggen
	ZD742	Panavia Tornado GR1T [CZ]	RAF No 17 Sqn, Bruggen
	ZD743	Panavia Tornado GR1 [CX]	RAF No 17 Sqn, Bruggen
	ZD744	Panavia Tornado GR1 [BD]	RAF No 14 Sqn, Bruggen
	ZD745	Panavia Tornado GR1 [BM]	RAF No 14 Sqn, Bruggen
	ZD746	Panavia Tornado GR1 [AB]	RAF No 9 Sqn, Bruggen
	ZD747	Panavia Tornado GR1 [AL]	RAF No 9 Sqn, Bruggen
	ZD748	Panavia Tornado GR1 [AK]	RAF No 9 Sqn, Bruggen
	ZD749	Panavia Tornado GR1 [U]	RAF SAOEU, Boscombe Down
	ZD788	Panavia Tornado GR1 [CB]	RAF No 17 Sqn, Bruggen
	ZD789	Panavia Tornado GR1 [AM]	RAF No 9 Sqn, Bruggen
	ZD790	Panavia Tornado GR1	RAF No 31 Sqn, Bruggen
	ZD792	Panavia Tornado GR1 [CF]	RAF No 17 Sqn, Bruggen
	ZD793	Panavia Tornado GR1 [CA]	RAF No 17 Sqn, Bruggen
	ZD809	Panavia Tornado GR1 [BA]	RAF No 14 Sqn, Bruggen
	ZD810	Panavia Tornado GR1 [AA]	RAF No 9 Sqn, Bruggen
	ZD811	Panavia Tornado GR1 [DF]	RAF No 31 Sqn, Bruggen
	ZD812	Panavia Tornado GR1T [BW]	RAF No 14 Sqn, Bruggen
	ZD842	Panavia Tornado GR1T [CY]	RAF No 17 Sqn, Bruggen
	ZD843	Panavia Tornado GR1 [DH]	RAF No 31 Sqn, Bruggen
	ZD844	Panavia Tornado GR1 [DE]	RAF No 31 Sqn, Bruggen
	ZD845	Panavia Tornado GR1 [AF]	RAF No 9 Sqn, Bruggen
	ZD846	Panavia Tornado GR1 [BL]	RAF No 14 Sqn, Bruggen
	ZD847	Panavia Tornado GR1 [CH]	RAF No 17 Sqn, Bruggen
	ZD848	Panavia Tornado GR1 [DM]	RAF No 31 Sqn, Bruggen
	ZD849	Panavia Tornado GR1 [BT]	RAF No 14 Sqn, Bruggen
	ZD850	Panavia Tornado GR1 [CL]	RAF No 17 Sqn, Bruggen
	ZD851	Panavia Tornado GR1 [AJ]	RAF No 9 Sqn, Bruggen
	ZD890	Panavia Tornado GR1 [AE]	RAF No 9 Sqn, Bruggen
	ZD892	Panavia Tornado GR1 [BJ]	RAF No 14 Sqn, Bruggen
	ZD895	Panavia Tornado GR1 [BF]	RAF No 14 Sqn, Bruggen
	ZD899	Panavia Tornado F2T	MoD(PE), BAe Warton
	ZD900	Panavia Tornado F2T	MoD(PE), A&AEE Boscombe Down
	ZD901	Panavia Tornado F2T [AA]	RAF, stored St Athan
	ZD902	Panavia Tornado F2T	MoD(PE), DRA Farnborough
	ZD903	Panavia Tornado F2T [AB]	RAF, stored St Athan
	ZD904	Panavia Tornado F2T [AE]	RAF, stored St Athan
	ZD905	Panavia Tornado F2	RAF, stored St Athan
	ZD906	Panavia Tornado F2 [AN]	RAF, stored St Athan
	ZD932	Panavia Tornado F2 [AM]	RAF, stored St Athan
	ZD933	Panavia Tornado F2 [AO]	RAF, stored St Athan
	ZD934	Panavia Tornado F2T [AD]	RAF, stored St Athan
	ZD935	Panavia Tornado F2T	*Scrapped at RAF Coningsby*
	ZD936	Panavia Tornado F2	RAF, stored St Athan
	ZD937	Panavia Tornado F2 [A]	RAF St Athan, BDRT
	ZD938	Panavia Tornado F2	RAF, stored St Athan
	ZD939	Panavia Tornado F2 [AS]	MoD(PE), BAe Warton
	ZD940	Panavia Tornado F2	RAF, stored St Athan
	ZD941	Panavia Tornado F2 [AU]	RAF, stored St Athan
	ZD948	Lockheed TriStar KC1 (G-BFCA)	RAF No 216 Sqn, Brize Norton
	ZD949	Lockheed TriStar K1 (G-BFCB)	RAF No 216 Sqn, Brize Norton
	ZD950	Lockheed TriStar KC1 (G-BFCC)	RAF No 216 Sqn, Brize Norton
	ZD951	Lockheed TriStar K1 (G-BFCD)	RAF No 216 Sqn, Brize Norton
	ZD952	Lockheed TriStar KC1 (G-BFCE)	RAF No 216 Sqn, Brize Norton
	ZD953	Lockheed TriStar KC1 (G-BFCF)	RAF No 216 Sqn, Brize Norton
	ZD974	Schempp-Hirth Kestrel TX1 (BGA2875)	RAF, stored Syerston
	ZD975	Schempp-Hirth Kestrel TX1 (BGA2876)	RAF, stored Syerston
	ZD980	B-V Chinook HC1	RAF No 78 Sqn, Mount Pleasant, FI
	ZD981	B-V Chinook HC1 [BD]	RAF No 18 Sqn, Laarbruch
	ZD982	B-V Chinook HC2 [BI]	Boeing, Philadelphia (conversion)

Serial	Type	Owner or Operator	Notes
ZD983	B-V Chinook HC1 [EF]	RAF No 7 Sqn, Odiham	
ZD984	B-V Chinook HC1 [EE]	RAF No 7 Sqn, Odiham	
ZD990	BAe Harrier T4A [Q]	RAF HOCU/No 20(R) Sqn, Wittering	
ZD991	BAe Harrier T4 [V]	RAF HOCU/No 20(R) Sqn, Wittering	
ZD992	BAe Harrier T4	RAF, stored St Athan	
ZD993	BAe Harrier T4 [U]	MoD(PE), A&AEE Boscombe Down	
ZD996	Panavia Tornado GR1A [I]	RAF No 2 Sqn, Marham	
ZE116	Panavia Tornado GR1A [DG]	RAF No 31 Sqn, Bruggen	
ZE154	Panavia Tornado F3T [AD]	RAF, stored St Athan	
ZE155	Panavia Tornado F3	MoD(PE), A&AEE Boscombe Down	
ZE156	Panavia Tornado F3 [HE]	RAF No 111 Sqn, Leuchars	
ZE157	Panavia Tornado F3T [AB]	RAF, stored St Athan	
ZE158	Panavia Tornado F3 [DC]	RAF, ASF Leeming (on rebuild)	
ZE159	Panavia Tornado F3T [EG]	RAF No 23 Sqn, Leeming	
ZE160	Panavia Tornado F3T [EX]	RAF No 23 Sqn, Leeming	
ZE161	Panavia Tornado F3T [FG]	MoD(PE), A&AEE Boscombe Down	
ZE162	Panavia Tornado F3 [FK]	RAF No 25 Sqn, Leeming	
ZE163	Panavia Tornado F3T [AA]	RAF, stored St Athan	
ZE164	Panavia Tornado F3 [DA]	RAF No 11 Sqn, Leeming	
ZE165	Panavia Tornado F3 [FO]	RAF No 25 Sqn, Leeming	
ZE166	Panavia Tornado F3T [AF]	RAF F3 OCU/No 56(R) Sqn, Coningsby	
ZE167	Panavia Tornado F3	MoD(PE), A&AEE Boscombe Down	
ZE168	Panavia Tornado F3 [EB]	RAF No 23 Sqn, Leeming	
ZE199	Panavia Tornado F3T [FL]	RAF No 25 Sqn, Leeming	
ZE200	Panavia Tornado F3 [DB]	RAF No 11 Sqn, Leeming	
ZE201	Panavia Tornado F3 [ED]	RAF No 23 Sqn, Leeming	
ZE202	Panavia Tornado F3T [AG]	RAF F3 OCU/No 56(R) Sqn, Coningsby	
ZE203	Panavia Tornado F3 [FI]	RAF No 25 Sqn, Leeming	
ZE204	Panavia Tornado F3 [DD]	RAF No 11 Sqn, Leeming	
ZE205	Panavia Tornado F3T [AM]	RAF F3 OCU/No 56(R) Sqn, Coningsby	
ZE206	Panavia Tornado F3 [EW]	RAF No 23 Sqn, Leeming	
ZE207	Panavia Tornado F3 [GC]	RAF No 43 Sqn, Leuchars	
ZE208	Panavia Tornado F3T [AN]	RAF F3 OCU/No 56(R) Sqn, Coningsby	
ZE209	Panavia Tornado F3 [H]	RAF No 1435 Flt, Mount Pleasant Fl	
ZE210	Panavia Tornado F3 [FB]	RAF No 25 Sqn, Leeming	
ZE250	Panavia Tornado F3T [HZ]	RAF, ASF Leuchars (on repair)	
ZE251	Panavia Tornado F3 [DE]	RAF, stored St Athan	
ZE252	Panavia Tornado F3 [HH]	RAF No 111 Sqn, Leuchars	
ZE253	Panavia Tornado F3T [AC]	RAF F3 OCU/No 56(R) Sqn, Coningsby	
ZE254	Panavia Tornado F3 [CA]	RAF, stored St Athan	
ZE255	Panavia Tornado F3 [HI]	RAF, stored St Athan	
ZE256	Panavia Tornado F3T [AJ]	RAF F3 OCU/No 56(R) Sqn, Coningsby	
ZE257	Panavia Tornado F3 [HN]	RAF No 111 Sqn, Leuchars	
ZE258	Panavia Tornado F3 [GA]	RAF, stored St Athan	
ZE287	Panavia Tornado F3T [AH]	RAF F3 OCU/No 56(R) Sqn, Coningsby	
ZE288	Panavia Tornado F3 [GG]	RAF, stored St Athan	
ZE289	Panavia Tornado F3 [HF]	RAF, ASF Leuchars	
ZE290	Panavia Tornado F3T [AD]	RAF F3 OCU/No 56(R) Sqn, Coningsby	
ZE291	Panavia Tornado F3 [AZ]	RAF, ASF Leuchars	
ZE292	Panavia Tornado F3 [HA]	RAF, stored St Athan	
ZE293	Panavia Tornado F3T [HT]	RAF No 111 Sqn, Leuchars	
ZE294	Panavia Tornado F3 [AQ]	RAF, stored St Athan	
ZE295	Panavia Tornado F3 [AW]	RAF, stored Coningsby	
ZE296	Panavia Tornado F3T [GR]	RAF No 43 Sqn, Leuchars	
ZE338	Panavia Tornado F3 [HG]	RAF No 111 Sqn, Leuchars	
ZE339	Panavia Tornado F3 [BJ]	RAF No 29 Sqn, Coningsby	
ZE340	Panavia Tornado F3T [AE]	RAF F3 OCU/No 56(R) Sqn, Coningsby	
ZE341	Panavia Tornado F3 [HD]	RAF No 111 Sqn, Leuchars	
ZE342	Panavia Tornado F3 [BL]	RAF No 29 Sqn, Coningsby	
ZE343	Panavia Tornado F3T [AI]	RAF, stored St Athan	
ZE351	McD Phantom F-4J(UK) (9058M) [I]	RAF Finningley Fire Section	
ZE353	McD Phantom F-4J(UK) (9083M) [E]	RAF Manston, on display	
ZE354	McD Phantom F-4J(UK) (9084M) [R]	RAF Coningsby Fire Section	
ZE356	McD Phantom F-4J(UK) (9060M) [Q]	RAF Waddington Fire Section	
ZE359	McD Phantom F-4J(UK) [J]	Imperial War Museum, Duxford	
ZE360	McD Phantom F-4J(UK) (9059M) [O]	FSCTE, RAF Manston	

Notes	Serial	Type	Owner or Operator
	ZE361	McD Phantom F-4J(UK) (9057M) [P]	RAF Honington Fire Section
	ZE364	McD Phantom F-4J(UK) (9085M) [Z]	RAF Coltishall Fire Section
	ZE368	WS61 Sea King HAR3	RAF No 202 Sqn, St Mawgan
	ZE369	WS61 Sea King HAR3	RAF No 202 Sqn, B Flt, Brawdy
	ZE370	WS61 Sea King HAR3	RAF No 202 Sqn, St Mawgan
	ZE375	WS Lynx AH9	AAC, Fleetlands
	ZE376	WS Lynx AH9	Westland, Yeovil (conversion)
	ZE378	WS Lynx AH7	AAC Fleetlands
	ZE379	WS Lynx AH7	AAC No 655 Sqn, Aldergrove
	ZE380	WS Lynx AH9 [1]	AAC No 659 Sqn, Detmold
	ZE381	WS Lynx AH9	AAC No 659 Sqn, Detmold
	ZE382	WS Lynx AH9 [3]	AAC No 659 Sqn, Detmold
	ZE395	BAe 125 CC3	RAF No 32 Sqn, Northolt
	ZE396	BAe 125 CC3	RAF No 32 Sqn, Northolt
	ZE410	Agusta A109A (AE-334)	AAC No 8 Flight, Netheravon
	ZE411	Agusta A109A (AE-331)	AAC No 8 Flight, Netheravon
	ZE412	Agusta A109A	AAC No 8 Flight, Netheravon
	ZE413	Agusta A109A	AAC No 8 Flight, Netheravon
	ZE418	WS61 Sea King HAS5 [583]	RN No 706 Sqn, Culdrose
	ZE419	WS61 Sea King HAS6 [705/PW]	*Written off, 6 November 1993, off Islay*
	ZE420	WS61 Sea King HAS5 [592/CU]	RN No 706 Sqn, Culdrose
	ZE422	WS61 Sea King HAS6	RNAY Fleetlands
	ZE425	WS61 Sea King HC4 [26]	RN No 772 Sqn, Portland
	ZE426	WS61 Sea King HC4 [VL]	RN No 846 Sqn, Yeovilton
	ZE427	WS61 Sea King HC4 [UN]	RN No 845 Sqn, Yeovilton
	ZE428	WS61 Sea King HC4 [VH]	RN No 846 Sqn, Yeovilton
	ZE432	BAC 1-11/479 (DQ-FBV)	MoD(PE) ETPS, Boscombe Down
	ZE433	BAC 1-11/479 (DQ-FBQ)	MoD(PE) GEC/Ferranti, Edinburgh
	ZE438	BAe Jetstream T3 [576]	RN FONA/Heron Flight, Yeovilton
	ZE439	BAe Jetstream T3 [577]	RN FONA/Heron Flight, Yeovilton
	ZE440	BAe Jetstream T3 [578]	RN FONA/Heron Flight, Yeovilton
	ZE441	BAe Jetstream T3 [579]	RN FONA/Heron Flight, Yeovilton
	ZE477	WS Lynx 3	IHM, Weston-super-Mare
	ZE495	Grob Viking T1 (BGA3000)	RAF No 622 VGS, Upavon
	ZE496	Grob Viking T1 (BGA3001)	RAF CGMF, Syerston
	ZE497	Grob Viking T1 (BGA3002)	RAF No 662 VGS, Arbroath
	ZE498	Grob Viking T1 (BGA3003)	RAF CGMF, Syerston
	ZE499	Grob Viking T1 (BGA3004)	RAF ACCGS, Syerston
	ZE501	Grob Viking T1 (BGA3006)	RAF ACCGS, Syerston
	ZE502	Grob Viking T1 (BGA3007)	RAF No 618 VGS, West Malling
	ZE503	Grob Viking T1 (BGA3008)	RAF No 625 VGS, Hullavington
	ZE504	Grob Viking T1 (BGA3009)	RAF No 645 VGS, Catterick
	ZE520	Grob Viking T1 (BGA3010)	RAF No 622 VGS, Upavon
	ZE521	Grob Viking T1 (BGA3011)	RAF No 662 VGS, Arbroath
	ZE522	Grob Viking T1 (BGA3012)	RAF No 618 VGS, West Malling
	ZE524	Grob Viking T1 (BGA3014)	RAF No 626 VGS, Predannack
	ZE525	Grob Viking T1 (BGA3015)	ATC, Congleton, Cheshire
	ZE526	Grob Viking T1 (BGA3016)	RAF No 626 VGS, Predannack
	ZE527	Grob Viking T1 (BGA3017)	RAF No 645 VGS, Catterick
	ZE528	Grob Viking T1 (BGA3018)	RAF No 645 VGS, Catterick
	ZE529	Grob Viking T1 (BGA3019)	RAF No 636 VGS, Swansea
	ZE530	Grob Viking T1 (BGA3020)	RAF No 645 VGS, Catterick
	ZE531	Grob Viking T1 (BGA3021)	RAF ACCGS, Syerston
	ZE532	Grob Viking T1 (BGA3022)	RAF No 618 VGS, West Malling
	ZE533	Grob Viking T1 (BGA3023)	RAF No 622 VGS, Upavon
	ZE534	Grob Viking T1 (BGA3024)	RAF ACCGS, Syerston
	ZE550	Grob Viking T1 (BGA3025)	RAF No 622 VGS, Upavon
	ZE551	Grob Viking T1 (BGA3026)	RAF No 611 VGS, Swanton Morley
	ZE552	Grob Viking T1 (BGA3027)	RAF ACCGS, Syerston
	ZE553	Grob Viking T1 (BGA3028)	RAF CGMF, Syerston
	ZE554	Grob Viking T1 (BGA3029)	RAF ACCGS, Syerston
	ZE555	Grob Viking T1 (BGA3030)	RAF No 626 VGS, Predannack
	ZE556	Grob Viking T1 (BGA3031)	RAF No 661 VGS, Kirknewton
	ZE557	Grob Viking T1 (BGA3032)	RAF No 622 VGS, Upavon
	ZE558	Grob Viking T1 (BGA3033)	RAF No 634 VGS, St Athan
	ZE559	Grob Viking T1 (BGA3034)	RAF CGMF, Syerston
	ZE560	Grob Viking T1 (BGA3035)	RAF No 611 VGS, Swanton Morley
	ZE561	Grob Viking T1 (BGA3036)	RAF No 621 VGS, Hullavington
	ZE562	Grob Viking T1 (BGA3037)	RAF CGMF, Syerston
	ZE563	Grob Viking T1 (BGA3038)	RAF ACCGS, Syerston
	ZE564	Grob Viking T1 (BGA3039)	RAF No 661 VGS, Kirknewton

Serial	Type	Owner or Operator	Notes
ZE584	Grob Viking T1 (BGA3040)	RAF No 661 VGS, Kirknewton	
ZE585	Grob Viking T1 (BGA3041)	RAF No 614 VGS, Wethersfield	
ZE586	Grob Viking T1 (BGA3042)	RAF No 618 VGS, West Malling	
ZE587	Grob Viking T1 (BGA3043)	RAF No 611 VGS, Swanton Morley	
ZE589	Grob Viking T1 (BGA3045)	RAF CGMF, Syerston	
ZE590	Grob Viking T1 (BGA3046)	RAF No 645 VGS, Catterick	
ZE591	Grob Viking T1 (BGA3047)	RAF No 662 VGS, Arbroath	
ZE592	Grob Viking T1 (BGA3048)	RAF No 625 VGS, Hullavington	
ZE593	Grob Viking T1 (BGA3049)	RAF CGMF, Syerston	
ZE594	Grob Viking T1 (BGA3050)	RAF CGMF, Syerston	
ZE595	Grob Viking T1 (BGA3051)	RAF No 662 VGS, Arbroath	
ZE600	Grob Viking T1 (BGA3052)	RAF No 618 VGS, West Malling	
ZE601	Grob Viking T1 (BGA3053)	RAF No 636 VGS, Swansea	
ZE602	Grob Viking T1 (BGA3054)	RAF No 615 VGS, Kenley	
ZE603	Grob Viking T1 (BGA3055)	RAF No 617 VGS, Manston	
ZE604	Grob Viking T1 (BGA3056)	RAF No 617 VGS, Manston	
ZE605	Grob Viking T1 (BGA3057)	RAF No 618 VGS, West Malling	
ZE606	Grob Viking T1 (BGA3058)	RAF No 614 VGS, Wethersfield	
ZE607	Grob Viking T1 (BGA3059)	RAF No 625 VGS, Hullavington	
ZE608	Grob Viking T1 (BGA3060)	RAF CGMF, Syerston	
ZE609	Grob Viking T1 (BGA3061)	RAF CGMF, Syerston	
ZE610	Grob Viking T1 (BGA3062)	RAF No 615 VGS, Kenley	
ZE611	Grob Viking T1 (BGA3063)	RAF No 621 VGS, Hullavington	
ZE612	Grob Viking T1 (BGA3064)	RAF CGMF, Syerston (wreck)	
ZE613	Grob Viking T1 (BGA3065)	RAF No 618 VGS, West Malling	
ZE614	Grob Viking T1 (BGA3066)	RAF No 661 VGS, Kirknewton	
ZE625	Grob Viking T1 (BGA3067)	RAF No 643 VGS, Binbrook	
ZE626	Grob Viking T1 (BGA3068)	RAF No 636 VGS, Swansea	
ZE627	Grob Viking T1 (BGA3069)	RAF ACCGS, Syerston	
ZE628	Grob Viking T1 (BGA3070)	RAF No 626 VGS, Predannack	
ZE629	Grob Viking T1 (BGA3071)	RAF No 661 VGS, Kirknewton	
ZE630	Grob Viking T1 (BGA3072)	RAF No 662 VGS, Arbroath	
ZE631	Grob Viking T1 (BGA3073)	RAF No 662 VGS, Arbroath	
ZE632	Grob Viking T1 (BGA3074)	RAF No 618 VGS, West Malling	
ZE633	Grob Viking T1 (BGA3075)	RAF No 614 VGS, Wethersfield	
ZE634	Grob Viking T1 (BGA3076)	RAF CGMF, Syerston (wreck)	
ZE635	Grob Viking T1 (BGA3077)	RAF CGMF, Syerston	
ZE636	Grob Viking T1 (BGA3078)	RAF No 622 VGS, Upavon	
ZE637	Grob Viking T1 (BGA3079)	RAF CGMF, Syerston	
ZE650	Grob Viking T1 (BGA3080)	RAF No 662 VGS, Arbroath	
ZE651	Grob Viking T1 (BGA3081)	RAF No 625 VGS, Hullavington	
ZE652	Grob Viking T1 (BGA3082)	RAF No 614 VGS, Wethersfield	
ZE653	Grob Viking T1 (BGA3083)	RAF No 614 VGS, Wethersfield	
ZE654	Grob Viking T1 (BGA3084)	RAF No 614 VGS, Wethersfield	
ZE655	Grob Viking T1 (BGA3085)	RAF CGMF, Syerston	
ZE656	Grob Viking T1 (BGA3086)	RAF No 617 VGS, Manston	
ZE657	Grob Viking T1 (BGA3087)	RAF CGMF, Syerston	
ZE658	Grob Viking T1 (BGA3088)	RAF No 618 VGS, West Malling	
ZE659	Grob Viking T1 (BGA3089)	RAF No 611 VGS, Swanton Morley	
ZE677	Grob Viking T1 (BGA3090)	RAF CGMF, Syerston	
ZE678	Grob Viking T1 (BGA3091)	RAF No 621 VGS, Hullavington	
ZE679	Grob Viking T1 (BGA3092)	RAF No 631 VGS, Samlesbury	
ZE680	Grob Viking T1 (BGA3093)	RAF No 617 VGS, Manston	
ZE681	Grob Viking T1 (BGA3094)	RAF ACCGS, Syerston	
ZE682	Grob Viking T1 (BGA3095)	RAF No 611 VGS, Swanton Morley	
ZE683	Grob Viking T1 (BGA3096)	RAF No 621 VGS, Hullavington	
ZE684	Grob Viking T1 (BGA3097)	RAF No 618 VGS, West Malling	
ZE685	Grob Viking T1 (BGA3098)	RAF No 661 VGS, Kirknewton	
ZE686	Grob Viking T1 (BGA3099)	MoD(PE), Slingsby Kirkbymoorside	
ZE690	BAe Sea Harrier FRS2	MoD(PE)/BAe Brough (conversion)	
ZE691	BAe Sea Harrier FRS1	RN, St Athan	
ZE692	BAe Sea Harrier FRS1 [713]	RN No 801 Sqn, Yeovilton	
ZE693	BAe Sea Harrier FRS1 [127/N]	RN No 800 Sqn, Yeovilton	
ZE694	BAe Sea Harrier FRS1 [003/R]	RN No 801 Sqn, Yeovilton	
ZE695	BAe Sea Harrier FRS2 [711/OEU]	RN No 899 Sqn OEU, Yeovilton	
ZE696	BAe Sea Harrier FRS2	MoD(PE)/BAe Brough (conversion)	
ZE697	BAe Sea Harrier FRS2	RN No 899 Sqn OEU, Yeovilton	
ZE698	BAe Sea Harrier FRS2	MoD(PE)/BAe Dunsfold (conversion)	
ZE700	BAe 146 CC2	RAF Queen's Flight, Benson	
ZE701	BAe 146 CC2	RAF Queen's Flight, Benson	
ZE702	BAe 146 CC2	RAF Queen's Flight, Benson	
ZE704	Lockheed Tristar C2 (N508PA)	RAF No 216 Sqn, Brize Norton	
ZE705	Lockheed Tristar C2 (N509PA)	RAF No 216 Sqn, Brize Norton	

Notes	Serial	Type	Owner or Operator
	ZE706	Lockheed Tristar C2A (N503PA)	RAF No 216 Sqn, Brize Norton
	ZE728	Panavia Tornado F3T [AL]	RAF, stored St Athan
	ZE729	Panavia Tornado F3 (fuselage)	RAF, stored St Athan
	ZE730	Panavia Tornado F3 [GL]	RAF No 43 Sqn, Leuchars
	ZE731	Panavia Tornado F3 [GK]	RAF No 43 Sqn, Leuchars
	ZE732	Panavia Tornado F3 [GI]	RAF No 43 Sqn, Leuchars
	ZE733	Panavia Tornado F3 [GE]	RAF No 43 Sqn, Leuchars
	ZE734	Panavia Tornado F3 [CX]	RAF No 5 Sqn, Coningsby
	ZE735	Panavia Tornado F3T [AL]	RAF, stored Coningsby
	ZE736	Panavia Tornado F3 [HA]	RAF, stored St Athan
	ZE737	Panavia Tornado F3 [FF]	RAF No 25 Sqn, Leeming
	ZE755	Panavia Tornado F3 [GB]	RAF No 43 Sqn, Leuchars
	ZE756	Panavia Tornado F3	RAF F3 OEU, Coningsby
	ZE757	Panavia Tornado F3 [GA]	RAF No 43 Sqn, Leuchars
	ZE758	Panavia Tornado F3 [C]	RAF No 1435 Flt, Mount Pleasant, FI
	ZE759	Panavia Tornado F3T (fuselage)	RAF, stored St Athan
	ZE760	Panavia Tornado F3 [GP]	RAF No 43 Sqn, Leuchars
	ZE761	Panavia Tornado F3 [CB]	RAF No 5 Sqn, Coningsby
	ZE762	Panavia Tornado F3 [GM]	RAF No 43 Sqn, Leuchars
	ZE763	Panavia Tornado F3 [DG]	RAF No 11 Sqn, Leeming
	ZE764	Panavia Tornado F3 [DH]	RAF No 11 Sqn, Leeming
	ZE785	Panavia Tornado F3	RAF, stored St Athan
	ZE786	Panavia Tornado F3T (fuselage)	RAF, stored St Athan
	ZE787	Panavia Tornado F3 [HM]	RAF No 111 Sqn, Leuchars
	ZE788	Panavia Tornado F3 [DF]	RAF No 11 Sqn, Leeming
	ZE789	Panavia Tornado F3 (fuselage)	RAF, stored St Athan
	ZE790	Panavia Tornado F3 [D]	RAF No 1435 Flt, Mount Pleasant, FI
	ZE791	Panavia Tornado F3 [A9]	RAF F3 OCU/No 56(R) Sqn, Coningsby
	ZE792	Panavia Tornado F3 [HL]	RAF No 111 Sqn, Leuchars
	ZE793	Panavia Tornado F3T [AK]	RAF, stored St Athan
	ZE794	Panavia Tornado F3 [HQ]	RAF No 111 Sqn, Leuchars
	ZE808	Panavia Tornado F3 [FA]	RAF No 25 Sqn, Leeming
	ZE809	Panavia Tornado F3 [HP]	RAF No 111 Sqn, Leuchars
	ZE810	Panavia Tornado F3 [AT]	RAF F3 OCU/No 56(R) Sqn, Coningsby
	ZE811	Panavia Tornado F3 [HB]	RAF No 111 Sqn, Leuchars
	ZE812	Panavia Tornado F3 [F]	RAF No 1435 Flt, Mount Pleasant, FI
	ZE830	Panavia Tornado F3T [GD]	RAF No 43 Sqn, Leuchars
	ZE831	Panavia Tornado F3 [GG]	RAF No 43 Sqn, Leuchars
	ZE832	Panavia Tornado F3 [A7]	RAF F3 OCU/No 56(R) Sqn, Coningsby
	ZE834	Panavia Tornado F3	RAF, on repair Leeming
	ZE835	Panavia Tornado F3 [HK]	RAF No 111 Sqn, Leuchars
	ZE836	Panavia Tornado F3 [AS]	RAF F3 OCU/No 56(R) Sqn, Coningsby
	ZE837	Panavia Tornado F3T [HY]	RAF No 111 Sqn, Leuchars
	ZE838	Panavia Tornado F3 [GH]	RAF No 111 Squadron, Leuchars
	ZE839	Panavia Tornado F3 [AR]	RAF No 43 Sqn, Leuchars
	ZE858	Panavia Tornado F3 [GO]	RAF F3 OCU/No 56(R) Sqn, Coningsby
			Written off nr Barnard Castle, Durham, 22 October 1993
	ZE862	Panavia Tornado F3T	RAF F3 OEU, Coningsby
	ZE887	Panavia Tornado F3 [DJ]	RAF No 11 Sqn, Leeming
	ZE888	Panavia Tornado F3T [EV]	RAF No 23 Sqn, Leeming
	ZE889	Panavia Tornado F3	RAF F3 OEU, Coningsby
	ZE907	Panavia Tornado F3 [EN]	RAF No 23 Sqn, Leeming
	ZE908	Panavia Tornado F3T [FC]	RAF No 25 Sqn, Leeming
	ZE911	Panavia Tornado F3[BE]	RAF No 29 Sqn, Coningsby
	ZE934	Panavia Tornado F3T [DX]	RAF No 11 Sqn, Leeming
	ZE936	Panavia Tornado F3 [EE]	RAF No 23 Sqn, Leeming
	ZE941	Panavia Tornado F3T [FE]	RAF No 25 Sqn, Leeming
	ZE942	Panavia Tornado F3 [DK]	RAF No 11 Sqn, Leeming
	ZE961	Panavia Tornado F3 [FD]	RAF No 25 Sqn, Leeming
	ZE962	Panavia Tornado F3 [FJ]	RAF No 25 Sqn, Leeming
	ZE963	Panavia Tornado F3T [ET]	RAF No 23 Sqn, Leeming
	ZE964	Panavia Tornado F3T [DY]	RAF No 11 Sqn, Leeming
	ZE965	Panavia Tornado F3T [DW]	RAF No 11 Sqn, Leeming
	ZE966	Panavia Tornado F3T [DZ]	RAF No 11 Sqn, Leeming
	ZE967	Panavia Tornado F3T [EU]	RAF No 23 Sqn, Leeming
	ZE968	Panavia Tornado F3	RAF F3 OEU, Coningsby
	ZE969	Panavia Tornado F3 [EA]	RAF No 23 Sqn, Leeming
	ZE982	Panavia Tornado F3 [DM]	RAF No 11 Sqn, Leeming
	ZE983	Panavia Tornado F3 [EZ]	RAF No 23 Sqn, Leeming
	ZF115	WS61 Sea King HC4	MoD(PE), ETPS, Boscombe Down
	ZF116	WS61 Sea King HC4 [20]	RN No 772 Sqn, Portland
	ZF117	WS61 Sea King HC4 [VK]	RN No 846 Sqn, Yeovilton

Serial	Type	Owner or Operator	Notes
ZF118	WS61 Sea King HC4 [ZT]	RN No 707 Sqn, Yeovilton	
ZF119	WS61 Sea King HC4 [ZS]	RN No 707 Sqn, Yeovilton	
ZF120	WS61 Sea King HC4 [20]	RN, Fleetlands	
ZF121	WS61 Sea King HC4 [21]	RN No 772 Sqn, Portland	
ZF122	WS61 Sea King HC4 [22]	RN No 772 Sqn, Portland	
ZF123	WS61 Sea King HC4 [23/PO]	RN No 772 Sqn, Portland	
ZF124	WS61 Sea King HC4 [24]	RN No 772 Sqn, Portland	
ZF130	BAe 125-600B (G-BLUW)	MoD(PE), BAe Dunsfold	
ZF135	Shorts Tucano T1	RAF No 3 FTS, Cranwell	
ZF136	Shorts Tucano T1	RAF No 1 FTS, Linton-on-Ouse	
ZF137	Shorts Tucano T1	RAF No 1 FTS, Linton-on-Ouse	
ZF138	Shorts Tucano T1	RAF, stored Shawbury	
ZF139	Shorts Tucano T1	RAF No 3 FTS, Cranwell	
ZF140	Shorts Tucano T1	RAF No 3 FTS, Cranwell	
ZF141	Shorts Tucano T1	RAF No 3 FTS, Cranwell	
ZF142	Shorts Tucano T1	RAF, stored Shawbury	
ZF143	Shorts Tucano T1	RAF No 3 FTS, Cranwell	
ZF144	Shorts Tucano T1	RAF No 3 FTS, Cranwell	
ZF145	Shorts Tucano T1	RAF No 1 FTS, Linton-on-Ouse	
ZF160	Shorts Tucano T1	RAF No 3 FTS, Cranwell	
ZF161	Shorts Tucano T1	RAF No 6 FTS, Finningley	
ZF162	Shorts Tucano T1	RAF No 6 FTS, Finningley	
ZF163	Shorts Tucano T1	RAF No 1 FTS, Linton-on-Ouse	
ZF164	Shorts Tucano T1	RAF No 1 FTS, Linton-on-Ouse	
ZF165	Shorts Tucano T1	RAF No 3 FTS, Cranwell	
ZF166	Shorts Tucano T1	RAF CFS, Scampton	
ZF167	Shorts Tucano T1	RAF No 3 FTS, Cranwell	
ZF168	Shorts Tucano T1	RAF, stored Shawbury	
ZF169	Shorts Tucano T1	RAF CFS, Scampton	
ZF170	Shorts Tucano T1	RAF No 1 FTS, Linton-on-Ouse	
ZF171	Shorts Tucano T1	RAF No 3 FTS, Cranwell	
ZF172	Shorts Tucano T1	RAF CFS, Scampton	
ZF200	Shorts Tucano T1	RAF No 3 FTS, Cranwell	
ZF201	Shorts Tucano T1	RAF No 3 FTS, Cranwell	
ZF202	Shorts Tucano T1	RAF No 3 FTS, Cranwell	
ZF203	Shorts Tucano T1	RAF CFS, Scampton	
ZF204	Shorts Tucano T1	RAF CFS, Scampton	
ZF205	Shorts Tucano T1	RAF CFS, Scampton	
ZF206	Shorts Tucano T1	RAF CFS, Scampton	
ZF207	Shorts Tucano T1	RAF No 3 FTS, Cranwell	
ZF208	Shorts Tucano T1	RAF No 1 FTS, Linton-on-Ouse	
ZF209	Shorts Tucano T1	RAF CFS, Scampton	
ZF210	Shorts Tucano T1	RAF No 3 FTS, Cranwell	
ZF211	Shorts Tucano T1	RAF No 1 FTS, Linton-on-Ouse	
ZF212	Shorts Tucano T1	RAF No 3 FTS, Cranwell	
ZF238	Shorts Tucano T1	RAF No 1 FTS, Linton-on-Ouse	
ZF239	Shorts Tucano T1	RAF No 3 FTS, Cranwell	
ZF240	Shorts Tucano T1	RAF No 3 FTS, Cranwell	
ZF241	Shorts Tucano T1	RAF No 3 FTS, Cranwell	
ZF242	Shorts Tucano T1	RAF No 6 FTS, Finningley	
ZF243	Shorts Tucano T1	RAF No 1 FTS, Linton-on-Ouse	
ZF244	Shorts Tucano T1	RAF No 1 FTS, Linton-on-Ouse	
ZF245	Shorts Tucano T1	RAF CFS, Scampton	
ZF263	Shorts Tucano T1	RAF No 3 FTS, Cranwell	
ZF264	Shorts Tucano T1	RAF No 3 FTS, Cranwell	
ZF265	Shorts Tucano T1	RAF CFS, Scampton	
ZF266	Shorts Tucano T1	RAF CFS, Scampton	
ZF267	Shorts Tucano T1	RAF No 3 FTS, Cranwell	
ZF268	Shorts Tucano T1	RAF CFS, Scampton	
ZF269	Shorts Tucano T1	RAF CFS, Scampton	
ZF270	Shorts Tucano T1	RAF No 3 FTS, Cranwell	
ZF284	Shorts Tucano T1	RAF No 3 FTS, Cranwell	
ZF285	Shorts Tucano T1	RAF No 3 FTS, Cranwell	
ZF286	Shorts Tucano T1	RAF CFS, Scampton	
ZF287	Shorts Tucano T1	RAF No 3 FTS, Cranwell	
ZF288	Shorts Tucano T1	RAF No 6 FTS, Finningley	
ZF289	Shorts Tucano T1	RAF No 3 FTS, Cranwell	
ZF290	Shorts Tucano T1	RAF No 6 FTS, Finningley	
ZF291	Shorts Tucano T1	RAF No 3 FTS, Cranwell	
ZF292	Shorts Tucano T1	RAF No 3 FTS, Cranwell	
ZF293	Shorts Tucano T1	RAF No 1 FTS, Linton-on-Ouse	
ZF294	Shorts Tucano T1	RAF No 3 FTS, Cranwell	
ZF295	Shorts Tucano T1	RAF No 3 FTS, Cranwell	

Notes	Serial	Type	Owner or Operator
	ZF315	Shorts Tucano T1	RAF No 1 FTS, Linton-on-Ouse
	ZF317	Shorts Tucano T1	RAF No 1 FTS, Linton-on-Ouse
	ZF318	Shorts Tucano T1	RAF CFS, Scampton
	ZF319	Shorts Tucano T1	RAF No 3 FTS, Cranwell
	ZF320	Shorts Tucano T1	RAF No 1 FTS, Linton-on-Ouse
	ZF338	Shorts Tucano T1	RAF No 3 FTS, Cranwell
	ZF339	Shorts Tucano T1	RAF No 3 FTS, Cranwell
	ZF340	Shorts Tucano T1	RAF No 3 FTS, Cranwell
	ZF341	Shorts Tucano T1	RAF No 3 FTS, Cranwell
	ZF342	Shorts Tucano T1	RAF No 3 FTS, Cranwell
	ZF343	Shorts Tucano T1	RAF CFS, Scampton
	ZF344	Shorts Tucano T1	RAF No 1 FTS, Linton-on-Ouse
	ZF345	Shorts Tucano T1	RAF CFS, Scampton
	ZF346	Shorts Tucano T1	RAF No 1 FTS, Linton-on-Ouse
	ZF347	Shorts Tucano T1	RAF No 3 FTS, Cranwell
	ZF348	Shorts Tucano T1	RAF No 3 FTS, Cranwell
	ZF349	Shorts Tucano T1	RAF No 3 FTS, Cranwell
	ZF350	Shorts Tucano T1	RAF No 3 FTS, Cranwell
	ZF372	Shorts Tucano T1	RAF CFS, Scampton
	ZF373	Shorts Tucano T1	RAF No 3 FTS, Cranwell
	ZF374	Shorts Tucano T1	RAF No 3 FTS, Cranwell
	ZF375	Shorts Tucano T1	RAF No 3 FTS, Cranwell
	ZF376	Shorts Tucano T1	RAF No 1 FTS, Linton-on-Ouse
	ZF377	Shorts Tucano T1	RAF No 3 FTS, Cranwell
	ZF378	Shorts Tucano T1	RAF CFS, Scampton
	ZF379	Shorts Tucano T1	RAF No 1 FTS, Linton-on-Ouse
	ZF380	Shorts Tucano T1	RAF CFS, Scampton
	ZF405	Shorts Tucano T1	RAF No 6 FTS, Finningley
	ZF406	Shorts Tucano T1	RAF CFS, Scampton
	ZF407	Shorts Tucano T1	RAF No 1 FTS, Linton-on-Ouse
	ZF408	Shorts Tucano T1	RAF No 1 FTS, Linton-on-Ouse
	ZF409	Shorts Tucano T1	RAF No 3 FTS, Cranwell
	ZF410	Shorts Tucano T1	RAF No 1 FTS, Linton-on-Ouse
	ZF411	Shorts Tucano T1	RAF No 1 FTS, Linton-on-Ouse
	ZF412	Shorts Tucano T1	RAF No 1 FTS, Linton-on-Ouse
	ZF413	Shorts Tucano T1	RAF No 6 FTS, Finningley
	ZF414	Shorts Tucano T1	RAF No 3 FTS, Cranwell
	ZF415	Shorts Tucano T1	RAF No 3 FTS, Cranwell
	ZF416	Shorts Tucano T1	RAF No 1 FTS, Linton-on-Ouse
	ZF417	Shorts Tucano T1	RAF, stored Shawbury
	ZF418	Shorts Tucano T1	RAF No 6 FTS, Finningley
	ZF444	PBN 2T Islander (G-WOTG)	*Marks not taken up - painted as G-WOTG*
	ZF445	Shorts Tucano T1	RAF No 6 FTS, Finningley
	ZF446	Shorts Tucano T1	RAF No 6 FTS, Finningley
	ZF447	Shorts Tucano T1	RAF No 3 FTS, Cranwell
	ZF448	Shorts Tucano T1	RAF No 6 FTS, Finningley
	ZF449	Shorts Tucano T1	RAF No 1 FTS, Linton-on-Ouse
	ZF450	Shorts Tucano T1	RAF No 1 FTS, Linton-on-Ouse
	ZF483	Shorts Tucano T1	RAF No 1 FTS, Linton-on-Ouse
	ZF484	Shorts Tucano T1	RAF No 1 FTS, Linton-on-Ouse
	ZF485	Shorts Tucano T1 (G-BULU)	RAF No 3 FTS, Cranwell
	ZF486	Shorts Tucano T1	RAF No 1 FTS, Linton-on-Ouse
	ZF487	Shorts Tucano T1	RAF No 1 FTS, Linton-on-Ouse
	ZF488	Shorts Tucano T1	RAF No 1 FTS, Linton-on-Ouse
	ZF489	Shorts Tucano T1	RAF No 3 FTS, Cranwell
	ZF490	Shorts Tucano T1	RAF No 1 FTS, Linton-on-Ouse
	ZF491	Shorts Tucano T1	RAF No 1 FTS, Linton-on-Ouse
	ZF492	Shorts Tucano T1	RAF No 1 FTS, Linton-on-Ouse
	ZF510	Shorts Tucano T1	MoD(PE) ETPS, Boscombe Down
	ZF511	Shorts Tucano T1	MoD(PE) ETPS, Boscombe Down
	ZF512	Shorts Tucano T1	RAF No 3 FTS, Cranwell
	ZF513	Shorts Tucano T1	RAF No 1 FTS, Linton-on-Ouse
	ZF514	Shorts Tucano T1	RAF No 3 FTS, Cranwell
	ZF515	Shorts Tucano T1	RAF No 3 FTS, Cranwell
	ZF516	Shorts Tucano T1	RAF No 3 FTS, Cranwell
	ZF520	Piper PA-31 Navajo Chieftain 350 (N35823/G-BLZK)	MoD(PE), A&AEE Boscombe Down
	ZF521	Piper PA-31 Navajo Chieftain 350 (N27509)	MoD(PE), T&EE Llanbedr
	ZF522	Piper PA-31 Navajo Chieftain 350 (N4261A/G-RNAV/N27728)	MoD(PE), A&AEE Boscombe Down
	ZF534	BAe EAP	MoD(PE), stored BAe Warton
	ZF537	WS Lynx AH9	MoD(PE)/Westland, Yeovil (conversion)

Serial	Type	Owner or Operator	Notes
ZF538	WS Lynx AH9 [1]	AAC No 653 Sqn, Wattisham	
ZF539	WS Lynx AH9 [5]	AAC No 659 Sqn, Detmold	
ZF540	WS Lynx AH9	MoD(PE)/Westland, Yeovil (conversion)	
ZF557	WS Lynx HAS3CTS [670]	RN No 815 Sqn OEU, Portland	
ZF558	WS Lynx HAS3CTS [672]	RN No 815 Sqn OEU, Portland	
ZF560	WS Lynx HAS8 [323]	MoD(PE)/Westland, Yeovil (conversion)	
ZF562	WS Lynx HAS3CTS	RN AMG, Portland	
ZF563	WS Lynx HAS3CTS [671]	RN No 815 Sqn OEU, Portland	
ZF573	PBN 2T Islander CC2A (G-SRAY)	RAF Northolt Station Flight	
ZF578	BAC Lightning F53 (670)	Wales Aircraft Museum, Cardiff Airport	
ZF580	BAC Lightning F53 (672)	BAe Samlesbury, at main gate	
ZF583	BAC Lightning F53 (681)	Solway Aviation Society, Carlisle	
ZF584	BAC Lightning F53 (682)	Ferranti Ltd, South Gyle, Edinburgh	
ZF588	BAC Lightning F53 (693)	East Midlands Airport Aero Park	
ZF594	BAC Lightning F53 (696)	North-East Aircraft Museum, Usworth	
ZF598	BAC Lightning T55 (713)	Midland Air Museum, Coventry	
ZF622	Piper PA-31 Navajo Chieftain 350	MoD(PE), A&AEE Boscombe Down	
ZF641	WS/Agusta EH-101 [PP1]	MoD(PE)/Westland, Yeovil	
ZF644	WS/Agusta EH-101 [PP4]	MoD(PE)/Westland, Yeovil	
ZF649	WS/Agusta EH-101 Merlin [PP5]	MoD(PE)/Westland, Yeovil	
ZG101	WS/Agusta EH-101 (mock-up) [GB]	Westland/Agusta, Yeovil	
ZG468	WS70 Blackhawk	Westland Helicopters, Yeovil	
ZG471	BAe Harrier GR7 [AB]	RAF No 3 Sqn, Laarbruch	
ZG472	BAe Harrier GR7 [O]	RAF SAOEU, Boscombe Down	
ZG474	BAe Harrier GR7 [WL]	RAF No 4 Sqn, Laarbruch	
ZG475	BAe Harrier GR7 [U]	RAF SAOEU, Boscombe Down	
ZG476	BAe Harrier GR7 [WT]	RAF No 4 Sqn, Incirlik	
ZG477	BAe Harrier GR7 [WI]	RAF No 4 Sqn, Incirlik	
ZG478	BAe Harrier GR7 [WY]	RAF No 4 Sqn, Incirlik	
ZG479	BAe Harrier GR7 [AI]	RAF No 3 Sqn, Laarbruch	
ZG480	BAe Harrier GR7 [WZ]	RAF No 4 Sqn, Incirlik	
ZG500	BAe Harrier GR7 [WV]	RAF No 4 Sqn, Laarbruch	
ZG501	BAe Harrier GR7 [E]	RAF SAOEU, Boscombe Down	
ZG502	BAe Harrier GR7 [WF]	RAF No 3 Sqn, Incirlik	
ZG503	BAe Harrier GR7 [AG]	RAF No 3 Sqn, Laarbruch	
ZG504	BAe Harrier GR7 [WG]	RAF No 3 Sqn, Incirlik	
ZG505	BAe Harrier GR7 [WJ]	RAF No 3 Sqn, Incirlik	
ZG506	BAe Harrier GR7 [CM]	RAF No 3 Sqn, Laarbruch	
ZG507	BAe Harrier GR7 [CA]	RAF No 4 Sqn, Laarbruch	
ZG508	Bae Harrier GR7 [CG]	RAF No 4 Sqn, Laarbruch	
ZG509	BAe Harrier GR7 [CH]	RAF No 3 Sqn, Laarbruch	
ZG510	BAe Harrier GR7 [AE]	RAF No 3 Sqn, Laarbruch	
ZG511	BAe Harrier GR7 [AL]	RAF No 3 Sqn, Laarbruch	
ZG512	BAe Harrier GR7 [CI]	RAF No 4 Sqn, Laarbruch	
ZG530	BAe Harrier GR7 [CL]	RAF No 4 Sqn, Laarbruch	
ZG531	BAe Harrier GR7 [CN]	RAF No 4 Sqn, Laarbruch	
ZG532	BAe Harrier GR7 [CC]	RAF No 4 Sqn, Laarbruch	
ZG533	BAe Harrier GR7 [CF]	RAF No 4 Sqn, Laarbruch	
ZG705	Panavia Tornado GR1A [A]	RAF No 13 Sqn, Marham	
ZG706	Panavia Tornado GR1A [E]	RAF SAOEU, Boscombe Down	
ZG707	Panavia Tornado GR1A [B]	RAF No 13 Sqn, Marham	
ZG708	Panavia Tornado GR1A [C]	RAF No 13 Sqn, Marham	
ZG709	Panavia Tornado GR1A [I]	RAF No 13 Sqn, Marham	
ZG710	Panavia Tornado GR1A [D]	RAF No 13 Sqn, Marham	
ZG711	Panavia Tornado GR1A [E]	RAF No 13 Sqn, Marham	
ZG712	Panavia Tornado GR1A [F]	RAF No 13 Sqn, Marham	
ZG713	Panavia Tornado GR1A [G]	RAF No 13 Sqn, Marham	
ZG714	Panavia Tornado GR1A [H]	RAF No 13 Sqn, Marham	
ZG725	Panavia Tornado GR1A [J]	RAF No 13 Sqn, Marham	
ZG726	Panavia Tornado GR1A [K[	RAF No 13 Sqn, Marham	
ZG727	Panavia Tornado GR1A [L]	RAF No 13 Sqn, Marham	
ZG728	Panavia Tornado F3 [CI]	RAF No 5 Sqn, Coningsby	
ZG729	Panavia Tornado GR1A [M]	RAF No 13 Sqn, Marham	
ZG730	Panavia Tornado F3 [CC]	RAF No 5 Sqn, Coningsby	
ZG731	Panavia Tornado F3 [CG]	RAF No 5 Sqn, Coningsby	
ZG732	Panavia Tornado F3 [BC]	RAF No 29 Sqn, Coningsby	
ZG733	Panavia Tornado F3 [BK]	RAF No 29 Sqn, Coningsby	
ZG734	Panavia Tornado F3 [BA]	RAF No 29 Sqn, Coningsby	
ZG735	Panavia Tornado F3 [CO]	RAF No 5 Sqn, Coningsby	
ZG750	Panavia Tornado GR1T [Y]	RAF No 13 Sqn, Marham	
ZG751	Panavia Tornado F3 [CW]	RAF No 5 Sqn, Coningsby	

Notes	Serial	Type	Owner or Operator
	ZG752	Panavia Tornado GR1T [Z]	RAF No 13 Sqn, Marham
	ZG753	Panavia Tornado F3 [CH]	RAF No 5 Sqn, Coningsby
	ZG754	Panavia Tornado GR1T [AW]	RAF No 9 Sqn, Bruggen
	ZG755	Panavia Tornado F3 [BD]	RAF No 29 Sqn, Coningsby
	ZG756	Panavia Tornado F3 [AX]	RAF No 9 Sqn, Bruggen
	ZG757	Panavia Tornado F3 [CA]	RAF No 5 Sqn, Coningsby
	ZG768	Panavia Tornado F3 [AX]	RAF F3 OCU/No 56(R) Sqn, Coningsby
	ZG769	Panavia Tornado GR1T [AY]	RAF No 9 Sqn, Bruggen
	ZG770	Panavia Tornado F3 [AP]	RAF F3 OCU/No 56(R) Sqn, Coningsby
	ZG771	Panavia Tornado GR1T [DW]	RAF No 31 Sqn, Bruggen
	ZG772	Panavia Tornado F3 [CN]	RAF No 5 Sqn, Coningsby
	ZG773	Panavia Tornado GR4	MoD(PE), BAe Warton (conversion)
	ZG774	Panavia Tornado F3 [A4]	RAF F3 OCU/No 56(R) Sqn, Coningsby
	ZG775	Panavia Tornado GR1 [CC]	RAF No 17 Sqn, Bruggen
	ZG776	Panavia Tornado F3 [BD]	RAF No 29 Sqn, Coningsby
	ZG777	Panavia Tornado GR1 [CK]	RAF No 17 Sqn, Bruggen
	ZG778	Panavia Tornado F3 [BG]	RAF No 29 Sqn
	ZG779	Panavia Tornado GR1 [CM]	RAF No 17 Sqn, Bruggen
	ZG780	Panavia Tornado F3 [BH]	RAF No 29 Sqn, Coningsby
	ZG791	Panavia Tornado GR1 [DC]	RAF No 31 Sqn, Bruggen
	ZG792	Panavia Tornado GR1 [BH]	RAF No 14 Sqn, Bruggen
	ZG793	Panavia Tornado F3 [CY]	RAF No 5 Sqn, Coningsby
	ZG794	Panavia Tornado GR1 [DJ]	RAF No 31 Sqn, Bruggen
	ZG795	Panavia Tornado F3 [AY]	RAF F3 OCU/No 56(R) Sqn, Coningsby
	ZG796	Panavia Tornado F3 [AV]	RAF F3 OCU/No 56(R) Sqn, Coningsby
	ZG797	Panavia Tornado F3 [BF]	RAF No 29 Sqn, Coningsby
	ZG798	Panavia Tornado F3 [CD]	RAF No 5 Sqn, Coningsby
	ZG799	Panavia Tornado F3 [AQ]	RAF F3 OCU/No 56(R) Sqn, Coningsby
	ZG816	WS61 Sea King HAS6 [708/PW]	RN No 819 Sqn, Prestwick
	ZG817	WS61 Sea King HAS6 [504]	RN No 810 Sqn, Culdrose
	ZG818	WS61 Sea King HAS6 [271/N]	RN No 814 Sqn, Culdrose
	ZG819	WS61 Sea King HAS6 [018/R]	RN AMG, Culdrose
	ZG820	WS61 Sea King HC4 [F]	RN No 845 Sqn, Yeovilton
	ZG821	WS61 Sea King HC4 [D]	RN No 845 Sqn, Yeovilton
	ZG822	WS61 Sea King HC4 [VN]	RN No 846 Sqn, Yeovilton
	ZG844	PBN 2T Islander AL1 (G-BLNE)	AAC No 1 Flt, Aldergrove
	ZG845	PBN 2T Islander AL1 (G-BLNT)	AAC Islander Training Flt, Middle Wallop
	ZG846	PBN 2T Islander AL1 (G-BLNU)	AAC No 1 Flt, Aldergrove
	ZG847	PBN 2T Islander AL1 (G-BLNV)	AAC No 1 Flt, Aldergrove
	ZG848	PBN 2T Islander AL1 (G-BLNY)	AAC No 1 Flt, Aldergrove
	ZG856	Bae Harrier GR7 [CJ]	RAF No 4 Sqn, Laarbruch
	ZG857	Bae Harrier GR7 [AH]	RAF No 3 Sqn, Laarbruch
	ZG858	Bae Harrier GR7 [CB]	RAF No 3 Sqn, Laarbruch
	ZG859	Bae Harrier GR7 [P]	RAF HOCU/No 20(R) Sqn, Wittering
	ZG860	Bae Harrier GR7 [T]	RAF SAOEU, Boscombe Down
	ZG861	Bae Harrier GR7 [AA]	RAF No 3 Sqn, Laarbruch
	ZG862	BAe Harrier GR7 [CO]	RAF No 4 Sqn, Laarbruch
	ZG875	WS61 Sea King HAS6 [014]	RN AMG, Culdrose
	ZG879	Powerchute Raider Mk 1	MoD(PE)/Powerchute, Hereford
	ZG884	WS Lynx AH9	MoD(PE), A&AEE Boscombe Down
	ZG885	WS Lynx AH9 [2]	AAC No 659 Sqn, Detmold
	ZG886	WS Lynx AH9 [3]	AAC No 653 Sqn, Wattisham
	ZG887	WS Lynx AH9 [4]	AAC No 659 Sqn, Detmold
	ZG888	WS Lynx AH9 [5]	AAC No 653 Sqn, Wattisham
	ZG889	WS Lynx AH9 [6]	AAC No 653 Sqn, Wattisham
	ZG914	WS Lynx AH9 [6]	AAC No 659 Sqn, Detmold
	ZG915	WS Lynx AH9 [7]	AAC No 659 Sqn, Detmold
	ZG916	WS Lynx AH9 [8]	AAC No 659 Sqn, Detmold
	ZG917	WS Lynx AH9 [J]	AAC No 659 Sqn, Detmold
	ZG918	WS Lynx AH9 [10]	AAC No 659 Sqn, Detmold
	ZG919	WS Lynx AH9 [7]	AAC No 653 Sqn, Wattisham
	ZG920	WS Lynx AH9 [8]	AAC No 653 Sqn, Wattisham
	ZG921	WS Lynx AH9 [11]	AAC No 659 Sqn, Detmold
	ZG922	WS Lynx AH9 [9]	AAC No 653 Sqn, Wattisham
	ZG923	WS Lynx AH9 [10]	AAC No 653 Sqn, Wattisham
	ZG969	Pilatus PC-9 (HB-HQE)	BAe Brough
	ZG989	PBN 2T Islander Astor (G-BJYU/ G-DLRA)	MoD(PE), A&AEE Boscombe Down
	ZG993	PBN 2T Islander AL1 (G-BOMD)	AAC Islander Flight, Middle Wallop
	ZG994	PBN 2T Islander AL1 (G-BPLN)	AAC No 1 Flight, Aldergrove
	ZH101	Boeing E-3D Sentry AEW1	RAF No 8 Sqn, Waddington
	ZH102	Boeing E-3D Sentry AEW1	RAF No 8 Sqn, Waddington

Serial	Type	Owner or Operator	Notes
ZH103	Boeing E-3D Sentry AEW1	RAF No 8 Sqn, Waddington	
ZH104	Boeing E-3D Sentry AEW1	RAF No 8 Sqn, Waddington	
ZH105	Boeing E-3D Sentry AEW1	RAF No 8 Sqn, Waddington	
ZH106	Boeing E-3D Sentry AEW1	RAF No 8 Sqn, Waddington	
ZH107	Boeing E-3D Sentry AEW1	RAF No 8 Sqn, Waddington	
ZH115	Grob Vigilant T1	RAF No 635 VGS, Samlesbury	
ZH116	Grob Vigilant T1	RAF, stored Shawbury	
ZH117	Grob Vigilant T1	RAF CGMF, Syerston	
ZH118	Grob Vigilant T1	RAF ACCGS, Syerston	
ZH119	Grob Vigilant T1	RAF ACCGS, Syerston	
ZH120	Grob Vigilant T1	RAF No 616 VGS, Henlow	
ZH121	Grob Vigilant T1	RAF No 612 VGS, Halton	
ZH122	Grob Vigilant T1	RAF No 616 VGS, Henlow	
ZH123	Grob Vigilant T1	RAF No 624 VGS, Chivenor	
ZH124	Grob Vigilant T1	RAF No 642 VGS, Linton-on-Ouse	
ZH125	Grob Vigilant T1	RAF No 633 VGS, Cosford	
ZH126	Grob Vigilant T1	RAF No 642 VGS, Linton-on-Ouse	
ZH127	Grob Vigilant T1	RAF No 612 VGS, Halton	
ZH128	Grob Vigilant T1	RAF CGMF, Syerston	
ZH129	Grob Vigilant T1	RAF No 616 VGS, Henlow	
ZH144	Grob Vigilant T1	RAF No 616 VGS, Henlow	
ZH145	Grob Vigilant T1	RAF, stored Shawbury	
ZH146	Grob Vigilant T1	RAF No 637 VGS, Little Rissington	
ZH147	Grob Vigilant T1	RAF No 637 VGS, Little Rissington	
ZH148	Grob Vigilant T1	RAF No 637 VGS, Little Rissington	
ZH184	Grob Vigilant T1	RAF ACCGS, Syerston	
ZH185	Grob Vigilant T1	RAF, stored Shawbury	
ZH186	Grob Vigilant T1	RAF No 633 VGS, Cosford	
ZH187	Grob Vigilant T1	RAF No 663 VGS, Kinloss	
ZH188	Grob Vigilant T1	RAF ACCGS, Syerston	
ZH189	Grob Vigilant T1	RAF CGMF, Syerston	
ZH190	Grob Vigilant T1	RAF ACCGS, Syerston	
ZH191	Grob Vigilant T1	RAF No 635 VGS, Samlesbury	
ZH192	Grob Vigilant T1	RAF No 663 VGS, Kinloss	
ZH193	Grob Vigilant T1	RAF No 663 VGS, Kinloss	
ZH194	Grob Vigilant T1	RAF No 612 VGS, Halton	
ZH195	Grob Vigilant T1	RAF ACCGS, Syerston	
ZH196	Grob Vigilant T1	RAF No 633 VGS, Cosford	
ZH197	Grob Vigilant T1	RAF No 642 VGS, Linton-on-Ouse	
ZH200	BAe Hawk 200	MoD(PE), BAe Warton	
ZH205	Grob Vigilant T1	RAF No 624 VGS, Chivenor	
ZH206	Grob Vigilant T1	RAF No 642 VGS, Linton-on-Ouse	
ZH207	Grob Vigilant T1	RAF, stored Shawbury	
ZH208	Grob Vigilant T1	RAF No 642 VGS, Linton-on-Ouse	
ZH209	Grob Vigilant T1	RAF No 613 VGS, Halton	
ZH210	Grob Vigilant T1 (wreck)	RAF CGMF Syerston	
ZH211	Grob Vigilant T1	RAF No 663 VGS, Kinloss	
ZH247	Grob Vigilant T1	RAF No 635 VGS, Samlesbury	
ZH248	Grob Vigilant T1	RAF CGMF, Syerston	
ZH249	Grob Vigilant T1	RAF No 616 VGS, Henlow	
ZH257	B-V CH-47C Chinook (AE-520)	RAF, stored Fleetlands	
ZH263	Grob Vigilant T1	RAF No 637 VGS, Little Rissington	
ZH264	Grob Vigilant T1	RAF No 642 VGS, Linton-on-Ouse	
ZH265	Grob Vigilant T1	RAF No 633 VGS, Cosford	
ZH266	Grob Vigilant T1	RAF No 633 VGS, Cosford	
ZH267	Grob Vigilant T1	RAF No 635 VGS, Samlesbury	
ZH268	Grob Vigilant T1	RAF No 613 VGS, Halton	
ZH269	Grob Vigilant T1	RAF No 624 VGS, Chivenor	
ZH270	Grob Vigilant T1	RAF ACCGS, Syerston	
ZH271	Grob Vigilant T1	RAF No 642 VGS, Linton-on-Ouse	
ZH272	Grob Vigilant T1	Fatigue test airframe, Grob, Germany	
ZH506	Shorts Tucano T52 (KAF 101)	Shorts, Belfast	
ZH507	Shorts Tucano T52 (KAF 102)	Shorts, Belfast	
ZH508	Shorts Tucano T52 (KAF 103)	Shorts, Belfast	
ZH509	Shorts Tucano T52 (KAF 104)	Shorts, Belfast	
ZH510	Shorts Tucano T52 (KAF 105)	Shorts, Belfast	
ZH511	Shorts Tucano T52 (KAF 106)	Shorts, Belfast	
ZH512	Shorts Tucano T52 (KAF 107)	Shorts, stored Shawbury	
ZH513	Shorts Tucano T52 (KAF 108)	Shorts, stored Shawbury	
ZH526	Shorts Tucano T52 (KAF 109)	Shorts, stored Shawbury	
ZH527	Shorts Tucano T52 (KAF 110)	Shorts, stored Shawbury	
ZH528	Shorts Tucano T52 (KAF 111)	Shorts, stored Shawbury	
ZH529	Shorts Tucano T52 (KAF 112)	Shorts, stored Shawbury	

Notes	Serial	Type	Owner or Operator
	ZH530	Shorts Tucano T52 (KAF 113)	Shorts, Belfast
	ZH531	Shorts Tucano T52 (KAF 114)	Shorts, stored Shawbury
	ZH532	Shorts Tucano T52 (KAF 115)	Shorts, stored Shawbury
	ZH533	Shorts Tucano T52 (KAF 116)	Shorts, stored Shawbury
	ZH536	PBN 2T Islander CC2 (G-BSAH)	RAF Northolt Station Flight
	ZH552	Panavia Tornado F3T [AZ]	RAF F3 OCU/No 56(R) Sqn, Coninsgby
	ZH553	Panavia Tornado F3T [BY]	RAF No 29 Sqn, Coningsby
	ZH554	Panavia Tornado F3T [GJ]	RAF No 43 Sqn, Leuchars
	ZH555	Panavia Tornado F3T [CV]	RAF No 5 Sqn, Coningsby
	ZH556	Panavia Tornado F3T [AK]	RAF F3 OCU/No 56(R) Sqn, Coningsby
	ZH557	Panavia Tornado F3T [AB]	RAF F3 OCU/No 56(R) Sqn, Coningsby
	ZH558	*Eurofighter 2000 Replica*	*Badly damaged, Dubai, Nov 93*
	ZH558	Panavia Tornado F3T [GF]	RAF No 43 Sqn, Leuchars
	ZH559	Panavia Tornado F3T [AO]	RAF F3 OCU/No 56(R) Sqn, Coningsby
	ZH563	DH115 Vampire T55 (U-1216)	Privately owned, Boscombe Down
	ZH573	BAe Hawk 60A	*To Zimbabwe AF as 611, 1 Sept 92*
	ZH574	BAe Hawk 60A	*To Zimbabwe AF as 612, 1 Sept 92*
	ZH580	WS Lynx Mk 95 (ZF559)	*To Portuguese Navy as 9201, 1992*
	ZH581	WS Lynx Mk 95 (ZF561)	*To Portuguese Navy as 9202, 1993*
	ZH582	WS Lynx Mk 95	For Portuguese Navy as 9203
	ZH583	WS Lynx Mk 95	For Portuguese Navy as 9204
	ZH584	WS Lynx Mk 95	For Portuguese Navy as 9205
	ZH586	Eurofighter 2000 (DA1/98+29)	BAe Warton
	ZH588	Eurofighter 2000 (DA2)	MoD(PE), BAe Warton
	ZH590	Eurofighter 2000 (DA4)	MoD(PE), BAe Warton
	ZH629	BAe Hawk 102	For Abu Dhabi AF as 1059
	ZH634	BAe Hawk 102	For Abu Dhabi AF as 1060
	ZH635	BAe Hawk 102	For Abu Dhabi AF as 1061
	ZH636	BAe Hawk 102	For Abu Dhabi AF as 1062
	ZH637	BAe Hawk 102	For Abu Dhabi AF as 1063
	ZH638	BAe Hawk 102	For Abu Dhabi AF as 1064
	ZH639	BAe Hawk 102	For Abu Dhabi AF as 1065
	ZH640	BAe Hawk 102	For Abu Dhabi AF as 1066
	ZH641	BAe Hawk 102	For Abu Dhabi AF as 1067
	ZH642	BAe Hawk 102	For Abu Dhabi AF as 1068
	ZH647	WS/Agusta EH-101 (G-EHIL)	MoD(PE)/Westland, Yeovil
	ZH653	BAe Harrier T10	BAe, for RAF
	ZH654	BAe Harrier T10	BAe, for RAF
	ZH655	BAe Harrier T10	BAe, for RAF
	ZH656	BAe Harrier T10	BAe, for RAF
	ZH657	BAe Harrier T10	BAe, for RAF
	ZH658	BAe Harrier T10	BAe, for RAF
	ZH659	BAe Harrier T10	BAe, for RAF
	ZH660	BAe Harrier T10	BAe, for RAF
	ZH661	BAe Harrier T10	BAe, for RAF
	ZH662	BAe Harrier T10	BAe, for RAF
	ZH663	BAe Harrier T10	BAe, for RAF
	ZH664	BAe Harrier T10	BAe, for RAF
	ZH665	BAe Harrier T10	BAe, for RAF
	ZH669	BAe Hawk 103	*To RAF of Oman as 101*
	ZH670	BAe Hawk 103	*To RAF of Oman as 102*
	ZH671	BAe Hawk 103	*To RAF of Oman as 103*
	ZH672	BAe Hawk 103	*To RAF of Oman as 104*
	ZH675	BAe Hawk 51A	*To Finnish AF as HW-351*
	ZH699	BAe Hawk 51A	*To Finnish AF as HW-352*
	ZH700	BAe Hawk 51A	For Finnish AF as HW-353
	ZH701	BAe Hawk 51A	For Finnish AF as HW-354
	ZH702	BAe Hawk 51A	For Finnish AF as HW-355
	ZH703	BAe Hawk 51A	For Finnish AF as HW-356
	ZH704	BAe Hawk 51A	For Finnish AF as HW-357
	ZH710	BAe Hawk 203	For RAF of Oman as 121
	ZH711	BAe Hawk 203	For RAF of Oman as 122
	ZH712	BAe Hawk 203	For RAF of Oman as 123
	ZH713	BAe Hawk 203	For RAF of Oman as 124
	ZH714	BAe Hawk 203	For RAF of Oman as 125
	ZH719	BAe Hawk 203	For RAF of Oman as 126
	ZH720	BAe Hawk 203	For RAF of Oman as 127
	ZH721	BAe Hawk 203	For RAF of Oman as 128
	ZH722	BAe Hawk 203	For RAF of Oman as 129
	ZH729	BAe Hawk 203	For RAF of Oman as 130
	ZH730	BAe Hawk 203	For RAF of Oman as 131
	ZH731	BAe Hawk 203	For RAF of Oman as 132
	ZH735	BAe Hawk 108	For Malaysian AF

Serial	Type	Owner or Operator	Notes
ZH738	BAe Hawk 108	For Malaysian AF	
ZH745	BAe Hawk 108	For Malaysian AF	
ZH746	BAe Hawk 108	For Malaysian AF	
ZH747	BAe Hawk 108	For Malaysian AF	
ZH748	BAe Hawk 108	For Malaysian AF	
ZH752	BAe Hawk 108	For Malaysian AF	
ZH753	BAe Hawk 108	For Malaysian AF	
ZH754	BAe Hawk 108	For Malaysian AF	
ZH757	BAe Hawk 108	For Malaysian AF	
ZJ100	BAe Hawk 102D	BAe Warton	
ZJ201	BAe Hawk 200RDA	BAe Warton	

Tornado F3 ZE907 of No 23 Sqn in the sun at RAF Akrotiri. *PRM*

Wearing its grey paint scheme for operations over Northern Iraq — Harrier GR7 ZD461 of No 1 Sqn based at Wittering. *Phil Boyden/BAe Defence*

Canberra PR9 XH134 coded AA with No 39 (No 1 PRU) Sqn. *Geoff Lee/BAe Defence*

Jaguar GR1A XX116 was the all black display aircraft flown by No 16(R) Sqn from Lossiemouth in 1993. *PRM*

A pair of Jaguar GR1As (XZ362 and XZ373) operated by No 54 Sqn — painted in air defence grey for their deployments to Turkey and Italy. *Geoff Lee/BAe Defence*

Gnat T1 XM693 is really XP504 and is now registered G-TIMM with Kennet Aircraft at Cranfield. *PRM*

ZD403 a Harrier GR7 of No 20(R) Sqn, the Harrier OCU. *PRM*

A trio of Tornado F3s from the RAF Coningsby Wing — ZE340 (AE) No.56 Sqn, ZG734 (BA) No.29 Sqn and ZH55E (CV) of No.5 Sqn. Coningsby/PA-Defence

1764M/K4972	7499M/WT555	7806M/TA639	7973M/WS807
2292M/K8203	7510M/WT694	7809M/XA699	7976M/XK418
2365M/K6035	7525M/WT619	7816M/WG763	7979M/XM529
3118M/H5199/BK892	7530M/WT648	7817M/TX214	7980M/XM561
3858M/X7688	7532M/WT651	7822M/XP248	7982M/XH892
4354M/BL614	7533M/WT680	7825M/WK991	7983M/XD506
5377M/EP120	7544M/WN904	7827M/XA917	7984M/XN597
5378M/AR614	7548M/PS915	7829M/XH992	7986M/WG777
5405M/LF738	7554M/FS890	7839M/WV781	7988M/XL149
5466M/*BN230*/(LF751)	7555M/AR614	7840M/XK482	7990M/XD452
5690M/MK356	7564M/XE982	7841M/WV783	7997M/XG452
5718M/BM597	7570M/XD674	7847M/WV276	7998M/*XM515*/(XD515)
5758M/DG202	7582M/*WP180*/(WP190)	7851M/WZ706	8005M/WG768
5854M/WH903	7583M/WP185	7852M/XG506	8009M/XG518
6457M/ML427	7602M/WE600	7854M/XM191	8010M/XG547
6490M/LA255	7605M/WS692	7855M/XK416	8012M/VS562
6850M/TE184	7606M/WV562	7859M/XP283	8016M/XT677
6944M/RW386	7607M/TJ138	7860M/XL738	8017M/XL762
6946M/RW388	7615M/WV679	7862M/XR246	8018M/XN344
6948M/DE673	7616M/WW388	7863M/WZ679	8019M/WZ869
6960M/MT847	7618M/WW442	7864M/XP244	8021M/XL824
7000M/TE392	7621M/WV686	7865M/TX226	8022M/XN341
7008M/EE549	7622M/WV606	7866M/XH278	8023M/XD463
7014M/N6720	7625M/WD356	7867M/XH980	8027M/XM555
7015M/NL985	7630M/VZ304	7868M/WZ736	8032M/XH837
7035M/*K25671*/(DE306)	7631M/VX185	7869M/WK935	8033M/XD382
7060M/VF301	7641M/XA634	7870M/XM556	8034M/XL703
7090M/EE531	7645M/WD293	7872M/*WZ826*/(XD826)	8041M/XF690
7118M/LA198	7646M/VX461	7881M/WD413	8043M/XF836
7119M/LA226	7648M/XF785	7882M/XD525	8046M/XL770
7150M/PK683	7663M/XA571	7883M/XT150	8049M/WE168
7154M/WB188	7673M/WV332	7886M/XR985	8050M/XG329
7174M/VX272	7688M/WW421	7887M/XD375	8051M/XN929
7175M/VV106	7693M/WV483	7890M/XD453	8052M/WH166
7200M/VT812	7696M/WV493	7891M/XM693	8054AM/XM410
7241M/*X4474*/(TE311)	7697M/WV495	7894M/XD818	8054BM/XM417
7243M/TE462	7698M/WV499	7895M/WF784	8055AM/XM402
7244M/*X4277*/(TB382)	7703M/WG725	7898M/XP854	8055BM/XM425
7245M/RW382	7704M/TW536	7899M/XG540	8056M/XG337
7246M/TD248	7705M/WL505	7900M/WA576	8057M/XR243
7256M/TB752	7706M/WB584	7902M/WZ550	8062M/XR669
7257M/TB252	7709M/WT933	7906M/WH132	8063M/WT536
7279M/TB752	7711M/PS915	7917M/WA591	8070M/EP120
7281M/TB252	7712M/WK281	7920M/WL360	8072M/PK624
7285M/VV119	7715M/XK724	7923M/XT133	8073M/TB252
7288M/PK724	7716M/WS776	7925M/WV666	8074M/TE392
7293M/RW393	7718M/WA577	7928M/XE849	8075M/RW382
7323M/VV217	7719M/WK277	7930M/WH301	8076M/XM386
7325M/R5868	7722M/XA571	7931M/RD253	8077M/XN594
7326M/VN485	7728M/WZ458	7932M/WZ744	8078M/XM351
7362M/475081/(VP546)	7729M/WB758	7933M/XR220	8079M/XN492
7416M/WN907	7734M/XD536	7937M/WS843	8080M/XM480
7421M/WT660	7736M/WZ559	7938M/XH903	8082M/XM409
7422M/WT684	7737M/XD602	7939M/XD596	8085M/XM467
7428M/WK198	7739M/XA801	7940M/XL764	8086M/TB752
7432M/WZ724	7741M/VZ477	7955M/XH767	8088M/XN602
7438M/WP905	7750M/*WK864*/(WL168)	7957M/XF545	8092M/WK654
7443M/WX853	7751M/WL131	7959M/WS774	8094M/WT520
7458M/WX905	7755M/WG760	7960M/WS726	8102M/WT486
7464M/XA564	7758M/PM651	7961M/WS739	8103M/WR985
7467M/WP978	7759M/PK664	7964M/WS760	8106M/WR982
7470M/XA553	7761M/XH318	7965M/WS792	8108M/WV703
7473M/XE946	7762M/XE670	7967M/WS788	8113M/WV753
7491M/WT569	7770M/WT746	7970M/WP907	8114M/WL798
7496M/WT612	7796M/WJ676	7971M/XK699	8117M/WR974

RAF Maintenance cross-reference

8118M/WZ549
8119M/WR971
8121M/XM474
8128M/WH775
8131M/WT507
8133M/WT518
8139M/XJ582
8140M/XJ571
8141M/XN688
8142M/XJ560
8143M/XN691
8153M/WV903
8154M/WV908
8155M/WV797
8156M/XE339
8158M/XE369
8159M/XD528
8160M/XD622
8161M/XE993
8162M/WM913
8163M/XP919
8164M/*WN105*/(WF299)
8165M/WH791
8169M/WH364
8171M/XJ607
8173M/XN685
8176M/WH791
8177M/*WM311*/(WM224)
8179M/XN928
8180M/XN930
8182M/XN953
8183M/*XN972*/(XN962)
8184M/WT520
8186M/WR977
8187M/WH791
8189M/WD646
8190M/XJ918
8192M/XR658
8196M/XE920
8198M/WT339
8203M/XD377
8205M/XN819
8206M/WG419
8207M/WD318
8208M/WG303
8209M/WG418
8210M/WG471
8211M/WK570
8212M/WK587
8213M/WK626
8214M/WP864
8215M/WP869
8217M/WZ866
8229M/XM355
8230M/XM362
8231M/XM375
8232M/*ZD713*/(XM381)
8233M/XM408
8234M/XN458
8235M/XN549
8236M/XP573
8237M/XS179
8238M/XS180
8239M/XS210
8344M/WH960
8345M/XG540
8346M/XN734
8350M/WH840
8352M/XN632
8355M/*KG374*/(KN645)
8357M/WK576
8359M/WF825
8360M/WP863

8361M/WB670
8362M/WG477
8363M/WG463
8364M/WG464
8365M/XK421
8366M/XG454
8367M/XG474
8368M/XF926
8369M/WE139
8370M/N1671
8371M/XA847
8372M/K8042
8373M/P2617
8375M/NX611
8376M/RF398
8377M/R9125
8378M/*T9707*
8379M/DG590
8380M/Z7197
8382M/VR930
8383M/K9942
8384M/X4590
8385M/N5912
8386M/NV778
8387M/T6296
8388M/XL993
8389M/VX573
8390M/SL542
8392M/SL674
8393M/XK987
8394M/WG422
8395M/WF408
8396M/XK740
8399M/WR539
8401M/XP686
8402M/XN769
8406M/XP831
8407M/XP585
8408M/XS186
8409M/XS209
8410M/XR662
8413M/XM192
8414M/XM173
8417M/XM144
8422M/XM169
8427M/XM172
8429M/XH592
8431M/XR651
8435M/XN512
8436M/XN554
8437M/WG362
8439M/WZ846
8440M/WD935
8442M/XP411
8445M/XK968
8447M/XP359
8453M/XP745
8457M/XS871
8458M/XP672
8459M/XR650
8460M/XP680
8462M/XX477
8463M/XP355
8464M/XJ758
8465M/W1048
8466M/L-866
8467M/WP912
8468M/MM5701/(BT474)
8470M/584219
8471M/701152
8472M/120227/(VN679)
8473M/WP180/(WP190)
8474M/494083

8475M/360043/(PJ876)
8476M/24
8477M/4101/(DG200)
8479M/730301
8481M/191614
8482M/112372/(VK893)
8483M/420430
8484M/5439
8485M/997
8486M/BAPC 99
8487M/J-1172
8488M/WL627
8491M/WJ880
8492M/WJ872
8493M/XR571
8494M/XP557
8495M/XR672
8498M/XR670
8501M/XP640
8502M/XP686
8503M/XS451
8506M/XF383
8507M/XS215
8508M/XS218
8509M/XT141
8513M/XN724
8514M/XS176
8515M/WH869
8535M/XN776
8538M/XN781
8546M/XN728
8548M/WT507
8549M/WT534
8551M/XN774
8554M/TG511
8559M/XN467
8560M/XR569
8565M/*WT720*/(E-408)
8566M/XV279
8568M/XP503
8569M/XR535
8570M/XR954
8572M/XM706
8573M/XM708
8575M/XP542
8576M/XP502
8578M/XR534
8579M/XR140
8580M/XP516
8581M/WJ775
8582M/XE874
8583M/BAPC 94
8585M/XE670
8586M/XE643
8587M/XP677
8588M/XR681
8589M/XR700
8590M/XM191
8591M/XA813
8595M/XH278
8596M/LH208
8598M/WP270
8602M/*PF179*/(XR541)
8606M/XP530
8608M/XP540
8609M/XR953
8610M/XL502
8611M/WF128
8615M/XP532
8617M/XM709
8618M/*XM693*/(XP504)
8620M/XP534
8621M/XR538

8622M/XR980
8623M/XR998
8624M/*XR991*/(X
8627M/XP558
8628M/XJ380
8630M/WG362
8631M/XR574
8633M/MK732
8634M/WP314
8638M/XS101
8640M/XR977
8642M/XR537
8645M/XD163
8647M/XP338
8648M/XK526
8653M/XS120
8654M/XL898
8655M/XN126
8656M/XP405
8657M/VZ634
8661M/XJ727
8662M/XR458
8666M/XE793
8667M/WP972
8668M/WJ821
8671M/XJ435
8672M/XP351
8673M/XD165
8674M/XP395
8676M/XL577
8677M/*XF519*/(XJ
8678M/XE656
8679M/XF526
8680M/XF527
8681M/XG164
8682M/XP404
8684M/XJ634
8685M/XF516
8687M/XJ639
8691M/WT518
8693M/WH863
8695M/WJ817
8696M/WH773
8699M/ZD232
8702M/XG196
8703M/VW453
8704M/XN643
8706M/XF383
8708M/XF509
8709M/XG209
8710M/XG274
8711M/XG290
8713M/XG225
8714M/XK149
8718M/XX396
8719M/XT257
8720M/XP353
8721M/XP354
8723M/XL567
8724M/XW923
8726M/XP299
8727M/XR486
8728M/WT532
8729M/WJ815
8730M/XD186
8731M/XP361
8732M/XJ729
8733M/XL318
8736M/XF375
8739M/XH170
8741M/XW329
8743M/WD790
8746M/XH171

100

8747M/WJ629	8867M/XK532	8957M/XN582	9052M/WJ717
8749M/XH537	8868M/WH775	8958M/XN501	9053M/XT755
8751M/XT255	8869M/WH957	8959M/XN472	9054M/XT766
8752M/XR509	8870M/WH964	8960M/XM455	9055M/XT770
8753M/WL795	8871M/WJ565	8961M/XS925	9056M/XS488
8755M/*WH699*/(WJ637)	8873M/XR453	8967M/XV263	9057M/ZE361
8756M/XL427	8874M/XE597	8968M/XM471	9058M/ZE351
8757M/XM656	8875M/XE624	8969M/XR753	9059M/ZE360
8762M/WH740	8876M/*VM791*/(XA312)	8974M/XM473	9060M/ZE356
8763M/WH665	8877M/XP159	8978M/XX837	9061M/XW335
8764M/XP344	8879M/XX948	8979M/XV747	9062M/XW351
8767M/XX635	8880M/XF435	8981M/XW764	9064M/XT867
8768M/A-522	8881M/XG254	8983M/XM478	9065M/XV577
8769M/A-528	8882M/XR396	8984M/XN551	9066M/XV582
8770M/XL623	8883M/XX946	8986M/XV261	9067M/XV586
8771M/XM602	8884M/VX275	8987M/XM358	9070M/XV581
8772M/WR960	8886M/XA243	8988M/XN593	9071M/XT853
8777M/XX914	8887M/WK162	8990M/XM419	9072M/XW768
8778M/XM598	8888M/XA231	8991M/XR679	9073M/XW924
8779M/XM607	8889M/XN239	8992M/XP547	9074M/XV738
8780M/WK102	8890M/WT532	8993M/XS219	9075M/XV753
8781M/WE982	8892M/XL618	8994M/XS178	9076M/XV808
8782M/XH136	8894M/XT669	8995M/XM425	9077M/XZ967
8783M/XW272	8895M/XX746	8996M/XM414	9078M/XV752
8784M/VP976	8896M/XX821	8997M/XX669	9079M/YZ130
8785M/XS642	8897M/XX969	8998M/XT864	9083M/ZE353
8786M/XN495	8898M/XX119	9001M/XV778	9084M/ZE354
8791M/XP329	8899M/XX756	9002M/XW763	9085M/ZE364
8792M/XP345	8900M/XZ368	9003M/XZ390	9087M/XX753
8793M/XP346	8901M/XZ383	9004M/XZ370	9088M/XV587
8794M/XP398	8902M/XV739	9005M/XZ374	9090M/XW353
8796M/XK943	8903M/XX747	9006M/XX967	9091M/XW434
8797M/XX947	8904M/XX966	9007M/XX968	9092M/XH669
8799M/WV787	8905M/XX975	9008M/XX140	9093M/WK124
8800M/XG226	8906M/XX976	9009M/XX763	9095M/XW547
8805M/XT772	8907M/XZ371	9010M/XX764	9096M/WV322
8806M/XP140	8908M/XZ382	9011M/XM412	9097M/XW366
8807M/XL587	8909M/XV784	9012M/XN494	9098M/XV406
8810M/XJ825	8910M/XL160	9014M/XN584	9099M/XT900
8813M/VT260	8911M/XH673	9015M/XW320	9100M/XL188
8814M/XM927	8917M/XM372	9016M/XN640	9101M/WL756
8816M/XX734	8918M/XX109	9017M/ZE449	9102M/XS241
8818M/XK527	8919M/XT486	9018M/XW365	9103M/XV411
8819M/XS479	8920M/XT469	9019M/XX824	9107M/XV482
8820M/VP952	8921M/XT466	9020M/XX825	9108M/XT475
8822M/VP957	8923M/XX819	9021M/XX826	9109M/XW312
8824M/VP971	8924M/XP701	9022M/XX958	9110M/XX736
8826M/XV638	8925M/XP706	9023M/XX844	9111M/XW421
8828M/XS587	8931M/XV779	9024M/XL192	9112M/XM475
8829M/XE653	8932M/XR718	9026M/XP629	9113M/XV500
8830M/XF515	8933M/XX297	9027M/XP556	9114M/XL162
8831M/XG160	8934M/XR749	9028M/XP563	9115M/XV863
8832M/XG172	8935M/XR713	9029M/XS217	9117M/XV161
8833M/XL569	8937M/XX751	9030M/XR674	9118M/XV253
8836M/XL592	8938M/WV746	9031M/XP688	9119M/XW303
8838M/*34037*/(429356)	8939M/XP741	9032M/XR673	9120M/XW419
8839M/XG194	8940M/XR716	9033M/XS181	9122M/XZ997
8840M/XG252	8941M/XT456	9034M/XP638	9123M/XT773
8844M/XJ676	8942M/XN185	9036M/XM350	9124M/XW427
8845M/XS572	8943M/XE799	9037M/XN302	9125M/XW410
8847M/XX344	8944M/WZ791	9038M/XV810	9126M/XW413
8848M/XZ135	8945M/XX818	9039M/XN586	9127M/XW432
8851M/XT595	8946M/XZ389	9040M/XZ138	9128M/XW292
8852M/XV337	8947M/XX726	9041M/XW763	9129M/XW294
8853M/XT277	8948M/XX757	9042M/XL954	9130M/XW327
8855M/XT284	8949M/XX743	9044M/XS177	9131M/*DD931*
8857M/XW544	8950M/XX956	9045M/XN636	9132M/XX977
8860M/XW549	8951M/XX727	9046M/XM349	9133M/*413573*
8861M/XW528	8952M/XX730	9047M/XW409	9134M/XT288
8862M/XN473	8953M/XX959	9048M/XM403	9136M/XT891
8863M/XG154	8954M/XZ384	9049M/XW404	9137M/XN579
8864M/WJ678	8955M/XX110	9050M/XG577	9139M/XV863
8865M/XN641	8956M/XN577	9051M/XM472	9140M/XZ287

RAF Maintenance cross-reference

9141M/XV118	9153M/XW360	9166M/XW323	9177M/XW328
9143M/XN589	9154M/XW321	9167M/XV744	9178M/XS793
9144M/XV353	9155M/WL679	9168M/XZ132	9179M
9145M/XV863	9157M/XV422	9169M/XW547	9180M
9146M/XW299	9158M/XV467	9170M/XZ994	9181M
9147M/XW301	9159M/XV468	9171M/XT895	9182M
9148M/XW436	9161M/XZ998	9172M/XW304	9183M
9149M/XW375	9162M/XZ991	9173M/XW418	9184M
9150M/*FX760*	9163M/XV415	9174M/XZ131	9185M
9151M/XT907	9164M/XK695	9175M/P1344	9186M/XF967
9152M/XV424	9165M/XV408	9176M/XW430	

A flight of Hawker Hunters from No 208 Sqn, Lossiemouth headed by T8B XF995. *PRM*

Ships' Numeric Code — Deck Letters Analysis

	0	1	2	3	4	5	6	7	8	9
32	AZ	GIB	AV	AB			AW	AL	BA	BA
33	BZ	BZ	LP	BM	SN	CF	CV	CV	CT	CT
34		AG	BT	BT	GW	NC	BW	BW	CM	CM
35	CL	CL	SD	SD	SM					
36	MC	NF	NF	MA	MA	AY	AY			
37			NL		VB	VB	XB			
40			BX	BX	IR	LN	LN	YK		
41	GC	EB	CW	CW		MM		NM		
42	EX	SU								
43					ED	ED		GT		
44				MR						
45								LA		
46			WM							
47				RM						

RN Code – Squadron – Base – Aircraft Cross-Check

Code Numbers	Deck/Base Letters	Unit	Location	Aircraft Type(s)
000 — 005	R	801 Sqn	Yeovilton	Sea Harrier FRS1
010 — 020	R	820 Sqn	Culdrose	Sea King HAS6
122 — 129	N	800 Sqn	Yeovilton	Sea Harrier FRS1
130 — 139	—	819 Sqn	Prestwick	Sea King HAS6
180 — 187	—	849 Sqn	Culdrose	Sea King AEW2A
264 — 274	N	814 Sqn	Culdrose	Sea King HAS6
300 — 308	PO	815 Sqn	Portland	Lynx HAS3
320 — 474	*	815 Sqn	Portland	Lynx HAS3
500 — 510	—	810 Sqn	Culdrose	Sea King HAS6
538 — 559	CU	705 Sqn	Culdrose	Gazelle HT2
560 — 575	CU	750 Sqn	Culdrose	Jetstream T2
576 — 579	-	FONA	Yeovilton	Jetstream T3
580 — 599	—	706 Sqn	Culdrose	Sea King HAS6
620 — 628	PO	772 Sqn	Portland	Sea King HC4
630 — 638	PO	702 Sqn	Portland	Lynx HAS3
640 — 648	PO	702 Sqn	Portland	Lynx HAS3
670 — 672	PO	815 Sqn OEU	Portland	Lynx HAS3 CTS
699 — 709	PW	819 Sqn	Prestwick	Sea King HAS6
710 — 717	VL	899 Sqn	Yeovilton	Sea Harrier FRS1/2
718 — 722	VL	899 Sqn	Yeovilton	Harrier T4/T4N
820 — 826	CU	771 Sqn	Culdrose	Sea King HAR5
860 — 868	VL	FRADU	Yeovilton	Hunter GA11
870 — 880	VL	FRADU	Yeovilton	Hunter T7/T8
901 — 912	—	FGF	Plymouth	Chipmunk T10

*See above separate Ships' Deck Letter Analysis
Note that only the 'last two' digits of the Code are worn by some aircraft types, especially helicopters.

RN Landing Platform and Shore Station Code-letters

Notes	Serial	Type	Owner or Operator	
	323	AB	HMS *Ambuscade* (F172)	Type 21 (815 Sqn)
	341	AG	HMS *Avenger* (F185)	Type 21 (815 Sqn)
	327	AL	HMS *Alacrity* (F174)	Type 21 (815 Sqn)
	472	AM	HMS *Andromeda* (F57)	Leander (815 Sqn)
	—	AS	RFA *Argus* (A135)	Aviation Training ship
	322	AV	HMS *Active* (F171)	Type 21 (815 Sqn)
	326	AW	HMS *Arrow* (F173)	Type 21 (815 Sqn)
	365/6	AY	HMS *Argyll* (F232)	Type 23 (815 Sqn)
	320	AZ	HMS *Amazon* (F169)	Type 21 (815 Sqn)
	328/9	BA	HMS *Brave* (F94)	Type 22 (815 Sqn)
	—	BD	RFA *Sir Bedivere* (L3004)	Landing ship
		BE	RFA *Blue Rover* (A270)	Fleet tanker
	333	BM	HMS *Birmingham* (D86)	Type 42 (815 Sqn)
	342/3	BT	HMS *Brilliant* (F90)	Type 22 (815 Sqn)
		BV	HMS *Black Rover* (A273)	Fleet tanker
	346/7	BW	HMS *Broadsword* (F88)	Type 22 (815 Sqn)
	402/3	BX	HMS *Battleaxe* (F89)	Type 22 (815 Sqn)
	330/1	BZ	HMS *Brazen* (F91)	Type 22 (815 Sqn)
	335	CF	HMS *Cardiff* (D108)	Type 42 (815 Sqn)
	350/1	CL	HMS *Cumberland* (F85)	Type 22 (815 Sqn)
	348/9	CM	HMS *Chatham* (F87)	Type 22 (815 Sqn)
	338/9	CT	HMS *Campbeltown* (F86)	Type 22 (815 Sqn)
	—	CU	RNAS Culdrose (HMS *Seahawk*)	
	336/7	CV	HMS *Coventry* (F98)	Type 22 (815 Sqn)
	412/3	CW	HMS *Cornwall* (F99)	Type 22 (815 Sqn)
	—	DC	HMS *Dumbarton Castle* (P268)	Fishery protection
		DG	RFA *Diligence* (A132)	Maintenance
	411	EB	HMS *Edinburgh* (D97)	Type 42 (815 Sqn)
	434/5	ED	HMS *Endurance* (A176)	Ice Patrol (815 Sqn)
	420	EX	HMS *Exeter* (D89)	Type 42 (815 Sqn)
	—	FA	RFA *Fort Austin* (A386)	Support ship
	—	FG	RFA *Fort Grange* (A385)	Support ship
		FL	RNAY Fleetlands	
	—	FS	HMS *Fearless* (L10)	Assault
	410	GC	HMS *Gloucester* (D96)	Type 42 (815 Sqn)
	321	GIB	Gibraltar Airport	(815 Sqn)
		GD	RFA *Sir Galahad* (L3005)	Landing ship
	—	GN	RFA *Green Rover* (A268)	Fleet tanker
	—	GR	RFA *Sir Geraint* (L3027)	Landing ship
	437	GT	HMS *Grafton* (F241)	Type 23
	—	GV	RFA *Gold Rover* (A271)	Fleet tanker
	344	GW	HMS *Glasgow* (D88)	Type 42 (815 Sqn)
	—	GY	RFA *Grey Rover* (A269)	Fleet tanker
	—	HC	HMS *Hecla* (A133)	Survey ship
	—	HR	HMS *Herald*	Survey ship
	—	ID	HMS *Intrepid* (L11)	Assault
	404	IR	HMS *Iron Duke* (F234)	Type 23 (815 Sqn)
	—	L	HMS *Illustrious* (R06)	Carrier
	457	LA	HMS *Lancaster* (F229)	Type 23 (815 Sqn)
	—	LC	HMS *Leeds Castle* (P258)	Fishery protection
	405/6	LN	HMS *London* (F95)	Type 22 (815 Sqn)
	332	LP	HMS *Liverpool* (D92)	Type 42 (815 Sqn)
	—	LS	RNAS Lee-on-Solent (HMS *Daedalus*)	
	363/4	MA	HMS *Marlborough* (F233)	Type 23 (815 Sqn)
	360	MC	HMS *Manchester* (D95)	Type 42 (815 Sqn)
	415	MM	HMS *Monmouth* (F235)	Type 23
	444	MR	HMS *Montrose* (F236)	Type 23
	—	N	HMS *Invincible* (R05)	Carrier
	345	NC	HMS *Newcastle* (D87)	Type 42 (815 Sqn)
	361/2	NF	HMS *Norfolk* (F230)	Type 23 (815 Sqn)
	372	NL	HMS *Northumberland* (F238)	Type 23
	417	NM	HMS *Nottingham* (D91)	Type 42 (815 Sqn)
	—	OD	RFA *Olmeda* (A124)	Fleet tanker
	—	ON	RFA *Olna* (A123)	Fleet tanker
	—	OW	RFA *Olwen* (A122)	Fleet tanker
		PO	RNAS Portland (HMS *Osprey*)	

RN Landing Platforms

Serial	Type	Owner or Operator	Notes
—	PV	RFA *Sir Percival* (L3036)	Landing ship
—	PW	Prestwick Airport (HMS *Gannet*)	
—	R	HMS *Ark Royal* (R09)	Carrier
—	RG	RFA *Regent* (A486)	Support ship
474	RM	HMS *Richmond* (F239)	Type 23
—	RS	RFA *Resource* (A480)	Support ship
352/3	SD	HMS *Sheffield* (F96)	Type 23 (815 Sqn)
355	SM	HMS *Somerset* (F240)	Type 23
334	SN	HMS *Southampton* (D90)	Type 42 (815 Sqn)
422	SU	HMS *Sutherland* (F242)	Type 23
—	TM	RFA *Sir Tristram* (L3505)	Landing ship
374/5	VB	HMS *Beaver* (F93)	Type 22 (815 Sqn)
—	VL	RNAS Yeovilton (HMS *Heron*)	
462	WM	HMS *Westminster* (F237)	Type 23
376	XB	HMS *Boxer* (F92)	Type 22 (815 Sqn)
407	YK	HMS *York* (D98)	Type 42 (815 Sqn)
—	—	RFA *Fort Victoria* (A387)	Auxiliary Oiler
—	—	RFA *Fort George* (A388)	Auxiliary Oiler

No 660 Sqn Army Air Corps operates this Scout AH1 in Hong Kong. *PRM*

ZA149 is a VC10 K3 flown by No 101 Sqn at RAF Brize Norton. *PRM*

Newly converted Sea Harrier FRS2 (ZD615) carries the dual markings of 899 Sqn and the Operational Evaluation Unit. *Phil Boyden/BAe Defence*

British-based Historic Aircraft in Overseas Markings

Some *historic, classic and warbird* aircraft carry the markings of overseas air arms and can be seen in the UK, mainly preserved in museums and collections or taking part in air shows.

Serial	Type	Owner or Operator	Notes
Argentina			
A-515	FMA IA58 Pucara (ZD485)	RAF Cosford Aerospace Museum	
A-517	FMA IA58 Pucara (G-BLRP)	Privately owned, Channel Islands	
A-522	FMA IA58 Pucara (8768M)	FAA Museum, RNAS Yeovilton	
A-528	FMA IA58 Pucara (8769M)	North-East Aircraft Museum, Usworth	
A-533	FMA IA58 Pucara (ZD486)	Museum of Army Flying, Middle Wallop	
A-549	FMA IA58 Pucara (ZD487)	Imperial War Museum, Duxford	
AE-406	Bell UH-1H Iroquois	Museum of Army Flying, Middle Wallop	
AE-409	Bell UH-1H Iroquois [656]	Museum of Army Flying, Middle Wallop	
AE-422	Bell UH-1H Iroquois	FAA Museum, RNAS Yeovilton	
PA-12	SA330L Puma HC1 (ZE449/ 9017M)	RAF Odiham, BDRT	
0729	Beech T-34C Turbo Mentor	FAA Museum, RNAS Yeovilton	
Australia			
A2-4	Supermarine Seagull V (VH-ALB)	RAF Museum, Hendon	
A16-199	Lockheed Hudson IIIA (G-BEOX/ FH174) [SF-R]	RAF Museum, Hendon	
A17-48	DH Tiger Moth (N48DH/G-BPHR)	Privately owned, Swindon	
Belgium			
FT-36	Lockheed T-33A	Dumfries & Galloway Aviation Museum, Tinwald Downs	
HD-75	Hanriot HD1 (OO-APJ/ G-AFDX/N75)	RAF Museum, Hendon	
MT-11	Fouga CM-170R Magister (G-BRFU)	Vintage Aircraft Team, Cranfield	
V-58	Stampe SV4B (G-DANN)	Privately owned, Redhill	
Canada			
232	Hawker Sea Fury FB11 (TG114/ N232J)	Privately owned, North Weald	
920	VS Stranraer (CF-BXO) [Q-N]	RAF Museum, Hendon	
9059	Bristol Bolingbroke IVT	Privately owned, Portsmouth	
9754	Consolidated PBY-5A Catalina (*JV928*/G-BLSC) [P]	Plane Sailing, Duxford	
9893	Bristol Bolingbroke IVT	Imperial War Museum store, Duxford	
9940	Bristol Bolingbroke IVT	Royal Scottish Museum of Flight, East Fortune	
16693	Auster J/1N Alpha (G-BLPG) [693]	Privately owned, Headcorn	
18013	DHC Chipmunk 22 (G-TRIC) [013]	Privately owned, Little Gransden	
18393	Avro Canada CF-100 (G-BCYK)	Imperial War Museum, Duxford	
18671	DHC Chipmunk 22 (G-BNZC/ WP905) [671]	British Aerial Museum, Duxford	
20310	CCF Harvard IV (G-BSBG/ 52-8562)	Privately owned, Shoreham	
20385	CCF T-6J Harvard IV (G-BGPB/ 53-4619)	Privately owned, North Weald	
21417	Canadair CT-133 Silver Star	Yorkshire Air Museum, Elvington	
23140	NA Sabre [AX] (fuselage)	Midland Air Museum, Coventry	
116622	Piasecki HUP-3 Retriever (116622/N6699D)	IHM, Weston-super-Mare	
Croatia			
5	Nord 1203 (G-BEDB)	Privately owned, Chirk	
Czech Republic			
3794	Mikoyan MiG-15	Imperial War Museum, Duxford	
Denmark			
E-402	Hawker Hunter F51 ●	Privately owned, Bournemouth	
E-419	Hawker Hunter F51	North-East Aircraft Museum, Usworth	
E-420	Hawker Hunter F51 (G-9-442)	Privately owned, Marlow	

Historic Aircraft

Serial	Type	Owner or Operator
E-421	Hawker Hunter F51	Brooklands Museum, Weybridge
E-423	Hawker Hunter F51 (G-9-444)	Second World War Aircraft Preservation Society, Lasham
E-424	Hawker Hunter F51 (G-9-445)	S Yorks Air Museum, Firbeck
E-425	Hawker Hunter F51	Midland Air Museum, Coventry
E-427	Hawker Hunter F51 (G-9-447)	Privately owned, Bruntingthorpe
E-430	Hawker Hunter F51	Privately owned, Charlwood, Surrey
ET-272	Hawker Hunter T7	Macclesfield Historical Aviation Society, Marthall
ET-273	Hawker Hunter T7 (cockpit) ●	Jet Heritage Ltd, Bournemouth
L-866	Consolidated Catalina (8466M)	RAF Cosford Aerospace Museum
R-756	Lockheed F-104G Starfighter	Midland Air Museum, Coventry
S-881	Sikorsky S-55C	IHM, Weston-super-Mare
S-882	Sikorsky S-55C	IHM, Weston-super-Mare
S-884	Sikorsky S-55C	Privately owned, New Waltham, Humberside
S-885	Sikorsky S-55C	Privately owned
S-886	Sikorsky S-55C	IHM, Weston-super-Mare
S-887	Sikorsky S-55C	IHM, Weston-super-Mare
Egypt		
0446	Mikoyan MiG-21UM	DRA Farnborough Fire Section
2684	Mikoyan MiG-19	DRA Farnborough Fire Section
7907	Sukhoi Su-7	DRA Farnborough Fire Section
France		
9	Dassault Mystère IVA [004]	RAF Bentwaters
16	Dassault Mystère IVA	RAF Lakenheath
25	Dassault Mystère IVA	RAF Woodbridge
36	Dassault Mystère IVA [EABDR 8]	RAF Upper Heyford BDRT
37	Nord 3400 [MAB] (G-ZARA)	Privately owned, Boston
45	SNCAN Stampe SV4C (G-BHFG)	Privately owned, Goodwood
46	Dassault Mystère IVA [EABDR 9]	RAF Upper Heyford
50	Dassault Mystère IVA	RAF Woodbridge
57	Dassault Mystère IVA [8-MT]	Imperial War Museum, Duxford
59	Dassault Mystère IVA [2-SF]	Wales Aircraft Museum, Cardiff
68	Nord 3400 [MHA]	Privately owned, Coventry
70	Dassault Mystère IVA [8-NV]	Midland Air Museum, Coventry
75	Dassault Mystère IVA [11]	RAF Lakenheath
79	Dassault Mystère IVA [8-NB]	Norfolk & Suffolk Aviation Museum, Flixton
83	Dassault Mystère IVA [8-MS]	Newark Air Museum, Winthorpe
84	Dassault Mystère IVA [8-NF]	Robertsbridge Aviation Society, Headcorn
85	Dassault Mystère IVA	Privately owned, Bruntingthorpe
99	Dassault Mystère IVA	RAF Lakenheath
101	Dassault Mystère IVA [8-MN]	Bomber County Aviation Museum, Hemswell
104	Dassault Mystère IVA	RAF Bentwaters, BDRT
108	SO1221 Djinn [CDL]	International Helicopter Museum, Weston-super-Mare
113	Dassault Mystère IVA	RAF Lakenheath
120	SNCAN Stampe SV4C (G-AZGC)	Privately owned, Reading
121	Dassault Mystère IVA [8-MY]	City of Norwich Aviation Museum
126	Dassault Mystère IVA	RAF Lakenheath
133	Dassault Mystère IVA	RAF Woodbridge
143	MS733 Alcyon (G-MSAL)	Privately owned, Booker
145	Dassault Mystère IVA	RAF Lakenheath
FR145	SO1221 Djinn [CDL]	Privately owned, Luton Airport
146	Dassualt Mystère IVA [8-MC]	North-East Aircraft Museum, Usworth
157	Morane MS230 (G-AVEB) [01/M373]	Privately owned, Booker
192	MH1521M Broussard (G-BKPT)	Privately owned, Chiseldon
241	Dassault Mystère IVA [2]	RAF Lakenheath
276	Dassault Mystère IVA	RAF Woodbridge
285	Dassault Mystère IVA	RAF Lakenheath
300	Dassault Mystère IVA [5]	RAF Lakenheath
309	Dassault Mystère IVA [8]	RAF Lakenheath
318	Dassault Mystère IVA [8-NY]	Dumfries & Galloway Aviation Museum, Tinwald Downs
319	Dassault Mystère IVA [8-ND]	Rebel Air Museum, Andrewsfield
14286	Lockheed T-33A [WK]	Imperial War Museum, Duxford
16718	Lockheed T-33A [314-UJ]	City of Norwich Aviation Museum

Serial	Type	Owner or Operator	Notes
42163	NA F-100D Super Sabre [11-YG]	Dumfries & Galloway Aviation Museum, Tinwald Downs	
42204	NA F-100D Super Sabre [11-MQ]	RAF Alconbury	
54433	Lockheed T-33A [WD]	Norfolk & Suffolk Aviation Museum, Flixton	
63938	NA F-100F Super Sabre [11-MU]	Lashenden Air Warfare Museum, Headcorn	
114700	NA T-6G Texan	Aces High, North Weald	
MS824	Morane-Saulnier Type N Replica (G-AWBU)	Privately owned, Booker	
S3398	Spad XIII Replica (G-BFYO) [2]	FAA Museum, RNAS Yeovilton	
S4523	Spad S.VII (N4727V) [1]	Imperial War Museum, Duxford	

Germany

Serial	Type	Owner or Operator	Notes
C19/18	Albatros D.V Replica (BAPC118)	South Yorks Aviation Museum, Firbeck	
C850/17	Albatros Replica	Macclesfield Historical Aviation Society Marthall	
D5397/17	Albatros D.VA Replica (G-BFXL)	FAA Museum, RNAS Yeovilton	
1Z+NK	Amiot AAC1 (Port.AF 6316)	IWM, Duxford	
LG+01	Bucker Bu.133C Jungmeister (G-AYSJ)	Privately owned, Duxford	
BU+CC	CASA 1.131E Jungmann (G-BUCC/G-BUEM)	Privately owned, Billingshurst	
BU+CK	CASA 1.131E Jungmann (G-BUCK)	Privately owned, White Waltham	
S5+B06	CASA 1.131E Jungmann 2000 (G-BSFB)	Privately owned, Stretton	
6J+PR	CASA 2.111D (G-AWHB)	Aces High Ltd, North Weald	
14	Fiat G.46-3B (G-BBII)	Privately owned, stored Rendcomb	
—	Fieseler Fi103 (V-1) (BAPC 92)	RAF Museum, Hendon	
—	Fieseler Fi103 (V-1) (BAPC 93)	Imperial War Museum, Duxford	
—	Fieseler Fi103 (V-1) (8583M/ BAPC 94)	RAF Cosford Aerospace Museum	
—	Fieseler Fi103 (V-1) (BAPC 158)	Defence School, Chattenden	
442795	Fieseler Fi103 (V-1) (BAPC 199)	Science Museum, South Kensington	
475081	Fieseler Fi156C-7 Storch [GM+AK] (VP546/7362M)	RAF Cosford Aerospace Museum	
28368	Flettner Fl282/B-V20 Kolibri (frame only)	Midland Air Museum, Coventry	
100143	Focke-Achgelis Fa330A	Imperial War Museum, Duxford	
100502	Focke-Achgelis Fa330A	Lincolnshire Aviation Heritage Centre, East Kirkby	
100509	Focke-Achgelis Fa330A	Science Museum, stored S Kensington	
100545	Focke-Achgelis Fa330A	FAA Museum, stored Wroughton	
100549	Focke-Achgelis Fa330A	Greater Manchester Museum of Science and Industry	
2100	Focke Wulf FW189A-1 [V7+1H]	Privately owned, Lancing	
2+1	Focke Wulf FW190 Replica (G-SYFW)[7334]	Privately owned, Guernsey, CI	
4	Focke Wulf FW190 Replica (G-BSLX)	Privately owned, Shoreham	
8	Focke Wulf FW190 Replica (G-WULF)	Privately owned, Dunkeswell	
733682	Focke Wulf FW190A-8/R7	Imperial War Museum, Lambeth	
584219	Focke Wulf FW190F-8/U1 (8470M) [38]	RAF Museum, Hendon	
4253/18	Fokker D.VII Replica (G-BFPL)	Privately owned, Duxford	
626/18	Fokker D.VII Replica (N6268) (really a Travelair 2000)	Blue Max Movie Aircraft Museum, Booker	
8417/18	Fokker D.VII	RAF Museum, Hendon	
102/18	Fokker Dr.1 Dreidekker Replica (BAPC 88)	FAA Museum, RNAS Yeovilton	
152/17	Fokker Dr.1 Dreidekker Replica (G-ATJM)	Privately owned, Rendcomb, Glos	
152/17	Fokker Dr.1 Dreidekker Replica (N5523V)	Privately owned, Booker	
425/17	Fokker Dr.1 Dreidekker Replica (BAPC 133)	Newark Air Museum, Winthorpe	
425/17	Fokker Dr.1 Dreidekker Replica (G-BEFR)	Privately owned, Dunkeswell	
450/17	Fokker Dr.1 Dreidekker Replica	Museum of Army Flying, Middle Wallop	
210/16	Fokker EIII (BAPC 56)	Science Museum, South Kensington	
422/15	Fokker EIII replica (G-AVJO)	Privately owned, Booker	
701152	Heinkel He111H-23 (8471M) [NT+SL]	RAF Museum, Hendon	

Historic Aircraft

Notes	Serial	Type	Owner or Operator
	120227	Heinkel He162A-2 Salamander (VN679/8472M) [2]	RAF Museum, Hendon
	120235	Heinkel He162A Salamander	Imperial War Museum, Lambeth
	—	Hispano HA 1112 (G-BOML)	Privately owned, Duxford
	494083	Junkers Ju87G-2 (8474M) [RI+JK]	RAF Museum, Hendon
	6234	Junkers Ju87R-4 [L1+FW]	Privately owned, Lancing
	360043	Junkers Ju88R-1 (PJ876/8475M) [D5+EV]	RAF Museum, Hendon
	22+35	Lockheed F104G Starfighter	Second World War Aircraft Preservation Society, Lasham
	22+57	Lockheed F104G Starfighter	Starfighter Preservation Group, New Waltham
	7198/18	LVG C.VI (G-AANJ)	Shuttleworth Collection, Old Warden
	14	Messerschmitt Bf109 Replica (BAPC 67)	Kent Battle of Britain Museum, Hawkinge
	1480	Messerschmitt Bf109 Replica (BAPC 66) [6]	Kent Battle of Britain Museum, Hawkinge
	6357	Messerschmitt Bf109 Replica (BAPC 74) [6]	Kent Battle of Britain Museum, Hawkinge
	1190	Messerschmitt Bf109E-3 ●	Privately owned, Bournemouth
	4101	Messerschmitt Bf109E-3 (DG200/8477M) [12]	RAF Museum, Hendon
	6	Messerschmitt Bf109G-2/Trop (RN228/8478M/G-USTV)	Imperial War Museum, Duxford
	4502	Messerschmitt Bf110E-2 [M8+ZE]	Privately owned, Lancing
	730301	Messerschmitt Bf110G-4 (8479M) [D5+RL]	RAF Museum, Hendon
	191316	Messerschmitt Me163B Komet	Science Museum, South Kensington
	191614	Messerschmitt Me163B Komet (8481M)	RAF Cosford Aerospace Museum
	191659	Messerschmitt Me163B Komet (8480M) [15]	Royal Scottish Museum of Flight, East Fortune
	191660	Messerschmitt Me163B Komet [3]	Imperial War Museum, Duxford
	112372	Messerschmitt Me262A-2a (VK893/8482M) [9K-XK]	RAF Cosford Aerospace Museum
	420430	Messerschmitt Me410A-1/U2 (8483M) [3U+CC]	RAF Cosford Aerospace Museum
	20+48	Mikoyan MiG-23BN [702]	DRA Farnborough
	7A+WN	Morane-Saulnier MS500 (G-AZMH)	Privately owned, Chalmington, Dorset
	FI+S	Morane-Saulnier MS505 (G-BIRW)	Royal Scottish Museum of Flight, East Fortune
	TA+RC	Morane-Saulnier MS 505 Criquet (G-BPHZ)	Privately owned, Duxford
	NJ+C11	Nord 1002 (G-ATBG)	Privately owned, Duxford
	14	Pilatus P-2 (J-108/G-BJAX)	Privately owned, Duxford
	CC+43	Pilatus P-2 (U-143/G-CJCI)	Privately owned, Norwich
	97+04	Putzer Elster B (G-APVF)	Privately owned, Tadlow
	+114	SNCAN 1101 Noralpha (G-BSMD)	Privately owned, Abbotsley
	D-692	Staaken Z-1 Flitzer (G-BVAW)	Privately owned, Aberdare
	98+10	Sukhoi Su-22M-4	DRA Farnborough
Greece			
	52-6541	Republic F-84F Thunderflash	North-East Aircraft Museum, Usworth
	51-6151	Canadair F-86D Sabre (really 51-6171)	North-East Aircraft Museum, Usworth
Hungary			
	501	Mikoyan MiG-21PF	Privately owned, St Athan
	503	Mikoyan MiG-21SMT (G-BRAM)	Aces High, North Weald
India			
	Q497	EE Canberra T4 (WE191)	BAe Warton Fire Service
Iraq			
	333	DH Vampire T55	Military Aircraft Preservation Group, Marthall
	26186	Bell 214ST (tail only)	Museum of Army Flying, Middle Wallop
Israel			
	41	NA P-51D Mustang (472028)	Privately owned, Teesside Airport
Italy			
	MM5701	Fiat CR42 (BT474/8468M) [13-95]	RAF Museum, Hendon

110

Serial	Type	Owner or Operator	Notes
MM53211	Fiat G.46-4 (BAPC 79)	Privately owned, Duxford	
MM53432	NA T-6D Texan [RM-11]	Privately owned, South Wales	
MM53692	CCF T-6G Texan	RAeS Medway Branch, Rochester	
MM54099	NA T-6G Texan (G-BRBC) [RR-56]	Privately owned, Chigwell	
MM542372	PA.18-95 Super Cub	Privately owned, Kesgrave	
W7	Avia FL.3 (G-AGFT)	Privately owned, Leicester	

Japan

24	Kawasaki Ki100-1B (8476M) (BAPC 83)	RAF Cosford Aerospace Museum	
5439	Mitsubishi Ki46-III (8484M/ BAPC 84)	RAF Cosford Aerospace Museum	
AI-110	Mitsubishi Zero Replica (N15798)	Privately owned, North Weald	
—	Yokosuka MXY 7 Ohka II (8485M/ BAPC 98)	Greater Manchester Museum of Science and Industry	
15-1585	Yokosuka MXY 7 Ohka II (BAPC 58)	FAA Museum, RNAS Yeovilton	
I—13	Yokosuka MXY 7 Ohka II (8486M/ BAPC 99)	RAF Cosford Aerospace Museum	
—	Yokosuka MXY 7 Ohka II (BAPC 159)	Defence School, Chattenden	

Netherlands

115	Hawker Fury FB10 (IAF243/ N28SF/VH-HFX/G-BTTA)	The Old Flying Machine Co, Duxford	
204	Lockheed SP-2H Neptune [V]	RAF Cosford Aerospace Museum	
361	Hawker Fury FB10 (N36SF)	Privately owned, Benson	
E-15	Fokker S-11 Instructor (G-BIYU)	Privately owned, White Waltham	
E-31	Fokker S-11 Instructor (G-BEPV)	Privately owned, Elstree	
N-202	Hawker Hunter F6 (nose only) [10]	Pinewood Studios, Elstree	
N-250	Hawker Hunter F6 (nose only) [G-9-185]	Science Museum, Wroughton	
N-268	Hawker Hunter F6 (Qatar QA-10)	Yorkshire Air Museum, Elvington	
N-315	Hawker Hunter T7	Privately owned, Batley	
R-163	Piper L-21B Super Cub (G-BIRH)	Privately owned, Lee-on-Solent	
R-167	Piper L-21B Super Cub (54-2457/G-LION)	Privately owned, Bishops Stortford	

New Zealand

NZ5648	Goodyear FG-1D Corsair (NX55JP) [1]	Old Flying Machine Co, Duxford	

Norway

56321	Saab S91B Safir (G-BKPY) [U-AB]	Newark Air Museum, Winthorpe	

Poland

05	WSK SM-2 (Mi-2)	IHM, Weston-super-Mare	
07	WSK SM-1 (Mi-1) (2007)	IHM, Weston-super-Mare	
1120	MiG-15bis	RAF Museum, Hendon	
3309	WSK SBLim-2A (MiG-15UTI)	Privately owned	
6247	WSK SBLim-2A (MiG-15UTI) (622 047/G-OMIG)	Privately owned, North Weald	
09008	WSK SBLim-2A (MiG-15UTI)	Privately owned, Shoreham	

Portugal

1513	NA Harvard II	Privately owned, Cranfield	
1662	NA Harvard III(G-ELMH)	Privately owned, Sudbury	
1681	NA T-6G Texan (G-BSBD)	Privately owned, Shoreham	
1736	CCF Harvard IV (G-BSBF)	Privately owned, Shoreham	
1741	CCF Harvard IV (G-BSBC/ G-HRVD)	Privately owned, Wellesbourne	
1788	CCF Harvard IV (G-BSBB)	Privately owned, Shoreham	
3460	Dornier 27-1 (G-BMFG)	Privately owned, Old Buckenham	

Qatar

QA12	Hawker Hunter FGA 78	Lovaux Ltd., Bournemouth (dismantled)	
QP30	WS Lynx Mk 28	RNAS Lee-on-Solent	
QP31	WS Lynx Mk 28	RNAW Almondbank	
QP32	WS Lynx Mk 28	RNAW Almondbank	

Russia (& former Soviet Union)

03	Mil Mi-24D (3532461715415)	Privately owned, Hawarden	
04	Mikoyan MiG-23ML (024003607)	Privately owned, Hawarden	

Historic Aircraft

Notes	Serial	Type	Owner or Operator
	05	Yak-50 (832507)	Privately owned, Strathallan
	06	Let L-29 Delfin (591636)	Privately owned, Hawarden
	06	Mil Mi-24D (3532464505029)	Privately owned, Cumbernauld
	07	Yak-18M (G-BMJY)	Privately owned, North Weald
	09	Let L-29 Delfin (591378)	Privately owned, Cumbernauld
	18	Let L-29 Delfin (591771)	Privately owned, Cumbernauld
	20	Lavochkin La-11	Privately owned, Duxford
	20	Yak-52 (790404)	Privately owned, Strathallan
	23	Mikoyan MiG-27 (83712515040)	Privately owned, Hawarden
	27	Yak C.11 (EAF 705/G-OYAK)	Privately owned, North Weald
	35	Sukhoi Su-17M-3 (25102)	Privately owned, Hawarden
	37	Let L-29 Delfin (491119)	Privately owned, Cumbernauld
	40	Let L-29 Delfin (491165)	Privately owned, Cumbernauld
	50	Mikoyan MiG-23MF (023003508)	Privately owned, Hawarden
	51	Let L-29 Delfin (491273)	Privately owned, Cumbernauld
	52	Yak-52 (LY-AKQ)	Privately owned, Gransden
	54	Sukhoi Su-17 (69004)	Privately owned, Hawarden
	56	Yak-52 (811504)	Privately owned, Strathallan
	69	Yak-50 (G-BTZB)	Privately owned, Duxford
	71	Mikoyan MiG-27K (61912507006)	Privately owned, Hawarden
	165221	WSK-Mielec An-2T (G-BTCU)[77]	Privately owned, Henstridge
	899404	Yak-52 (LY-AKV/G-CCCP)	Privately owned, Gransden

South Africa

Notes	Serial	Type	Owner or Operator
	6130	Lockheed Ventura II (AJ469)	RAF Cosford Aerospace Museum (stored)

Spain

Notes	Serial	Type	Owner or Operator
	C4E-88	Messerschmitt Bf-109E	Tangmere Military Aviation Museum
	C4K-102	Hispano HA 1.112 Mil (N9938)	Privately owned, Duxford
	E3B-153	CASA 1.131E Jungmann (G-BPTS) [781-75]	Privately owned, Duxford
	E3B-369	CASA 1.131E Jungmann (G-BPDM) [781-32]	Privately owned, Shoreham
	E3B-540	CASA 1.131E Jungmann (G-BRSH) [781-25]	Privately owned, Breighton
	EM-01	DH60G Moth (G-AAOR) [30-76]	Privately owned, Shoreham

Sweden

Notes	Serial	Type	Owner or Operator
	29640	SAAB J-29F [20-08]	Midland Air Museum, Coventry
	32028	SAAB 32A Lansen (G-BMSG)	Privately owned, Cranfield
	35075	SAAB J-35J Draken [40]	Imperial War Museum, Duxford

Switzerland

Notes	Serial	Type	Owner or Operator
	A-10	CASA 1.131E Jungmann (G-BECW)	Privately owned, Headcorn
	A-806	Pilatus P3-03 (G-BTLL)	Privately owned, Biggin Hill
	A-867	Pilatus P3-05 (G-BUKM)	Privately owned, Shipdham
	J-1008	DH Vampire FB6	Mosquito Aircraft Museum, London Colney
	J-1149	DH Vampire FB6 (G-SWIS) ●	Jet Heritage, Bournemouth
	J-1172	DH Vampire FB6 (8487M)	Greater Manchester Museum of Science and Industry
	J-1173	DH Vampire FB6 (G-DHXX) ●	Privately owned, Bournemouth
	J-1605	DH Venom FB50 (G-BLID)	Privately owned, Charlwood, Surrey
	J-1614	DH Venom FB50 (G-BLIE)	Privately owned, Glasgow
	J-1632	DH Venom FB50 (G-VNOM)	Privately owned, Cranfield
	J-1704	DH Venom FB54	RAF Cosford Aerospace Museum
	J-1758	DH Venom FB54 (G-BLSD/N203DM)	Aces High Ltd, North Weald
	U-80	Bucker Bu.133D Jungmeister (G-BUKK)	Privately owned, White Waltham
	U-110	Pilatus P-2 (G-PTWO)	Privately owned, Earls Colne
	U-142	Pilatus P-2 (G-BONE)	Privately owned, Goudhurst
	U-1214	DH Vampire T55 (G-DHVV) ●	Privately owned, Bournemouth
	U-1219	DH Vampire T55 (G-DHWW) ●	Privately owned, Bournemouth
	U-1230	DH Vampire T55 (G-DHZZ) ●	Privately owned, Bournemouth

USA

Notes	Serial	Type	Owner or Operator
	I-492	Ryan PT-22 (G-BPUD)	Privately owned, Swanton Morley
	01532	Northrop F-5E Tiger II (Replica)	RAF Alconbury on display
	O-17899	Convair VT-29B	Imperial War Museum, Duxford
	100	Grumman F8F-2P Bearcat (121714/NX700HL) [S]	The Fighter Collection, Duxford
	111989	Cessna L-19A Bird Dog (N33600)	Museum of Army Flying, Middle Wallop

Historic Aircraft

Serial	Type	Owner or Operator	Notes
112	Boeing-Stearman PT-13D Kaydet (G-BSWC)	Privately owned, Rendcomb	
115042	NA T-6G Texan (G-BGHU) [TA-042]	Privately owned, Headcorn	
115302	Piper L-18C Super Cub (G-BJTP) [TP]	Privately owned, Winterbourne, Bristol	
1164	Beech D.18S (G-BKGL/ RCAF 5193)	British Aerial Museum, Duxford	
118	Boeing-Stearman PT-13A Kaydet (G-BSDS)	Privately owned, Norwich	
1180	Boeing-Stearman N2S-3 Kaydet (G-BRSK)	Privately owned, Old Buckenham	
121821	Vultee BT-15 Valiant (N513L)	Aces High, North Weald	
122351	Beech C-45G (G-BKRG)	Aces High, North Weald	
124485	Boeing B-17G Flying Fortress (485784/G-BEDF) [DF-A]	B-17 Preservation Ltd., Duxford	
126922	Douglas AD-4NA Skyraider (G-RAID) [937-JS]	The Fighter Collection, Duxford	
1411	Grumman G.44A Widgeon (N444M)	Privately owned, Biggin Hill	
14419	Lockheed T-33A	Midland Air Museum, Coventry	
140547	NA T-28C Trojan (N2800Q)	Privately owned, Duxford	
146-11042	Wolf WII Replica (G-BMZX) [7]	Privately owned, Haverfordwest	
146-11083	Wolf WII Replica (G-BNAI) [5]	Privately owned, Haverfordwest	
146289	NA T-28C Trojan (N99153) [2W]	Norfolk & Suffolk Aviation Museum, Flixton	
14863	NA AT-6D Harvard 3 (G-BGOR)	Privately owned, Headcorn	
150225	Westland Wessex (G-AWOX) [123]	IHM, Weston-super-Mare	
151632	NA TB-25N Mitchell (NL9494Z) (really 430925)	Privately owned, Coventry	
15195	Fairchild PT-19A Cornell	RAF Museum, stored Cardington	
153008	McD F-4N Phantom	RAF Alconbury, BDRT	
155848	McD F-4S Phantom [WT-11/ VMFA-232]	FAA Museum, stored RNAS Yeovilton	
159233	McD AV-8A Harrier [CG-33/ VMA-231]	FAA Museum, RNAS Yeovilton	
160810	Bell AH-1T Sea Cobra (fuselage)	GEC, Rochester	
16579	Bell UH-1H Iroquois	IHM, Weston-super-Mare	
16769	Lockheed T-33A	RAF Mildenhall Fire Section	
17473	Lockheed T-33A	Midland Air Museum, Coventry	
17657	Douglas A-26K Invader (nose)	Booker Aircraft Museum	
18-2001	Piper L-18C Super Cub (G-BIZV) (really 52-2401)	Privately owned, Oxenhope	
19252	Lockheed T-33A	Tangmere Military Aviation Museum	
2	Boeing-Stearman N2S-5 Kaydet (G-AZLE)	Privately owned, Denham	
208	Boeing-Stearman N2S-5 Kaydet (N75664/42-17223)	Privately owned, Spanhoe Lodge, Northants	
217448	Boeing-Stearman PT-17 Kaydet (N3922B/42-17642)	Privately owned, Old Buckenham	
217786	Boeing-Stearman PT-13D Kaydet (G-BRTK) [177]	Privately owned, Old Buckenham	
224211	Douglas C-47A Dakota (G-BPMP) [M2-Z]	Privately owned, Coventry	
226671	Republic P-47M Thunderbolt (NX47DD)	The Fighter Collection, Duxford	
23	Fairchild PT-23 (43-437/N49272)	Privately owned, Halfpenny Green	
231983	Boeing B-17G Flying Fortress (44-83735/F-BDRS) [IY-G]	Imperial War Museum, Duxford	
236800	Piper L-4A Cub (G-BHPK) [44-A] (really 42-38410)	Privately owned, Tibenham	
243809	Waco CG-4A Hadrian (BAPC 185)	Museum of Army Flying, Middle Wallop	
24518	Kaman HH-43F Huskie (24535)	Midland Air Museum, Coventry	
26	Boeing-Stearman A75N-1 Kaydet (G-BAVO)	Privately owned, Streethay, Lichfield	
27	NA SNJ-7 Texan (G-BRVG/ 42-85895)	Intrepid Aviation, North Weald	
2807	NA T-6G Texan (G-BHTH) [V-103]	Privately owned, Thruxton	
28521	CCF Harvard IV (G-BSBE) [TA-521]	Privately owned, Shoreham	
295	Ryan PT-22 (N56028/41-20806)	Privately owned, Oaksey Park, Wilts	
29963	Lockheed T-33A	Wales Aircraft Museum, Cardiff	

Historic Aircraft

Notes	Serial	Type	Owner or Operator
	30861	NA TB-25J Mitchell (N9089Z)	Privately owned, North Weald
	314887	Fairchild Argus III (G-AJPI)	Privately owned, Liverpool
	315509	Douglas C-47A (G-BHUB) [W7-S]	Imperial War Museum, Duxford
	3-1923	Aeronca O-58B Defender (G-BRHP)	Privately owned, Chiseldon
	31952	Aeronca O-58B Defender (G-BRPR)	Privately owned, Ross-on-Wye
329417		Piper L-4A Cub (G-BDHK) (really 42-38400)	Privately owned, Coleford
32947		Piper L-4H Cub (G-BGXA) [44-F] (really 43-29471)	Privately owned, Martley, Worcs
	329601	Piper L-4H Cub (G-AXHR) [D-44]	Privately owned, Nayland
	329854	Piper L-4H Cub (G-BMKC) [R-44]	Privately owned, St Just
	329934	Piper L-4H Cub (G-BCPH) [72-B]	Privately owned, White Waltham
33		Boeing-Stearman N2S-5 Kaydet (G-THEA)	Privately owned, Duxford
	330485	Piper L-4H Cub (G-AJES) [44-C]	Privately owned, Saltash
	34037	NA TB-25N Mitchell (N9115Z/ 8838M) (really 429366)	RAF Museum, Hendon
343251		Boeing-Stearman N2S-5 Kaydet (G-NZSS/N4325/Bu.43517)	Privately owned, Cumbernauld
	37414	McD F-4C Phantom (FY63)	Midland Air Museum, Coventry
	37699	McD F-4C Phantom (FY63)	MIdland Air Museum, Coventry
379		Boeing-Stearman PT-13D Kaydet (G-ILLE/42-14865)	Privately owned, Compton Abbas
38674		Thomas-Morse S4 Scout Replica (G-MTKM)	Privately owned, Rugby
390		Boeing-Stearman N2S-3 Kaydet (G-BTRJ/N68235/Bu.07256)	Privately owned, Swanton Morley
40467		Grumman F6F-5K Hellcat (G-BTCC) [19]	The Fighter Collection, Duxford
	40707	McD F-4C Phantom (FY64)	RAF Lakenheath, BDRT
41		NA T-6G Texan (G-DDMV/ 49-3209) [BA]	Privately owned, Sywell
	41-33275	NA AT6C Harvard (G-BICE) [CE]	Privately owned, Ipswich
413573		NA P-51D Mustang (9133M/ N6526D) (really 473415) [B6-V]	RAF Museum, Hendon
41386		Thomas-Morse S4 Scout Replica (G-MJTD)	Privately owned, Hitchin
	42-12417	NA AT-16 Harvard IIB (B-163)	Thameside Aviation Museum
	42157	NA F-100D Super Sabre	North-East Aviation Museum, Usworth
	42165	NA F-100D Super Sabre [VM]	Imperial War Museum, Duxford
	42174	NA F-100D Super Sabre [UH]	Midland Air Museum, Coventry
	42196	NA F-100D Super Sabre [LT]	Norfolk & Suffolk Aviation Museum, Flixton
	42223	NA F-100D Super Sabre	Newark Air Museum, Winthorpe
	42265	NA F-100D Super Sabre	RAF Lakenheath
	42-58678	Taylorcraft DF-65 (G-BRIY) [IY]	Privately owned, North Weald
	42-69097	Bell P-63A Kingcobra (G-BTWR)	The Fighter Collection, Duxford
	42-78044	Aeronca 11AC Chief (G-BRXL)	Privately owned, Denham
	430823	NA TB-25J Mitchell (N1042B) [69]	Aces High Ltd, North Weald
	431171	NA B-25J Mitchell (N7614C)	Imperial War Museum, Duxford
44		Piper PA-18-95 Super Cub (G-BJLH) [K-33]	Privately owned, Felthorpe
441		Boeing-Stearman N2S-4 Kaydet (G-BTFG/N4467N/Bu.30010)	Privately owned, Bryngwyn Bach, Clwyd
	44-14574	NA P-51D Mustang (fuselage)	East Essex Aviation Museum, Clacton
442		Boeing-Stearman PT-17 Kaydet (G-BPTB/N55581/40-1885)	Privately owned, Paddock Wood
	445562	Douglas A-26 Invader (N7079G)	Privately owned, North Weald
	44-79609	Piper L-4H Cub (G-BHXY) [PR]	Privately owned, Aldergrove
	44-80594	Piper L-4J Cub (G-BEDJ)	Privately owned, White Waltham
	454467	Piper L-4J Cub (G-BILI) [44-J]	Privately owned, Bristol
	454537	Piper L-4J Cub (G-BFDL) [04-J]	Privately owned, Breighton
	45-49192	Republic P-47D Thunderbolt (N47DD)	Imperial War Museum, Duxford
	461748	Boeing B-29A Superfortress (G-BHDK) [Y]	Imperial War Museum, Duxford
463221		NA P-51D Mustang (G-BTCD) (really 473149) [G4-S]	The Fighter Collection, Duxford
	472216	NA P-51D Mustang (G-BIXL) [AJ-L]	Privately owned, North Weald
472258		NA P-51D Mustang (really 473979) [WZ-I]	Imperial War Museum, Lambeth

Serial	Type	Owner or Operator	Notes
472773	NA P-51D Mustang [AJ-C] (G-SUSY)	Privately owned, North Weald	
472917	CAC-18 Mustang 23 [AJ-A] (G-HAEC)	Privately owned, Duxford	
473877	NA P-51D Mustang (N167F) [B6-S]	Privately owned, Duxford	
474008	NA P-51D Mustang (N51RR) [VF-R]	Privately owned, North Weald	
479766	Piper L-4H Cub (G-BKHG) [63-D]	Privately owned, Goldcliff, Gwent	
480015	Piper L-4H Cub (G-AKIB)	Privately owned, Bodmin	
480133	Piper L-4J Cub (G-BDCD) [44-B]	Privately owned, Slinfold	
480321	Piper L-4J Cub (G-FRAN) [44-H]	Privately owned, Rayne, Essex	
480480	Piper L-4J Cub (G-BECN) [44-E]	Privately owned, Kersey, Suffolk	
480752	Piper L-4J Cub (G-BCXJ) [39-E]	Privately owned, Old Sarum	
483009	NA AT-6D Texan (really 244450) (G-BPSE)	Aces High, North Weald	
483868	Boeing B-17G Flying Fortress (N5237V) [A-N]	RAF Museum, Hendon	
511371	NA P-51D Mustang (NL1051S) [VF-S]	Privately owned, Leavesden	
51-14526	NA T-6G Texan (G-BRWB)	Privately owned, Duxford	
51-15227	NA T-6G Harvard (G-BKRA) [10]	Privately owned, Shoreham	
51-15673	Piper L-18C Super Cub (G-CUBI) (really 53-4781)	Privately owned, Felixkirk	
511701A	Beech C-45H (G-BSZC) [AF258]	Privately owned, Bryngwyn Bach	
52-8543	CCF Harvard IV (G-BUKY) [66]	Privately owned, Rochester	
53319	Grumman TBM-3R Avenger (G-BTDP) [319-RB]	Privately owned, North Weald	
540	Piper L-4H Cub (G-BCNX) (really 43-29877)	Privately owned, Monewden	
54137	CCF Harvard IV (G-CTKL/ RCAF3064)[69]	Privately owned, Shoreham	
54-21261	Lockheed T-33A (N33VC)	Privately owned, Duxford	
54-2447	Piper L-21B Super Cub (G-SCUB)	Privately owned, Anwick	
54-2474	Piper L-21B Super Cub (G-PCUB)	Privately owned, Headcorn	
54439	Lockheed T-33A	North-East Aviation Museum, Usworth	
5547	Lockheed T-33A (really 19036)	Newark Air Museum, Winthorpe	
60312	McDonnell F-101B Voodoo [AR]	Midland Air Museum, Coventry	
60689	Boeing B-52D Stratofortress	Imperial War Museum, Duxford	
607327	Piper PA.18-95 Super Cub [09-L] (G-ARAO)	Privately owned, Lambley	
61-2414	Boeing CH-47A Chinook	RAF Odiham, instructional use	
63000	NA F-100D Super Sabre [FW-000] (really 42160)	Wales Aircraft Museum, Cardiff	
63000	NA F-100D Super Sabre [FW-000] (really 42212)	RAF/USAF Croughton, at gate	
63319	NA F-100D Super Sabre [FW-319] (really 42269)	RAF Lakenheath, at gate	
63-419	McD F-4C Phantom (37419) [SA]	RAF Alconbury, BDRT	
63-428	Republic F-105G Thunderchief (really 24428)	USAF Croughton, Oxon	
63-449	McD F-4C Phantom (37449)	RAF Upper Heyford, BDRT	
63-471	McD F-4C Phantom (37471)	RAF Lakenheath, BDRT	
63-610	McD F-4C Phantom (37610)	RAF Lakenheath, BDRT	
66692	Lockheed U-2C	Imperial War Museum, Duxford	
67-120	GD F-111E (70120) [UH]	Imperial War Museum, Duxford	
67543	Lockheed P-38J Lightning (NX3145X) [MC-O]	The Fighter Collection, Duxford	
6771	Republic F-84F Thunderstreak (really 52-7133) (ex-FU-6)	Cosford Aerospace Museum, store	
68-011	GD F-111E (80011) [UH]	RAF Lakenheath, on display	
68-060	GD F-111E (80060) (pod)	Dumfries & Galloway Aviation Museum, Tinwald Downs	
70270	McDonnell F-101B Voodoo (fuselage)	Midland Air Museum, Coventry	
70-494	Republic F-105G Thunderchief (really 62-4434) [LN]	RAF Lakenheath, BDRT	
74-131	McD F-15A Eagle (40131) [LN]	RAF Lakenheath, BDRT	
77-259	Fairchild A-10A Thunderbolt (70259) [AR]	IWM, Duxford	
7797	Aeronca L-16A (G-BFAF)	Privately owned, Finmere	
796	Boeing-Stearman PT-13D Kaydet (N43SV)	Privately owned, Rendcomb	

Historic Aircraft

Notes	Serial	Type	Owner or Operator
	80-219	Fairchild GA-10A Thunderbolt (00219) [AR]	RAF Alconbury, on display
	80260	McDonnell F-101B Voodoo	RAF Molesworth
	8178	NA F-86A Sabre (G-SABR) [FU-178]	Privately owned, Bournemouth
	82062	DHC U-6A Beaver	Midland Air Museum, Coventry
	85	WAR P-47 Thunderbolt Replica (N47DL/G-BTBI)	Privately owned, Manchester
	854	Ryan PT-22 (G-BTBH/41-20854)	Privately owned, Wellesbourne Mountford
	855	Ryan PT-22 (N56421/41-15510)	Privately owned, Halfpenny Green
	86711	Grumman FM-2 Wildcat (N4845V) [M-F-48]	Privately owned, Duxford
	88297	Goodyear FG-1D Corsair (N8297/G-FGID) [29]	The Fighter Collection, Duxford
	88-9696	NA AT-6C Harvard IIA (G-TEAC) [688]	Privately owned, North Weald
	897	Aeronca 11AC Chief (G-BJEV)	Privately owned, English Bicknor
	91007	Lockheed T-33A (51-8566 G-TJET/G-NASA) [TR-007]	Privately owned, Cranfield
	93542	CCF Harvard IV (G-BRLV) [LTA-542]	Privately owned, White Waltham
	985	Boeing-Stearman PT-13D Kaydet (G-ERIX)(really 42-16930)	Privately owned, Sutton Bridge

Yugoslavia

Notes	Serial	Type	Owner or Operator
	13064	Republic P-47D Thunderbolt	RAF Museum Restoration Centre, Cardington
	30149	Soko P-2 Kraguj [149] (G-BRXK)	Privately owned, Liverpool

This Australian built Tiger Moth (G-BPHR) retains its RAAF serial A17-48. *PRM*

Irish Army Air Corps Military Aircraft Markings

Serial	Type	Owner or Operator	Notes
34	Miles Magister	Irish Aviation Museum Store, Dublin	
141	Avro Anson XIX	Irish Aviation Museum Store, Dublin	
157	VS Seafire III (RX158)	Privately owned, Battle, East Sussex	
164	DH Chipmunk T20	Engineering Wing, Baldonnel (stored)	
168	DH Chipmunk T20	No 2 Support Wing, Gormanston	
172	DH Chipmunk T20	Training Wing, Gormanston (stored)	
173	DH Chipmunk T20	South East Aviation Enthusiasts, Waterford	
176	DH Dove 4 (VP-YKF)	South East Aviation Enthusiasts, Waterford	
177	Percival Provost T51 (G-BLIW)	Privately owned, Shoreham	
181	Percival Provost T51	Privately owned, Thatcham	
183	Percival Provost T51	Irish Aviation Museum Store, Dublin	
184	Percival Provost T51	South East Aviation Enthusiasts, Waterford	
187	DH Vampire T55	Aviation Society of Ireland, stored, Waterford	
189	Percival Provost T51	Baldonnel, Fire Section	
191	DH Vampire T55	Irish Aviation Museum Store, Dublin	
192	DH Vampire T55	South East Aviation Enthusiasts, Waterford	
193	DH Vampire T55 (pod)	Baldonnel Fire Section	
195	Sud Alouette III	No 3 Support Wing, Baldonnel	
196	Sud Alouette III	No 3 Support Wing, Baldonnel	
197	Sud Alouette III	No 3 Support Wing, Baldonnel	
198	DH Vampire T11 (XE977)	Engineering Wing, Baldonnel	
199	DH Chipmunk T22	Training Wing store, Gormanston (spares)	
202	Sud Alouette III	No 3 Support Wing, Baldonnel	
203	Cessna FR172H	No 2 Support Wing, Gormanston	
205	Cessna FR172H	No 2 Support Wing, Gormanston	
206	Cessna FR172H	No 1 Support Wing, Baldonnel (rebuild)	
207	Cessna FR172H	No 2 Support Wing, Gormanston	
208	Cessna FR172H	No 2 Support Wing, Gormanston	
209	Cessna FR172H	No 2 Support Wing, Gormanston	
210	Cessna FR172H	No 2 Support Wing, Gormanston	
211	Sud Alouette III	No 3 Support Wing, Baldonnel	
212	Sud Alouette III	No 3 Support Wing, Baldonnel	
213	Sud Alouette III	No 3 Support Wing, Baldonnel	
214	Sud Alouette III	No 3 Support Wing, Baldonnel	
215	Fouga Super Magister	No 1 Support Wing, Baldonnel	
216	Fouga Super Magister	No 1 Support Wing, Baldonnel	
217	Fouga Super Magister	No 1 Support Wing, Baldonnel	
218	Fouga Super Magister	No 1 Support Wing, Baldonnel	
219	Fouga Super Magister	No 1 Support Wing, Baldonnel	
220	Fouga Super Magister	No 1 Support Wing, Baldonnel	
221	Fouga Super Magister [79/3-KE]	Engineering Wing, Baldonnel	
222	SIAI SF-260WE Warrior	Training Wing, Baldonnel	
225	SIAI SF-260WE Warrior	Training Wing, Baldonnel	
226	SIAI SF-260WE Warrior	Training Wing, Baldonnel	
227	SIAI SF-260WE Warrior	Training Wing, Baldonnel	
229	SIAI SF-260WE Warrior	Training Wing, Baldonnel	
230	SIAI SF-260WE Warrior	Training Wing, Baldonnel	
231	SIAI SF-260WE Warrior	Training Wing, Baldonnel	
233	SIAI SF-260MC	Engineering Wing, Baldonnel (stored)	
235	SIAI SF-260WE Warrior	Training Wing, Baldonnel	
237	Aérospatiale SA341F Gazelle	Advanced Flying Training School, Baldonnel	
238	BAe125/700B	Transport & Training Squadron, Baldonnel	
240	Beech King Air 200	Transport & Training Squadron, Baldonnel	
241	Aérospatiale SA341F Gazelle	Advanced Flying Training School, Baldonnel	
243	Cessna FR172K	No 2 Support Wing, Gormanston	
244	SA365F Dauphin II	No 3 Support Wing, Baldonnel	
245	SA365F Dauphin II	No 3 Support Wing, Baldonnel	
246	SA365F Dauphin II	No 3 Support Wing, Baldonnel	
247	SA365F Dauphin II	No 3 Support Wing, Baldonnel	
248	SA365F Dauphin II	No 3 Support Wing, Baldonnel	
250	Airtech CN.235	Transport & Training Squadron, Baldonnel	
251	Grumman Gulfstream IV	Transport & Training Squadron, Baldonnel	
252	Airtech CN.235 MP		
253	Airtech CN.235 MP		

Colourful Royal Netherlands Air Force F-16A of No 311 Sqn. *Andrew P. March*

Brazilian Air Force Boeing KC-137 2403 is based at Afonsos. *Andrew P. March.*

119

JbG 35 at Pferdsfeld operates this F-4F Phantom (37+12). *Andrew P. March*

Aircraft included in this section are a selection of those likely to be seen visiting UK civil and military airfields on transport flights, exchange visits, exercises and for air shows. It is not a comprehensive list of *all* aircraft operated by the air arms concerned.

ALGERIA
Force Aérienne Algerienne
   Lockheed C-130H
   Hercules
   4911 (7T-WHT)
   4912 (7T-WHS)
   4913 (7T-WHY)
   4914 (7T-WHZ)
   4924 (7T-WHR)
   4926 (7T-WHQ)
   4928 (7T-WHJ)
   4930 (7T-WHI)
   4934 (7T-WHF)
   4935 (7T-WHE)

   Lockheed C-130H-30
   Hercules
   4987 (7T-WHD)
   4989 (7T-WHL)
   4997 (7T-WHA)
   5224 (7T-WHB)

AUSTRALIA
Royal Australian Air Force
   Boeing 707-338C
   33 Sqn, Richmond, NSW
   A20-623
   A20-624
   A20-627
   A20-629

   Boeing 707-368C
   33 Sqn, Richmond, NSW
   A20-261

   Lockheed
   C-130H Hercules
   36 Sqn, Richmond, NSW
   A97-001
   A97-002
   A97-003
   A97-004
   A97-005
   A97-006
   A97-007
   A97-008
   A97-009
   A97-010
   A97-011
   A97-012

   Lockheed
   C-130E Hercules
   37 Sqn, Richmond, NSW
   A97-159
   A97-160
   A97-167
   A97-168
   A97-171
   A97-172

A97-177
A97-178
A97-180
A97-181
A97-189
A97-190

Lockheed
P-3C Orion
10/11 Sqns, Edinburgh, NSW
A9-656   11 Sqn
A9-657   11 Sqn
A9-658   11 Sqn
A9-659   11 Sqn
A9-660   11 Sqn
A9-661   11 Sqn
A9-662   11 Sqn
A9-663   11 Sqn
A9-664   11 Sqn
A9-665   11 Sqn
A9-751   10 Sqn
A9-752   10 Sqn
A9-753   10 Sqn
A9-755   10 Sqn
A9-756   10 Sqn
A9-757   10 Sqn
A9-758   10 Sqn
A9-759   10 Sqn
A9-760   10 Sqn

AUSTRIA
Oesterreichische
Luftstreitkrafte
   SAAB 105ÖE
   JbG, Linz;
   1/Uberwg, Zeltweg;
   2/Uberwg, Graz
   (yellow)
   1101/A JbG
   1102/B JbG
   1104/D JbG
   1105/E JbG
   1106/F
   1107/G JbG
   1108/H
   1109/I
   1110/J JbG
   (green)
   1111/A
   1112/B JbG
   1114/D JbG
   1116/F JbG
   1117/G JbG
   1119/I
   1120/J JbG
   (red)
   1122/B 2/Uberwg
   1123/C JbG
   1124/D

1125/E JbG
1126/F
1127/G
1128/H JbG
1129/I 1/Uberwg
1130/J JbG
(blue)
1131/A
1132/B JbG
1133/C JbG
1134/D JbG
1135/E JbG
1136/F
1137/G Jba
1139/I JbG
1140/J 1/Uberwg

Short SC7
Skyvan 3M
Flachenstaffel, Tulln
5S-TA
5S-TB

BELGIUM
Force Aérienne Belge/
   Belgische Luchtmacht
   D-BD Alpha Jet
   7/11 Smaldeel,
      Brustem (9Wg)
   AT01
   AT02
   AT03
   AT05
   AT06
   AT08
   AT09
   AT10
   AT11
   AT12
   AT13
   AT14
   AT15
   AT16
   AT17
   AT18
   AT19
   AT20
   AT21
   AT22
   AT23
   AT24
   AT25
   AT26
   AT27
   AT28
   AT29
   AT30
   AT31
   AT32
   AT33

Dassault Mirage 5BA
42 Smaldeel, Bierset
BA08
BA15
BA18
BA20
BA22
BA27
BA31
BA33
BA42
BA43
BA44
BA53
BA54
BA60

Dassault Mirage 5BD
42 Smaldeel, Bierset
BD04
BD09
BD10
BD11
BD12

Dassault Mirage 5BR
42 Smaldeel, Bierset
BR03
BR04
BR04
BR07
BR08
BR09
BR10
BR12
BR13
BR14
BR15
BR17
BR21
BR22
BR23
BR24
BR25
BR26
BR27

Boeing 727-29C
21 Smaldeel, Melsbroek
CB01
CB02

**Swearingen
Merlin IIIA**
21 Smaldeel, Melsbroek
CF01
CF02
CF04
CF05
CF06

**Lockheed
C-130H Hercules**
20 Smaldeel, Melsbroek
CH01
CH02
CH03
CH04
CH05
CH06
CH07
CH08
CH09
CH10
CH11
CH12

**Dassault
Falcon 20E**
21 Smaldeel, Melsbroek
CM01
CM02

**Hawker-Siddeley
HS748 Srs 2A**
21 Smaldeel, Melsbroek
CS01
CS02
CS03

General Dynamics F-16A
349,350 Smaldeel;
    Bevekom (1 Wg);
1,2 Smaldeel, Florennes
    (2 Wg);
23,31 Smaldeel,
    Kleine-Brogel (10 Wg)

FA01	349 Sm
FA02	350 Sm
FA03	349 Sm
FA04	350 Sm
FA05	349 Sm
FA09	349 Sm
FA10	349 Sm
FA16	349 Sm
FA17	349 Sm
FA18	350 Sm
FA19	350 Sm
FA20	350 Sm
FA21	349 Sm
FA22	350 Sm
FA23	350 Sm
FA25	349 Sm
FA26	349 Sm
FA27	349 Sm
FA28	350 Sm
FA30	349 Sm
FA31	349 Sm
FA32	350 Sm
FA34	349 Sm
FA36	350 Sm
FA37	349 Sm
FA38	350 Sm
FA39	350 Sm
FA40	349 Sm
FA43	349 Sm
FA44	350 Sm
FA45	349 Sm
FA46	349 Sm
FA47	349 Sm
FA48	349 Sm
FA49	350 Sm
FA50	350 Sm
FA51	350 Sm
FA53	350 Sm
FA55	349 Sm
FA56	23 Sm
FA57	23 Sm
FA58	31 Sm
FA60	31 Sm
FA61	23 Sm
FA65	31 Sm
FA66	31 Sm
FA67	23 Sm
FA68	31 Sm
FA69	23 Sm
FA70	31 Sm
FA71	23 Sm
FA72	31 Sm
FA73	23 Sm
FA74	31 Sm
FA75	23 Sm
FA76	31 Sm
FA77	23 Sm
FA78	31 Sm
FA80	31 Sm
FA81	23 Sm
FA82	31 Sm
FA83	23 Sm
FA84	31 Sm
FA86	31 Sm
FA87	31 Sm
FA88	31 Sm
FA89	23 Sm
FA90	31 Sm
FA91	350 Sm
FA92	31 Sm
FA93	23 Sm
FA94	31 Sm
FA95	23 Sm
FA96	31 Sm
FA97	1 Sm
FA98	2 Sm
FA99	1 Sm
FA100	2 Sm
FA101	1 Sm
FA102	2 Sm
FA103	2 Sm
FA104	2 Sm
FA106	2 Sm
FA107	1 Sm
FA108	2 Sm
FA109	1 Sm
FA110	2 Sm
FA111	1 Sm
FA112	2 Sm
FA113	23 Sm
FA114	2 Sm
FA115	1 Sm
FA116	2 Sm
FA117	1 Sm
FA118	2 Sm
FA119	1 Sm
FA120	2 Sm
FA121	1 Sm
FA122	2 Sm
FA123	1 Sm
FA124	23 Sm
FA125	1 Sm
FA126	23 Sm
FA127	2 Sm
FA128	2 Sm
FA129	1 Sm
FA130	2 Sm
FA131	1 Sm
FA132	2 Sm
FA133	1 Sm
FA134	2 Sm
FA135	1 Sm
FA136	2 Sm

General Dynamics F-16B
349 Sm, 350 Sm, OCS,
    Bevekom (1Wg);
1 Sm, 2 Sm, Florennes
    (2 Wg);

23 Sm, 31 Sm,
Kleine-Brogel (10 Wg)

FB01	OCS
FB02	OCS
FB03	OCS
FB04	1 Wg
FB05	OCS
FB07	OCS
FB08	350 Sm
FB09	OCS
FB10	10 Wg
FB12	OCS
FB14	2 Wg
FB15	10 Wg
FB17	10 Wg
FB18	10 Wg
FB19	10 Wg
FB20	10 Wg
FB21	1 Sm
FB22	10 Wg
FB23	1 Sm
FB24	2 Sm

Fouga CM170 Magister
33 Sm (9 Wg), Brustem

MT3
MT04
MT14
MT29
MT30
MT31
MT33
MT34
MT36
MT37
MT40
MT44
MT46
MT48
MT49

SIAI Marchetti SF.260MB/SF.260D*
Ecole de Pilotage
Elementaire (5 Sm),
Gossoncourt

ST01
ST03
ST04
ST05
ST06
ST08
ST09
ST10
ST12
ST13
ST14
ST15
ST16
ST17
ST18
ST19
ST20
ST21
ST22
ST23
ST24
ST25
ST26
ST27
ST28
ST30
ST31
ST32
ST33
ST34
ST35
ST36
ST37*
ST38*
ST39*
ST40*
ST41*
ST42*
ST43*
ST44*
ST45*
ST46*
ST47*
ST48*
ST49*
ST50*
ST51*

Belgische Landmacht
Sud Alouette II
16 Batalion, Butzweilerhof,
  Germany;
17 Battalion, Werl, Germany;
18 Battalion, Merzbrück,
  Germany;
Gendarmerie Nationale
(GN),Brasschaat;
SvHLV, Brasschaat

A04	16 Batt
A05	SvHLV
A12	17 Batt
A14	18 Batt
A15	17 Batt
A18	16 Batt
A22	SvHLV
A23	18 Batt
A24	18 Batt
A26	SvHLV
A31	SvHLV
A32	18 Batt
A34	17 Batt
A35	SvHLV
A37	18 Batt
A38	17 Batt
A40	17 Batt
A41	18 Batt
A42	SvHLV
A43	18 Batt
A44	18 Batt
A45	18 Batt
A46	16 Batt
A47	SvHLV
A48	17 Batt
A49	16 Batt
A50	SvHLV
A53	18 Batt
A54	SvHLV
A55	SvHLV
A57	16 Batt
A61	17 Batt
A62	17 Batt
A64	16 Batt
A65	18 Batt
A66	17 Batt
A68	16 Batt
A69	SvHLV
A70	18 Batt
A72	SvHLV
A73	SvHLV
A74	SvHLV
A75	18 Batt
A76	18 Batt
A77	SvHLV
A78	16 Batt
A79	16 Batt
A80	16 Batt
A90	GN
A92	GN
A93	GN
A94	GN
A95	GN

Britten-Norman BN-2A Islander
16 Batallion, Butzweilerhof,
  Germany;
17 Battalion, Werl, Germany;
18 Battalion, Merzbrück,
  Germany;
SvHLV, Brasschaat

B01/LA	SvHLV
B02/LB	
B03/LC	
B04/LD	SvHLV
B07/LG	SvHLV
B08/LH	SvHLV
B09/LI	
B10/LJ	SvHLV
B11/LK	SvHLV
B12/LL	SvHLV

Agusta A109HA/HO*
16 Batallion, Butzweilerhof,
  Germany;
17 Battalion, Werl, Germany;
18 Battalion, Merzbrück,
  Germany;
SvHLV, Brasschaat

H01*	
H02*	
H03*	
H04*	
H05*	
H06*	
H07*	
H08*	
H09*	
H10*	18 Batt
H11*	
H12*	
H13*	
H14*	SvHLV
H15*	18 Batt
H16*	
H17*	SvHLV
H18*	SvHLV
H19	18 Batt
H20	18 Batt
H21	18 Batt
H22	18 Batt
H23	
H24	
H25	
H26	
H27	
H28	

Force Navale
Belge/Belgische Zeemacht
SA316B Alouette III
Koksijde Heli Flight
M1   (OT-ZPA)
M2   (OT-ZPB)
M3   (OT-ZPC)

Westland Sea
King Mk48
40 Smaldeel, Koksijde
RS01
RS02
RS03
RS04
RS05

BRAZIL
Forca Aerea Brasileira
Boeing KC-137
2 GT 2 Esq, Afonsos
2401
2402
2403
2404

Lockheed
C-130E Hercules
1 GT,   Afonsos
2451   C-130E
2453   C-130E
2454   C-130E
2455   C-130E
2456   C-130E
2458   C-130E
2460   C-130E
2461   KC-130H
2462   KC-130H
2463   C-130H
2464   C-130H
2465   C-130H
2466   C-130H
2467   C-130H

Lockheed
RC-130E Hercules
6 GAV 1 Esq, Recife
2459

CANADA
Canadian Forces
Lockheed
CC-130E/CC-130E(SAR)*
Hercules
413 Sqn, Greenwood (SAR);
418 Sqn, Edmonton (SAR);
424 Sqn, Trenton (SAR);
426 Sqn, Trenton;
429 Sqn, Trenton;
435 Sqn, Edmonton;
436 Sqn, Trenton
130305* 424 Sqn
130306* 418 Sqn
130307* 424 Sqn
130308   436 Sqn
130310* 424 Sqn
130311   435 Sqn
130313   435 Sqn
130314* 424 Sqn
130315   436 Sqn

130316   429 Sqn
130317   436 Sqn
130319   436 Sqn
130320   436 Sqn
130323   436 Sqn
130324   436 Sqn
130325   436 Sqn
130326   435 Sqn
130327   436 Sqn
130328   436 Sqn

Lockheed
CC-130H/CC-130H(T)*
Hercules
130332   436 Sqn
130333   436 Sqn
130334
130335
130336
130337
130338* 435 Sqn
130339* 435 Sqn
130340* 435 Sqn
130341* 435 Sqn
130342* 435 Sqn

Boeing CC-137
(B.707-374C)
437 Sqn, Trenton
13701
13703
13704
13705

Lockheed
CP-140 Aurora
404/405/415 Sqns,
  Greenwood;
407 Sqn, Comox
140101
140102
140103
140104
140105   407 Sqn
140106
140107   407 Sqn
140108
140109   405 Sqn
140110   407 Sqn
140111   407 Sqn
140112
140113
140114
140115
140116
140117
140118   407 Sqn

Lockheed
CP-140A Arcturus
140119
140120
140121

Canadair CC-144/CE-144A*
Challenger
412 Sqn, Ottawa-Uplands;
414 Sqn, Comox;
434 Sqn, Shearwater
144601   412 Sqn
144602   412 Sqn
144603* 414 Sqn

144604   412 Sqn
144605* 434 Sqn
144606   412 Sqn
144607* 414 Sqn
144608* 414 Sqn
144609   412 Sqn
144610* 414 Sqn
144611* 434 Sqn
144613   412 Sqn
144614   412 Sqn
144615   412 Sqn
144616* 434 Sqn

Airbus CC-150 Polaris
(A310-304)
437 Sqn, Trenton
15001
15002
15003
15004
15005

CHILE
Fuerza Aérea de Chile
Boeing 707-321B/330/351C
902   351C
903   330B
904   321B

Extra EA-300
Los Halcones
021   [1]
022   [2]
023   [3]
024   [6]
025   [5]
027   [4]

Lockheed
C-130B/H Hercules
Grupo 10, Santiago
995   C-130H
996   C-130H
997   C-130B

CZECH AND SLOVAK
REPUBLICS
Some aircraft are still to be re-
located in the Republic to which
they belong, following the
division of the former
Czechoslovak Air Force on 1
January 1993.
In the lists below the bases have
been identified with the Republic
in which they are located
(Cz=Czech and Sl=Slovak).

Aero L.39 Albatros
30 BILP, Pardubice (Cz);
1 LSP, Prerov (Cz);
2 LSP, Kosice (Sl);
3 LSP, Piestany (Sl);
1 SLP, Ceske
  Budejovice (Cz);
11 SLP, Zatec (Cz);
81 SSLT, Sliac (Sl);
82 SSLT, Mosnov (Cz);
VU 030, Praha/Kbely (Cz)
0001   L.39MS   VU 030
0002   L.39MS   1 LSP

Reg	Type	Unit
0003	L.39MS	1 LSP
0103	L.39C	2 LSP
0105	L.39C	2 LSP
0106	L.39C	2 LSP
0107	L.39C	2 LSP
0113	L.39C	2 LSP
0115	L.39C	2 LSP
0441	L.39C	2 LSP
0442	L.39C	3 LSP
0444	L.39C	3 LSP
0445	L.39C	3 LSP
0447	L.39C	3 LSP
0448	L.39C	3 LSP
0449	L.39C	2 LSP
0502	L.39C	3 LSP
1701	L.39C	3 LSP
1702	L.39C	3 LSP
1725	L.39ZA	30 BILP
1730	L.39ZA	2 LSP
1735	L.39ZA	2 LSP
2341	L.39ZA	11 SLP
2343	L.39ZA	82 SSLT
2344	L.39ZA	82 SSLT
2350	L.39ZA	1 SLP
2415	L.39ZA	11 SLP
2421	L.39ZA	1 SLP
2424	L.39ZA	1 SLP
2427	L.39ZA	1 SLP
2430	L.39ZA	11 SLP
2436	L.39ZA	11 SLP
4605	L.39C	2 LSP
4606	L.39C	2 LSP
4607	L.39C	2 LSP
4701	L.39ZA	81 SSLT
4703	L.39ZA	81 SSLT
4705	L.39ZA	81 SSLT
4707	L.39ZA	30 BILP
4711	L.39ZA	81 SSLT
4806	L.39ZA	81 SSLT

Let 410
FLS, Hradec Kralove (Cz);
3 LSP, Piestany (Sl);
1 SMDLP, Kbely (Cz)

Reg	Type	Unit
0403	L.410M	1 SMDLP
0503	L.410M	3 LSP
1133	L.410T	1 SMDLP
1521	L.410FG	FLS

Mikoyan MiG-29/MiG-29UB*
3810
4401*
4402*
5113
5515
5817
5918
7702
8003
8304
8605
9308

Sukhoi Su-25K/Su-25BK*
30 BILP, Pardubice (Cz)
1004
1005
5006
5033
5036

6019
8075
8079
8080
8081
9093
9098
9099

CZECH REPUBLIC

Aero L.39/L.59(L.39MS) Albatros
1 LSP, Prerov;
30 BILP, Pardubice;
82 SSLT, Mosnov

Reg	Type	Unit
0004	L.39MS	1 LSP
0005	L.39MS	1 LSP
0006	L.39MS	1 LSP
0440	L.39C	1 LSP
2347	L.39ZA	82 SSLT
2418	L.39ZA	82 SSLT
2433	L.39ZA	82 SSLT
3903	L.39ZA	30 BILP
5013	L.39ZA	30 BILP
5015	L.39ZA	30 BILP
5017	L.39ZA	30 BILP
5019	L.39ZA	30 BILP

Antonov An-12BP
3 DLP, Praha/Kbely
2105

Antonov An-26
3 DLP, Praha/Kbely
2408
2409
2507
3209

Let 410
3 DLP, Praha/Kbely;
10 SPOJP, Pardubice;
17 SPOJP, Klecany

Reg	Type	Unit
0402	L.410M	3 DLP
0501	L.410M	3 DLP
0502	L.410M	3 DLP
0712	L.410UVP	3 DLP
0731	L.410UVP	3 DLP
0926	L.410T	17 SPOJP
0928	L.410T	17 SPOJP
0929	L.410T	3 DLP
1132	L.410T	17 SPOJP
1134	L.410T	17 SPOJP
1504	L.410UVP	3 DLP
1522	L.410FG	10 SPOJP
1523	L.410FG	10 SPOJP
1524	L.410FG	10 SPOJP
1526	L.410FG	10 SPOJP
2312	L.410UVP	3 DLP

Let 610
VU-030, Praha/Kbely
0005

Mikoyan MiG-29/MiG-29UB*
11 SLP, Ceske Budejovice
4012
5414
5616
8906
9207

Sukhoi Su-25K/Su-25BK*
30 BILP, Pardubice
1002
1003
3348*
5007
5008
5039
5040
6020
8076
8077
8078
9013
9014
9094

Tupolev Tu-134A
3 DLP, Praha/Kbely
1407

Tupolev Tu-154B-2
3 DLP, Praha/Kbely
0601

DENMARK

Kongelige Danske Flyvevaabnet

Lockheed C-130H Hercules
Eskadrille 721, Vaerløse
B-678
B-679
B-680

General Dynamics F-16
Eskadrille 723, Aalborg;
Eskadrille 726, Aalborg;
Eskadrille 727, Skrydstrup;
Eskadrille 730, Skrydstrup

F-16A

E-004	Esk 726
E-005	Esk 726
E-006	Esk 726
E-007	Esk 726
E-008	Esk 726
E-016	Esk 726
E-017	Esk 726
E-018	Esk 726
E-174	Esk 727
E-176	Esk 723
E-177	Esk 723
E-178	Esk 730
E-180	Esk 726
E-181	Esk 730
E-182	Esk 730
E-183	Esk 723
E-184	Esk 723
E-187	Esk 727
E-188	Esk 723
E-189	Esk 723
E-190	Esk 723
E-191	Esk 730
E-192	Esk 730
E-193	Esk 727
E-194	Esk 723
E-195	Esk 723
E-196	Esk 723
E-197	Esk 730
E-198	Esk 730
E-199	Esk 727

E-200 Esk 723
E-202 Esk 730
E-203 Esk 723
E-596 Esk 726
E-597 Esk 730
E-598 Esk 730
E-599 Esk 730
E-600 Esk 727
E-601 Esk 727
E-602 Esk 727
E-603 Esk 727
E-604 Esk 726
E-605 Esk 730
E-606 Esk 730
E-607 Esk 726
E-608 Esk 723
E-609 Esk 727
E-610 Esk 727
E-611 Esk 727

F-16B
ET-022 Esk 726
ET-197 Esk 726
ET-198 Esk 726
ET-199 Esk 726
ET-204 Esk 727
ET-205 Esk 730
ET-206 Esk 730
ET-207 Esk 727
ET-208 Esk 730
ET-210 Esk 726
ET-612 Esk 730
ET-613 Esk 727
ET-614 Esk 723
ET-615 Esk 727

Grumman Gulfstream III
Eskadrille 721, Vaerløse
F-249
F-313
F-330

SAAB T-17 Supporter
Flyveskolen, Avnø (FLSK);
Haerens Flyvetjaeneste (Danish Army), Vandel;
Eskadrille 721, Vaerløse
T-401 FLSK
T-402 Skrydstrup Stn Flt
T-403 Karup Stn Flt
T-404 Karup Stn Flt
T-405 Karup Stn Flt
T-407 Karup Stn Flt
T-408 FLSK
T-409 FLSK
T-410 Karup Stn Flt
T-411 FLSK
T-413 FLSK
T-414 Army
T-415 FLSK
T-417 Army
T-418 FLSK
T-419 FLSK
T-420 Esk 721
T-421 FLSK
T-422 FLSK
T-423 FLSK
T-425 Aalborg Stn Flt
T-426 FLSK
T-427 FLSK
T-428 FLSK
T-429 FLSK
T-430 FLSK
T-431 FLSK
T-432 FLSK

Sikorsky S-61A Sea King
Eskadrille 722, Vaerløse
Detachments at:
Aalborg, Ronne, Skrydstrup
U-240
U-275
U-276
U-277
U-278
U-279
U-280
U-481

Sovaernets Flyvetjaeneste (Navy)
Westland Lynx Mk 80/90*
Eskadrille 722, Vaerløse
S-035
S-134
S-142
S-170
S-175
S-181
S-191
S-249*
S-256*

Haerens Flyvetjaeneste (Army)
Hughes 500M
Vandel
H-201
H-202
H-203
H-205
H-206
H-207
H-209
H-210
H-211
H-213
H-244
H-245
H-246

Aérospatiale AS550C-2 Fennec
P-090
P-234
P-254
P-275
P-276
P-287
P-288
P-319
P-320
P-352
P-369

ECUADOR
Fuerza Aérea Ecuatoriana
Lockheed C-130H Hercules
FAE-812
FAE-893

EGYPT
Al Quwwat al-Jawwiya Ilmisriya
Lockheed C-130H/C-130H-30* Hercules
16 Sqn, Cairo West
1271/SU-BAB
1272/SU-BAC
1273/SU-BAD
1274/SU-BAE
1275/SU-BAF
1277/SU-BAI
1278/SU-BAJ
1279/SU-BAK
1280/SU-BAL
1281/SU-BAM
1282/SU-BAN
1283/SU-BAP
1284/SU-BAQ
1285/SU-BAR
1286/SU-BAS
1287/SU-BAT
1288/SU-BAU
1289/SU-BAV
1290/SU-BEW
1291/SU-BEX
1292/SU-BEY
1293/SU-BKS*
1294/SU-BKT*
1295/SU-BKU*

FRANCE
Armée de l'Air
Aérospatiale SN601 Corvette
CEV, Bretigny
1 MV
2 MW

Aérospatiale TB-30 Epsilon
GE.315, Cognac
1 315-UA
2 315-UB
3 FZ
4 315-UC
5 315-UD
6 315-UE
7 315-UF
8 315-UG
9 315-UH
10 315-UI
11 315-UJ
12 315-UK
13 315-UL
14 315-UM
15 315-UN
16 315-UO
17 315-UP
18 315-UQ
19 315-UR
20 315-US
21 315-UT
23 315-UV
24 315-UW
25 315-UX
26 315-UY
27 315-UZ
28 315-VA
29 315-VB
30 315-VC

31	315-VD
32	315-VE
33	315-VF
34	315-VG
35	315-VH
36	315-VI
37	315-VJ
38	315-VK
39	315-VL
40	315-VM
41	315-VN
42	315-VO
43	315-VP
44	315-VQ
45	315-VR
46	315-VS
47	315-VT
48	315-VU
49	315-VV
50	315-VW
51	2-BD
52	315-VX
53	315-VY
54	315-VZ
56	315-WA
57	F-ZVLB
58	315-WB
60	315-WC
61	315-WD
62	315-WE
63	315-WF
64	315-WG
65	315-WH
66	315-WI
67	315-WJ
68	315-WK
69	315-WL
70	315-WM
71	315-WN
72	315-WO
73	315-WP
74	315-WQ
75	315-WR
76	315-WS
77	315-WT
78	315-WU
79	315-WV
80	315-WW
81	315-WX
82	315-WY
83	315-WZ
84	315-XA
85	315-XB
86	315-XC
87	315-XD
88	315-XE
89	315-XF
90	315-XG
91	315-XH
92	315-XI
93	315-XJ
94	315-XK
95	315-XL
96	315-XM
97	315-XN
98	315-XO
99	315-XP
100	315-XQ
101	315-XR
102	315-XS
103	315-XT
104	315-XU

105	315-XV
106	315-XW
107	315-XX
108	315-XY
109	315-XZ
110	315-YA
111	315-YB
112	315-YC
113	315-YD
114	315-YE
115	315-YF
116	315-YG
117	315-YH
118	315-YI
119	315-YJ
120	315-YK
121	315-YL
122	315-YM
123	315-YN
124	315-YO
125	315-YP
126	315-YQ
127	315-YR
128	315-YS
129	315-YT
130	315-YU
131	315-YV
132	315-YW
133	315-YX
134	315-YY
135	315-YZ
136	315-ZA
137	315-ZB
138	315-ZC
139	315-ZD
140	315-ZE
141	315-ZF
142	315-ZG
143	315-ZH
144	315-ZI
145	315-ZJ
146	315-ZK
148	315-ZL
149	315-ZM
150	315-ZN
152	315-ZO
153	315-ZP
154	315-ZQ
155	315-ZR
158	315-ZS
159	315-ZT

Airtech CN-235
CEAM, Mont-de-Marsan;
ET.1/62, Creil

043	330-ID
045	330-IE
065	330-IF
066	330-IG
071	330-IH
072	330-II

Boeing C-135FR
ERV.93, Avord, Istres,
Mont-de-Marsan

38470	93-CA
38471	93-CB
38472	93-CC
38474	93-CE
475	93-CF
735	93-CG
12736	93-CH

737	93-CI
738	93-CJ
12739	93-CK
740	93-CL

Boeing KC-135R
ERV.93, Avord
23516
38033
71439

Boeing E-3F Sentry
EDCA.00/036, Avord

201	36-CA
202	36-CB
203	36-CC
204	36-CD

CASA 212
CEV

377	MO
378	MP
386	MQ
387	MR
388	MS

Cessna 310
CEV

045	AU
046	AV
185	AU
186	BI
187	BJ
188	BK
190	BL
192	BM
193	BG
194	BH
242	AW
244	AX
513	BE
820	CL
981	BF

Cessna 411
CEV

6	AD
8	AE
185	AC
248	AB

D-BD Alpha Jet
Patrouille de France (PDF),
 Salon de Provence;
EC.1/8, EC.2/8 Cazaux;
GE.314, Tours;
CEAM (330), Mont-de-
Marsan

01	F-ZJTS	CEV
02	F-ZWRU	
E1		CEV
E3	8-NC	EC2/8
E4		CEV
E5	8-NS	EC2/8
E7	8-MM	EC1/8
E8		
E9	314-TN	
E10	8-NM	EC2/8
E11	8-MW	EC1/8
E12		CEV
E13	314-LH	
E14	314-LE	

E15	314-TT		E97	314-LV		E170	314-LB		
E17	8-NK	EC2/8	E98	314-LA		E171			
E18	8-MD	EC1/8	E99	314-LW		E173			
E19	314-TS		E100		CEV	E174			
E20	8-ML	EC1/8	E101			E175	314-LU		
E21	314-UD		E102	8-MC	EC1/8	E176			

Dassault Falcon 20
CEV;
SIET.98/120, Cazaux;
ETEC.2/65, Villacoublay;
CITAC.339, Luxeuil

E22			E103			22	CS	(CEV)	
E23	F-TERO	PDF [8]	E104	314-TL		49	120-FA		
E24	314-TW		E105	330-BT		79	CT	(CEV)	
E25	314-LL		E106	314-LJ		86	CG	(CEV)	
E26	8-NP	EC2/8	E107			93	(F-RAED)	(ETEC)	
E27			E108	8-NI	EC2/8	96	CB	(CEV)	
E28	8-MI	EC1/8	E109	8-MU	EC1/8	104	CW	(CEV)	
E29	8-MF	EC1/8	E110	8-ND	EC2/8	115	339-JG		
E30	8-NR	EC2/8	E112			124	CC	(CEV)	
E31	314-UA		E113			131	CD	(CEV)	
E32	8-NQ	EC2/8	E114	314-UC		138	CR	(CEV)	
E33	8-NN	EC2/8	E115	8-MS	EC1/8	145	CU	(CEV)	
E34	314-TC		E116			167	(F-RAEB)	(ETEC)	
E35			E117	314-UL		182	339-JA		
E36	314-LD		E118	8-NT	EC2/8	186	339-JE		
E37	F-TERI	PDF [1]	E119	314-TR		188	CX	(CEV)	
E38	F-TERC	PDF [9]	E120	314-LM		238	F-RAEE	(ETEC)	
E40			E121	F-TERK	PDF [7]	252	CA	(CEV)	
E41	314-LC		E122	314-UG		260	(F-RAEA)	(ETEC)	
E42	314-LQ		E123	8-MQ	EC1/8	263	CY	(CEV)	
E43	314-TZ		E124			268	(F-RAEF)	(ETEC)	
E44		CEV	E125	F-TERH	PDF [4]	288	CV	(CEV)	
E45			E126	F-TERA	PDF [6]	291	(F-RAEG)	(ETEC)	
E46	F-ZJTJ	AMD-BA	E127	8-MB	EC1/8	342	(F-RAEC)	(ETEC)	
E47			E128	314-LS		375	CZ	(CEV)	
E48	8-MO	EC1/8	E129	8-NB	EC2/8	422	65-EH	(ETEC)	
E49	314-LP		E130	314-TI		451	339-JC		
E51	314-UB		E131	314-TY		483	339-JI		
E52	314-TX		E132	F-TERN	PDF [5]				

Dassault Falcon 50
ET.60, Villacoublay

E53	8-NW	EC2/8	E133			5	(F-RAFI)
E55	314-UN		E134			27	(F-RAFK)
E58	314-TD		E135			034	(F-RAFL)
E59			E136	314-LY		78	(F-RAFJ)

Dassault Falcon 900
ET.60, Villacoublay

E60			E137	314-TG		2	(F-RAFP)
E61			E138	314-UK		4	F-RAFQ

Dassault Mirage IVA/IVP
EB.1/91, Mont-de-Marsan;
EB.2/91, Cazaux

E63			E139	314-UF		2	AA	
E64	8-NH	EC2/8	E140	F-TERD	PDF [0]	4	AC	
E65			E141			5	AD	
E66	8-ME	EC1/8	E142			6	AE	
E67	8-MR	EC1/8	E143	314-UJ		7	AF	
E68	8-NA	EC2/8	E144	8-NU	EC2/8	8/01	AG	
E69	8-NX	EC2/8	E145			11	AJ	1/91
E70			E146	8-MG	EC1/8	12	AK	
E72	F-TERG	PDF [3]	E147			13	AL	
E73			E148	8-NJ	EC2/8	14	AM	
E74	8-N0	EC2/8	E149	314-LI		15	AN	
E75	314-TU		E150	8-NF	EC2/8	19	AR	
E76	314-TH		E151			20	AS	
E79	314-LN		E152	314-TA		21	AT	
E80		CEV	E153	314-TM		23	AV	1/91
E81	314-LR		E154	8-MA	EC1/8			
E82	314-TE		E155					
E83	8-NG	EC2/8	E156	8-MX	EC1/8			
E84	8-MH	EC1/8	E157	314-LG				
E85	330-BR		E158					
E86	314-TJ		E159	314-LT				
E87	8-MP	EC1/8	E160	314-LZ				
E88	314-TF		E161					
E89	F-TERE	PDF [2]	E162	314-LF				
E90	8-NE	EC2/8	E163	314-TQ				
E91	8-NL	EC2/8	E164	8-MJ	EC1/8			
E92			E165	314-TB				
E93	8-NV	EC2/8	E166	8-MN	EC1/8			
E94			E167	8-MV	EC1/8			
E95	314-LX		E168	8-MK	EC1/8			
E96	8-MT		E169	314-LK				

24	AW	
25	AX	2/91
26	AY	1/91
27	AZ	
31	BD	1/91
34	BG	
36	BI	1/91
37	BJ	
39	BL	
42	BO	
44	BQ	
47	BT	
48	BU	1/91
49	BV	
51	BX	
52	BY	2/91
53	BZ	2/91
54	CA	2/91
55	CB	
56	CC	
57	CD	1/91
59	CF	1/91
61	CH	2/91
62	CI	1/91

**Dassault
Mirage F.1C/F.1CT***
EC.12 Cambrai;
EC.13 Colmar;
EC.4/30 Djibouti;
EC.30, Rheims;
CEAM (330), Mont-de-Marsan

2		
3		
4	12-YE	(CEV)
5		
6		
9	12-ZQ	2/12
10	12-ZD	2/12
14	30-SJ	1/30
15		
16	30-SE	1/30
17		
18		
19		
20		
21		
22		
23		
24		
25	12-ZP	2/12
26		
27		
29		
30		
31		
32		
33	30-FS	3/30
35		
36	30-MP	2/30
37	30-MK	2/30
38	30-SB	1/30
39	12-ZM	2/12
40	30-FM	3/30
41		
42	30-MC	2/30
43		
44		
47		
49		
50	12-ZI	2/12

52		
54	30-MJ	2/30
55	30-MN	2/30
60	12-ZH	2/12
62	30-SC	1/30
63		
64		
67		
68	30-FN	3/30
69		
70		
71	30-SD	1/30
72		
73		
74		
75		
76	30-FF	3/30
77		
78		
79		
80	30-LN	4/30
81	30-LO	4/30
82		
83		
84		
85	30-LP	4/30
87	30-SI	1/30
90		
100	30-LC	4/30
101		
103	12-ZN	2/12
201		
202	30-LF	4/30
203	30-LQ	4/30
205		
206	30-LR	4/30
207		
210	30-LS	4/30
211	30-LT	4/30
213	30-SR	1/30
214	12-ZJ	2/12
216	30-SG	1/30
217	30-MR	2/30
218	30-SK	1/30
219	30-SL	1/30
220	12-ZG	2/12
221		
223	12-ZR	2/12
224	30-SS	1/30
225		
226*	13-QO	1/13
227*		CEV
228		
229*	13-QF	1/13
230*	13-QM	1/13
231	30-SO	1/30
232		
233*	13-QG	1/13
234*	13-QL	1/13
235		
236	12-ZE	2/12
237*	13-QH	1/13
238*	13-QK	1/13
239*	13-QD	1/13
240		
241		
242*	13-QJ	1/13
243*	13-QN	1/13
244		
245*	13-SA	2/13
246		
247		

248		
249	30-SQ	1/30
251		
252	30-MB	2/30
253	30-MM	2/30
254*	13-QC	1/13
255	12-ZB	2/12
256	12-ZF	2/12
257		
258	30-LA	4/30
259	30-SP	1/30
260	30-SF	1/30
261		
262*		
264	30-FL	3/30
265		
267*	13-QB	1/13
268	30-LI	4/30
271	30-SN	1/30
272	30-SA	1/30
273*	330-AI	
274*	330-AJ	
275	30-SM	1/30
277		
278*	13-QA	1/13
279		
280*	13-QE	1/13
281*	13-QI	1/13
282*	13-SB	2/13
283	30-MF	2/30

**Dassault Mirage
F.1CR**
ER.33, Strasbourg;
CEAM (330), Mont-de-Marsan;
CEV, Istres

601		CEV
602		CEV
603	33-CB	1/33
604	33-CE	1/33
605	33-NF	2/33
606	33-TS	
607		
608	33-NG	2/33
609		
610	33-CH	1/33
611	33-CO	1/33
612	33-NJ	2/33
613	33-NK	2/33
614	33-TO	
615	33-CU	1/33
616		
617	33-CI	1/33
619	33-TD	
620	33-CT	1/33
621		
622	33-CR	1/33
623	33-CM	1/33
624	33-NY	2/33
625		
627	33-NI	2/33
628	33-TC	
629	33-CG	1/33
630	33-NL	2/33
631	33-CD	1/33
632	33-NE	2/33
634	33-CK	1/33
635	33-TH	
636	33-CS	1/33
637	33-CP	1/33
638	33-TP	
640	33-TE	

641	33-NT	2/33
642	33-NC	2/33
643		
645	33-NO	2/33
646	33-TU	
647	33-TR	
648	33-CF	1/33
649	33-TF	
650	33-CJ	1/33
651	33-NB	2/33
653	33-TB	
654	33-CL	1/33
655	33-NR	2/33
656	33-NH	2/33
657		
658	33-TI	
659	33-CA	1/33
660	33-ND	2/33
661	33-TA	
662	33-NM	2/33

Dassault Mirage 2000B
CEAM (330), Mont-de-Marsan;
CEV;
EC.2, Dijon;
EC.5, Cambrai;
EC.12, Orange

01		CEV
501	2-EQ	CEV
502	2-FA	2/2
504		
505	2-FB	2/2
506	2-FC	2/2
507	2-FD	2/2
508	2-FE	2/2
509	2-FF	2/2
510	2-FG	2/2
511	2-FH	2/2
512	2-FI	2/2
513	2-FJ	2/2
514	2-FK	2/2
515	330-AN	
516	2-FM	2/2
517	2-FO	2/2
518	5-OJ	2/5
519	5-AM	3/5
520	5-AN	3/5
521	5-OL	2/5
522	5-NA	1/5
523	12-YA	1/12
524	12-KB	3/12
525	12-KN	3/12
526		
527		

Dassault Mirage 2000C
CEAM (330), Mont-de-Marsan;
CEV, Istres; EC.2, Dijon;
EC.5, Orange; EC.12 Cambrai

01		
03		CEV
04		
1	2-EP	CEV
2		CEV
3	2-FP	2/2
4	2-LB	3/2
5	2-FQ	2/2
8	2-EC	1/2
9	2-LO	3/2
11	2-EF	1/2
12	2-EH	1/2
13	2-EI	1/2
14	2-EO	1/2
15	2-EK	1/2
16	2-EL	1/2
17	2-EM	1/2
18	2-FL	2/2
19	2-LA	3/2
20	2-EQ	1/2
21	2-LF	3/2
22	2-LG	3/2
25	2-LK	3/2
27	2-LM	3/2
28	2-LN	3/2
29	2-ED	1/2
30	2-FN	2/2
32	2-EP	1/2
33	2-LQ	3/2
34	2-LI	3/2
35	2-EE	1/2
36	2-EN	1/2
37	2-EU	1/2
38	5-AR	3/5
39	5-OF	2/5
40	5-OI	2/5
41	5-AA	3/5
42	5-NC	1/5
43		
44		
45	5-OM	2/5
46	5-AD	3/5
47	5-AC	3/5
48	5-AF	3/5
49	5-AE	3/5
51	5-OG	2/5
52	5-OC	2/5
53	5-AH	3/5
54	5-AI	3/5
55	5-OH	2/5
56	5-OA	2/5
57	5-AJ	3/5
58	5-AK	3/5
59	5-OB	2/5
61	5-OD	2/5
62	5-AL	3/5
63	5-OK	2/5
64	330-AQ	
65	5-OO	2/5
66	5-ON	2/5
67		
68	5-AP	3/5
69		
70	5-AO	3/5
71		
72	5-OE	2/5
73		
74	5-OP	2/5
75		
76	5-NP	1/5
77	5-ND	1/5
78	5-NE	1/5
79	5-NF	1/5
80	330-AS	
81	330-AY	
82	330-AX	
83	5-NG	1/5
84	5-NH	1/5
85	5-NI	1/5
86	5-NJ	1/5
87	5-NK	1/5
88	5-NL	1/5
89	5-NM	1/5
90	5-NN	1/5
91	5-NO	1/5
92		
93	5-NR	1/5
94	12-KA	3/12
95	12-YB	1/12
96	12-KK	3/12
97	12-YF	1/12
98	12-YJ	1/12
99	12-YP	1/12
100	12-YH	1/12
101	12-YQ	1/12
102	12-YE	1/12
103	12-YN	1/12
104	12-KC	3/12
105	12-YL	1/12
106	12-KL	3/12
107	12-YR	1/12
108	330-AT	
109	12-YI	1/12
110		
111		
112	5-NB	1/5
113		
114	12-YG	1/12
115		
116	12-KG	2/12
117	12-YD	1/12
118	12-KH	3/12
119	12-KD	3/12
120	12-KM	3/12
121	12-KF	3/12
122		
123		
124		
125		
126		

Dassault Mirage 2000D
CEAM (330), Mont-de-Marsan;
EC.3, Nancy

D01	AMD-BA	
601	330-AK	
602	3-IB	3/3
603	3-IC	3/3
604	3-ID	3/3
605	3-IE	3/3
606	3-IF	3/3
607		
608		
609		
610		

Dassault Mirage 2000N
CEAM (330), Mont-de-Marsan;
EC.3, Nancy;
EC.1/4, EC.2/4 Luxeuil;
EC.3/4 Istres

301		
302	4-CA	3/4
303	4-CP	3/4
304	3-CB	3/4
305	4-BF	2/4
306	4-BE	2/4
307	4-BC	2/4
308	4-CD	3/4
309	4-BA	2/4
310	4-CE	3/4
311	4-BD	2/4

312	4-CF	3/4		**DHC 6 Twin Otter**			5144*	61-PF	
313				CEAM, Mont-de-Marsan;			5150*	61-PG	
314	4-CG	3/4		GAM.56 Evreux;			5151*	61-PH	
315	4-BG	2/4		ETEC.1/65 Villacoublay;			5152*	61-PI	
316	4-CH	3/4		EdC.70 Chateaudun			5153*	61-PJ	
317	4-BH	2/4		292	OW	GAM.56	5226*	61-PK	
318	4-CI	3/4		298	OY	GAM.56	5227*	61-PL	
319	4-BI	2/4		300	OZ	GAM.56			
320	4-CJ	3/4		603	MB	EdC.70			
322	4-CK	3/4		730	CA	ETEC	**Morane Saulnier 760**		
323	4-BK	2/4		742	65-CB	ETEC	**Paris**		
324	4-CL	3/4		743	CZ	ETEC	CEV;		
325	4-BL	2/4		745	CV	ETEC	EC.4, Luxeuil;		
326	4-CM	3/4		786	CT	ETEC	EC.13, Colmar;		
327	4-BM	2/4		790	65-CW	ETEC	ENOSA, Toulouse;		
329	4-BN	2/4					ETE.41, Metz;		
330	4-CO	3/4		**Douglas DC-8F**			ETE.43, Bordeaux;		
331	4-BO	2/4		EE.51 Evreux;			ETE.44, Aix-en-Provence;		
332	330-AR			ET.3/60 Charles de Gaulle			ET.65, Villacoublay;		
333	330-AG			45570	F-RAFE	EE.51	GI.312, Salon de Provence;		
334	330-AV			45819	F-RAFC	ET.3/60	CEAM (330), Mont-de-Marsan		
335	4-BJ	2/4		46013	F-RAFG	ET.3/60	1	330-DA	CEAM
336	4-BP	2/4		46043	F-RAFD	ET.3/60	14	41-AH	ETE.41
337	4-AB	2/4		46130	F-RAFF	ET.3/60	19		
338	4-AC	1/4					23		
339	4-AD	1/4		**Embraer EMB.121 Xingu**			24	65-LA	ET.65
340	4-AA	1/4		CEAM, Mont-de-Marsan;			25	41-AP	ETE.41
341	4-AF	1/4		CITAC.339, Luxeuil;			26	65-LN	ET.65
342	4-AG	1/4		ETE.43 Bordeaux;			27		
343	4-AH	1/4		ETE.44 Aix-en-Provence;			29	4-WA	EC.4
344	4-AJ	1/4		GE.319 Avord			30	65-LW	ET.65
345	4-AK	1/4		054	YX		34	43-BB	ETE.43
346	4-AL	1/4		064	YY		35	13-TB	EC.13
347	4-AM	1/4		072	YA		36	316-DH	ENOSA
348	3-JA	2/3		073	YB		38	41-AS	ETE.41
349	4-AO	1/4		075	YC		44	330-DR	CEAM
350	4-AP	1/4		076	YD		45	DI	ENOSA
351	4-AQ	1/4		078	YE		51	13-TA	EC.13
353				080	YF		53		
354	3-JC	2/3		082	YG		54	330-DQ	CEAM
355	3-JD	2/3		084	YH		56	DJ	ENOSA
356	3-JE	2/3		086	YI		57	65-LK	ET.65
357	3-JF	2/3		089	YJ		58	312-DG	GI.312
358	3-JG	2/3		091	YK		59		
359	3-JH	2/3		092	YL		60	312/DE	GI.312
360	3-JI	2/3		095	YM		61	312/DF	GI.312
361	3-JJ	2/3		096	YN		62		
362	3-JK	2/3		098	YO		68	NB	CEV
363	3-JL	2/3		099	YP		70	65-LF	ET.65
364	3-JM	2/3		101	YR		71	41-AC	ETE.41
365	3-JN	2/3		102	YS		73		
366	3-JO	2/3		103	YT (ETE.44)		75	316-DK	ENOSA
367	3-JP	2/3		105	YU		77	330-DD	CEAM
368	4-AR	1/4		107	YV		78	65-LI	ET.65
369	4-AS	1/4		108	YW		80		
370	4-AT	1/4		111	YQ		81	314-DD	CEAM
371	4-AV	1/4					83	NC	CEV
372	4-BR	2/4		**Embraer EMB.312F**			91	65-LU	ET.65
373	3-JV	2/3		**Tucano**			92	316/DL	ENOSA
374				438			93		
375	3-JB	2/3		439			94		
							97	330-DC	CEAM
Dassault Rafale-A				**Lockheed C-130H**			100	NG	CEV
01	CEV			**Hercules**			113	NI	CEV
				*C-130H-30 Hercules			114	NJ	CEV
Dassault Rafale-B				ET.2/61, Orleans			115	OV	CEV
B01	AMD-BA			5114	61-PA		116	ON	CEV
				5116	61-PB		117	AZ	CEV
Dassault Rafale-C				5119	61-PC		118	NQ	CEV
C01	CEV			5140	61-PD		119	NL	CEV
C02				5142*	61-PE				
C03									

Nord 262 Fregate

CEV, Istres;
ENOSA, Toulouse;
ETE.41, Metz;
ETE.43, Bordeaux;
ETE.44, Aix-en-Provence;
ETEC.1/65, Villacoublay;
EdC.070, Chateaudun;
CEAM (330), Mont-de-Marsan

01		CEV
3	OH	CEV
55	MH	CEV
58	MJ	CEV
64	AA	ETEC
66	AB	ETEC
67	MI	CEV
68	AC	ET.65
76	DA	ENOSA
77	AK	ETEC
78	AF	ETEC
80	AW	ET.65
81	AH	ET.65
83	DB	ENOSA
86	DD	ENOSA
87	DC	ENOSA
88	AL	ET.65
89	AZ	ET.65
91	AT	ETE.44
92	DE	ENOSA
93	MB	CEV
94	AU	ETE.44
95	AR	ET.65
105	MA	EdC
106	AY	ET.65
107	AX	ET.65
108	AG	ET.65
109	AM	ET.65
110	AS	ET.65

SEPECAT Jaguar A

EC.7, St Dizier;
EC.11, Toul;
CEAM (330), Mont-de-Marsan;
CITAC.339, Luxeuil

A1		
A2	11-MC	2/11
A3		CEV
A5	7-IE	3/7
A7	7-PG	2/7
A8		
A9	7-PB	2/7
A11	7-PA	2/7
A12	7-IF	3/7
A13	11-EM	1/11
A14	11-MA	2/11
A15	7-IJ	3/7
A16		
A17	7-HF	1/7
A19		
A21	7-IA	3/7
A22	11-RE	3/11
A23	7-HK	1/7
A24		
A25	11-MO	2/11
A26	7-HM	1/7
A27	11-MQ	2/11
A28	11-MG	2/11
A29	11-MB	2/11
A31		

A32		
A33	7-HL	1/7
A34	7-ID	3/7
A35		
A36	7-IP	3/7
A37	7-HA	1/7
A38	11-EG	1/11
A39	7-IT	3/7
A40	7-IQ	3/7
A41	7-HM	1/7
A43	11-EC	1/11
A44		
A46	7-IC	3/7
A47		
A48	7-PC	2/7
A49	11-ED	1/11
A50		
A53	11-RB	3/11
A54	11-EF	1/11
A55	7-HB	1/7
A58	11-RH	3/11
A59	7-IH	3/7
A60		
A61	11-RG	3/11
A64	7-IS	3/7
A65		
A66	7-IB	3/7
A70	11-RL	3/11
A72	7-PD	2/7
A73	7-HH	1/7
A74		
A75	7-HE	1/7
A76	7-HI	1/7
A79		
A80	7-HN	1/7
A82		
A84	11-RQ	3/11
A86		
A87		
A88	7-II	3/7
A89		
A90		
A92		
A93	7-HP	1/7
A94		
A96		
A98	7-IK	3/7
A99	11-EI	1/11
A100	11-EE	1/11
A101	11-MH	2/11
A103		
A104		
A107	11-MV	2/11
A108	11-MP	2/11
A112	11-EK	1/11
A113		
A115		
A117		
A118	7-IM	3/7
A119		
A120	11-MR	2/11
A121		
A122	11-EQ	1/11
A123		
A124		
A126		
A127	11-MM	2/11
A128	11-MD	2/11
A129		
A130	7-HJ	1/7
A131		
A133	11-EL	1/11

A135	11-RJ	3/11
A137	11-EM	1/11
A138	11-RX	3/11
A139	11-RC	3/11
A140	11-EN	1/11
A141	11-EO	1/11
A142		
A144	11-RW	3/11
A145	11-EP	1/11
A148	11-EQ	1/11
A149	11-RK	3/11
A150	11-ET	1/11
A151	11-ER	1/11
A152		
A153	11-RA	3/11
A154	11-RP	3/11
A157	11-ES	1/11
A158	11-RM	3/11
A159	11-RV	3/11
A160	11-RT	3/11

SEPECAT Jaguar E

E1		CEV
E2	7-HD	1/7
E3	339-WI	
E4		
E5		
E6	11-EZ	1/11
E7	7-PN	2/7
E8	339-WG	3/7
E9	7-PQ	2/7
E10	339-WF	
E11	7-PE	2/7
E12	339-WJ	
E13	11-RD	3/11
E15	7-PF	2/7
E16	7-HO	1/7
E18		
E19		
E20	11-RI	3/11
E21		
E22	7-PI	2/7
E23		
E24	339-WK	
E25	7-PK	2/7
E27	7-IG	3/7
E28	7-PR	2/7
E29	7-PL	2/7
E30		
E32	7-PO	2/7
E33		
E35	339-WH	
E36	7-PP	2/7
E37		
E39		
E40	7-PH	2/7

SOCATA TBM 700

ETE.43, Bordeaux;
ETEC.2/65, Villacoublay

33	65-XA	ETEC
35	65-XB	ETE.43
70	65-XC	ETE.43
77	65-XD	ETEC
78	65-XE	ETEC
80	65-XF	ETEC

Transall C-160
Transall C-160H[1]
Transall C-160NG[2]

ETOM.55, Dakar;
EE.59, Evreux (C160H);

ET.61 Orleans (C160A/F);	
ET.64 Evreux (C160NG)	
A02	61-MI
A04	BICEV
A06	61-ZB
F1	61-MA
F2	61-MB
F3	61-MC
F4	61-MD
F5	
F11	61-MF
F12	61-MG
F13	
R15	61-MJ
F16	61-MK
F17	
F18	61-MM
F42	61-MN
F43	61-MO
F44	61-MP
F45	61-MQ
F46	61-MR
F48	61-MT
F49	61-MU
F51	61-MW
F52	61-MX
F53	61-MY
F54	61-MZ
F55	61-ZC
F86	61-ZD
F87	61-ZE
F88	61-ZF
F89	61-ZG
F90	61-ZH
F91	61-ZI
F92	61-ZJ
F93	61-ZK
F94	61-ZL
F95	61-ZM
F96	61-ZN
F97	61-ZO
F98	61-ZP
F99	61-ZQ
F100	61-ZR
F153	61-ZS
F154	61-ZT
F155	61-ZU
F157	61-ZW
F158	61-ZX
F159	61-ZY
F160	61-ZZ
F201[2]	64-GA
F202[2]	64-GB
R203[2]	64-GC
F204[2]	64-GD
F205[2]	64-GE
F206[2]	64-GF
F207[2]	64-GG
F208[2]	64-GH
F210[2]	64-GJ
F211[2]	64-GK
F212[2]	64-GL
F213[2]	64-GM
F214[2]	64-GN
F215[2]	64-GO
F216[2]	GT
F217[2]	64-GQ
F218[2]	64-GR
F221[2]	64-GS
F222[2]	64-GV
F223[2]	64-GW

F224[2]	64-GX
F225[2]	64-GY
F226[2]	64-GZ
F230[1]	F-ZJUA
F231[1]	F-ZJUB
F232[1]	
H01[1]	59-BA
H02[1]	59-BB
H03[1]	59-BC
H04[1]	59-BD

Aéronavale/Marine
Aérospatiale SA.321G
Super Frelon
32 F, Lanveoc;
33 F, San Mandrier

101	(32F)
2	(32F)
105	(33F)
106	(32F)
118	(32F)
120	(32F)
122	(32F)
134	(32F)
137	(32F)
141	(32F)
44	(32F)
148	(33F)
149	(32F)
60	(32F)
162	(32F)
163	(33F)
164	(32F)
165	(32F)

Breguet 1050
Alizé
4F, Lann Bihoué;
6F, Nimes-Garons;
ES 59, Hyeres

11	(4F)
12	(4F)
17	(4F)
22	(6F)
24	(6F)
25	(6F)
26	(6F)
28	
30	(6F)
31	(59S)
33	(4F)
36	(6F)
41	(6F)
43	(4F)
47	(4F)
48	(4F)
49	
50	(6F)
51	(4F)
52	(4F)
53	(6F)
55	(6F)
56	(4F)
59	(6F)
60	(59S)
64	(6F)
65	(6F)
67	(59S)
68	(6F)
73	(6F)
76	(59S)

87	(59S)

Breguet Br 1150
Atlantic/Atlantique 2*
21F/22F, Nimes-Garons;
23F/24F, Lann Bihoué

03	(21F/22F)
04	(21F/22F)
2	(21F/22F)
3	(21F/22F)
7	(23F/24F)
11	(21F/22F)
13	(21F/22F)
21	(23F/24F)
23	(21F/22F)
24	(23F/24F)
25	(21F/22F)
31	(21F/22F)
35	(21F/22F)
41	(21F/22F)
44	(21F/22F)
45	(23F/24F)
48	(23F/24F)
49	(21F/22F)
50	(21F/22F)
51	(21F/22F)
52	(21F/22F)
53	(21F/22F)
54	(21F/22F)
55	(23F/24F)
56	(21F/22F)
57	(21F/22F)
61	(21F/22F)
65	(23F/24F)
66	(23F/24F)
67	(21F/22F)
68	(23F/24F)
01*	(21F/22F)
02*	(CEV)
03*	(CEV)
04*	(21F/22F)
1*	(23F/24F)
2*	(23F/24F)
3*	(23F/24F)
4*	(23F/24F)
5*	(23F/24F)
6*	(23F/24F)
7*	(23F/24F)
8*	(23F/24F)
9*	(23F/24F)
10*	
11*	(23F/24F)
12*	(23F/24F)
13*	
14*	
15*	
16*	
17*	
18*	
19*	
20*	
21*	
22*	
23*	
24*	
25*	
26*	
27*	
28*	
29*	
30*	

Dassault Super Etendard
11 F, Landivisiau;
17 F, Hyeres;
ES 59, Hyeres

1	(11F)
2	(59S)
3	(59S)
4	(11F)
5	(11F)
6	(59S)
8	(11F)
10	(11F)
11	(11F)
12	(11F)
13	(17F)
14	(11F)
15	(11F)
16	(17F)
17	
18	(59S)
19	(59S)
21	
23	(17F)
24	(17F)
25	(11F)
26	(11F)
28	(11F)
29	
30	(11F)
31	(11F)
32	(11F)
33	(17F)
34	(11F)
35	(17F)
37	(59S)
38	(59S)
39	
41	(59S)
42	
43	(11F)
44	(11F)
45	(17F)
46	(17F)
47	(17F)
48	(11F)
49	(59S)
50	(17F)
51	
52	(11F)
53	
54	(11F)
55	(17F)
57	(11F)
59	(17F)
60	(11F)
61	(11F)
62	
63	(11F)
64	(11F)
65	(17F)
66	(17F)
68	(CEV)
69	(11F)
71	(17F)

Dassault Falcon 10 (MER)
ES 3, Hyeres;
ES 57, Landivisiau

32	(3S)
101	(57S)
129	(57S)
133	(57S)
143	(57S)
185	(3S)

Dassault Falcon Guardian
ES 9 Noumea;
ES 12 Papeete;
CEPA, Istres

48	(12S)
65	(9S)
72	(12S)
77	(9S)
80	(CEPA)

Dassault Rafale-M

M01	AMD-BA
M02	AMD-BA

Embraer EMB.121 Xingu
ES 2, Lann Bihoué;
ES 11, Le Bourget;
ES 52, Lann Bihoué;
ES 57, Landivisiau

30	(11S)
47	(57S)
55	(52S)
65	(11S)
66	(52S)
67	(52S)
68	(52S)
69	(2S)
70	(11S)
71	(2S)
74	(11S)
77	(11S)
79	(11S)
81	(57S)
83	(11S)
85	(52S)
87	(52S)
90	(52S)

LTV F-8E (FN) Crusader
12 F, Landivisiau

3	
4	
5	
7	
8	
10	
11	
17	
19	
22	
23	
27	
29	
31	
32	
34	
35	(CEV)
37	
39	
40	
41	
42	
46	
85	
87	
88	

Morane Saulnier 760 Paris
ES 57, Landivisiau

32	
33	

Nord 262 Fregate
ES 2, Lann Bihoué;
ES 3, Hyeres;
ES 11, Le Bourget;
ES 56, Nimes-Garons;
ES 57, Landivisiau

1	(11S)
16	(56S)
28	(2S)
43	(11S)
45	(3S)
46	(56S)
51	(57S)
52	(56S)
53	(56S)
59	(2S)
60	(2S)
61	(3S)
62	(2S)
63	(3S)
65	(2S)
69	(56S)
70	(2S)
71	(2S)
72	(2S)
73	(56S)
75	(2S)
79	(56S)
100	(56S)
102	(11S)
104	(11S)

Piper Navajo
ES 3, Hyeres;
ES 10 Fréjus;
ES 56 Nimes-Garons

227	(3S)
903	(56S)
906	(3S)
916	(3S)
925	(3S)
927	(10S)
931	(3S)

Westland Lynx HAS2 (FN); HAS4 (FN)
31 F, San Mandrier;
34 F, Lanvéoc;
ES 20, St Raphael

260	(20S)
262	(35F)
263	(34F)
264	(31F)
265	(34F)
266	(34F)
267	
268	
269	(34F)
270	(31F)
271	(35F)
272	(34F)
273	(34F)
274	(34F)

275 (31F)
276 (34F)
278 (34F)
620 (34F)
621 (34F)
622 (34F)
623 (34F)
624 (34F)
625 (34F)
627 (34F)
801* (31F)
802* (34F)
803* (31F)
804* (35F)
806* (31F)
807* (31F)
808* (34F)
809* (31F)
810* (31F)
811* (34F)
812* (31F)
813* (31F)
814* (34F)

Aviation Legére de l'Armée de Terre (ALAT)
Cessna F.406 Caravan
3 GHL, Rennes
0008 AGS
0010 AGT

GERMANY
Luftwaffe, Marineflieger
Boeing 707-307C
FBS-BMVg, Köln-Bonn
10+01
10+02
10+03
10+04

Airbus A310-304
FBS-BMVg, Köln-Bonn
10+21
10+22
10+23

Tupolev Tu-154M
FBS-BMVg, Köln-Bonn
11+01
11+02

Canadair CL601-1A Challenger
FBS-BMVg, Köln-Bonn
12+01
12+02
12+03
12+04
12+05
12+06
12+07

HFB 320 Hansa Jet ECM
JbG 32, Lechfeld
16+21
16+23
16+24
16+25
16+26
16+27
16+28

VFW-Fokker 614-100
FBS-BMVg, Köln-Bonn
17+01
17+02
17+03

Mikoyan MiG-29
JG 73, Preschen
WTD 61, Ingolstadt
MiG-29A
29+01 JG 73
29+02 JG 73
29+03 JG 73
29+05 JG 73
29+07 JG 73
29+08 JG 73
29+09 JG 73
29+10 JG 73
29+11 JG 73
29+12 JG 73
29+14 JG 73
29+15 JG 73
29+16 JG 73
29+17 JG 73
29+18 JG 73
29+19 JG 73
29+20 JG 73
29+21 JG 73
98+06 WTD 61
98+08 WTD 61

MiG-29UB
29+22 JG 73
29+23 JG 73
29+24 JG 73
29+25 JG 73

McD F-4F Phantom
JbG 35, Pferdsfeld;
JG 71, Wittmundhaven;
JG 72, Hopsten;
JG 74, Neuburg/Donau;
TSLw 1, Kaufbeuren;
WTD 61, Ingolstadt
37+01 JG 72
37+03 JG 71
37+04 TSLw 1
37+05 JG 72
37+06 JbG 35
37+07 JG 72
37+08 JG 74
37+09 JbG 35
37+10 JbG 35
37+11 JG 74
37+12 JbG 35
37+13 JG 74
37+14 TSLw 1
37+15 WTD-61
37+16 WTD-61
37+17 JG 72
37+18 JG 72
37+19 JG 72
37+20 JbG 35
37+21 JbG 35
37+22 JG 71
37+23 JG 72
37+24 JG 72
37+25 JbG 35
37+26 JG 72
37+28 JG 74
37+29 JbG 35
37+30 JbG 35

37+31 JG 74
37+32 JG 74
37+33 JbG 35
37+34 JbG 35
37+35 JbG 35
37+36 JbG 35
37+37 JG 72
37+38 JbG 35
37+39 JG 71
37+40 JbG 35
37+41 JbG 35
37+42 JbG 35
37+43 JbG 35
37+44 JbG 35
37+45 JbG 35
37+46 JbG 35
37+47 JbG 35
37+48 JG 74
37+49 JG 74
37+50 JbG 35
37+52 JbG 35
37+53 JG 74
37+54 JG 74
37+55 JG 74
37+56 JG 74
37+57 JG 72
37+58 JbG 35
37+60 JG 74
37+61 JG 74
37+63 JG 74
37+64 JG 74
37+65 JG 74
37+66 JG 74
37+67 JG 74
37+69 JbG 35
37+70 JG 71
37+71 JG 74
37+73 JG 74
37+75 JG 71
37+76 JG 74
37+77 JG 74
37+78 JG 71
37+79 JG 74
37+81 JG 72
37+82 JbG 35
37+83 JG 71
37+84 JG 74
37+85 JG 74
37+86 JG 71
37+88 JG 72
37+89 JG 72
37+90 JG 72
37+91 WTD 61
37+92 JG 74
37+93 JG 72
37+94 JG 71
37+96 JG 74
37+97 JG 74
37+98 JG 71
38+00 JG 74
38+01 JG 72
38+02 JG 71
38+03 JG 71
38+04 JG 74
38+05 JG 74
38+06 JG 71
38+07 JG 71
38+08 JG 72
38+09 JG 72
38+10 JG 71
38+11 JG 72
38+12 JG 72

Reg	Unit	Reg	Unit	Reg	Unit
38+13	JbG 35	40+14		40+90	TG 31
38+14	JG 74	40+15		40+91	JbG 49
38+16	JG 71	40+16		40+92	
38+17	JG 72	40+17	TG 31	40+93	JbG 49
38+18	JG 72	40+18	JbG 49	40+94	JbG 49
38+20	JG 72	40+20	TG 31	40+95	TG 31
38+21	JG 72	40+21	JbG 49	40+96	JbG 49
38+24	JG 71	40+22	JbG 49	40+97	JbG 44
38+25	JG 72	40+23	TG 31	40+98	TG 31
38+26	JG 72	40+24		40+99	
38+27	JG 71	40+25	JbG 49	41+00	
38+28	JG 72	40+26	JbG 49	41+01	JbG 49
38+29	JG 72	40+27		41+02	JbG 49
38+30	JG 72	40+28	JbG 44	41+03	
38+31	JG 71	40+29	TG 31	41+04	JbG 49
38+32	JG 72	40+30	TG 31	41+05	TG 31
38+33	JG 72	40+31	TG 31	41+06	
38+34	JbG 35	40+32		41+07	TG 31
38+36	JG 71	40+33		41+08	JbG 44
38+37	JG 72	40+34		41+09	JbG 49
38+38	JbG 35	40+35	TG 31	41+10	TG 31
38+39	JG 72	40+36	TG 31	41+11	TG 31
38+40	JG 71	40+37		41+12	TG 31
38+42	JG 71	40+38	TG 31	41+13	
38+43	JG 72	40+39		41+14	JbG 49
38+44	JG 71	40+40	JbG 49	41+15	TG 31
38+45	JG 72	40+41		41+16	
38+46	JG 72	40+42	TG 31	41+17	
38+47	JG 71	40+43	TG 31	41+18	
38+48	JG 71	40+44	JbG 49	41+19	TG 31
38+49	JG 72	40+45		41+20	
38+50	JG 71	40+46		41+21	TG 31
38+51	JbG 35	40+47	JbG 49	41+22	TG 31
38+53	JG 72	40+48		41+23	JbG 49
38+54	JG 72	40+49	JbG 49	41+24	
38+55	JG 71	40+50	TG 31	41+25	JbG 49
38+56	JG 72	40+51	TG 31	41+26	JbG 49
38+57	JG 72	40+52	TG 31	41+27	
38+58	JG 71	40+53	JbG 44	41+28	TG 31
38+59	JG 71	40+54		41+29	
38+60	JG 71	40+56	WTD-61	41+30	WTD 61
38+61	JG 71	40+57	TG 31	41+31	JbG 44
38+62	JG 72	40+58		41+32	
38+63	JG 71	40+59	TSLw 3	41+33	
38+64	JG 71	40+60		41+34	JbG 49
38+66	JG 71	40+61	JbG 49	41+35	JbG 49
38+67	JG 72	40+62	JbG 44	41+36	JbG 49
38+68	JG 72	40+63		41+37	JbG 49
38+69	JG 71	40+64	TG 31	41+38	JbG 49
38+70	JG 71	40+65	JbG 49	41+39	WTD 61
38+72	JbG 35	40+66	JbG 44	41+40	TG 31
38+73	JG 72	40+67		41+41	TG 31
38+74	JG 72	40+68		41+42	JbG 49
38+75	JG 71	40+69	TG 31	41+43	
		40+70		41+44	

D-BD Alpha Jet
TG 31, Leipheim (stored);
JbG 44, Beja (Portugal);
JbG 49, Förstenfeldbruck;
WTD 61, Ingolstadt

Reg	Unit	Reg	Unit	Reg	Unit
40+01	WTD 61	40+71	JbG 44	41+45	JbG 49
40+02	WTD 61	40+72	JbG 44	41+46	JbG 44
40+03	JbG 49	40+73	JbG 49	41+47	
40+04		40+74	TG 31	41+48	
40+05	JbG 49	40+75		41+49	JbG 49
40+06	JbG 49	40+76	JbG 49	41+50	TG 31
40+07		40+77		41+51	
40+08	TG 31	40+78	TSLw 3	41+52	JbG 44
40+09	JbG 49	40+79	TG 31	41+53	JbG 49
40+11		40+80		41+54	TG 31
40+12	JbG 49	40+81		41+55	JbG 49
40+13	TG 31	40+82	TG 31	41+56	JbG 49
		40+84	JbG 49	41+57	WTD-61
		40+85	JbG 49	41+58	JbG 49
		40+86	JbG 44	41+59	JbG 49
		40+88	TG 31	41+60	
		40+89		41+61	JbG 49

Panavia Tornado
Strike/Trainer[1]/ECR[2]
TTTE, RAF Cottesmore;
AG 51, Schleswig/Jagel;
JbG 31, Nörvenich;
JbG 32, Lechfeld;
JbG 33, Böchel;
JbG 34, Memmingen;
JbG 38, Jever;
MBB, Manching;
MFG2, Eggebek;
TSLw 1, Kaufbeuren;
WTD 61, Ingolstadt

41+62		43+48	AG 51	44+28	JbG 31
41+63	JbG 49	43+50	AG 51	44+29	JbG 31
41+64	JbG 49	43+52	AG 51	44+30	JbG 31
41+65	TG 31	43+53	AG 51	44+31	JbG 31
41+66	JbG 49	43+54	AG 51	44+32	JbG 38
41+67	TG 31	43+55	AG 51	44+33	JbG 31
41+68	JbG 49	43+57	AG 51	44+34	JbG 32
41+70		43+58	AG 51	44+35	JbG 31
41+71	JbG 49	43+59	AG 51	44+36[1]	JbG 32
41+72	JbG 49	43+60	AG 51	44+37[1]	JbG 38
41+73	JbG 49	43+61	AG 51	44+38[1]	JbG 32
41+74	JbG 49	43+62	AG 51	44+39[1]	JbG 33
41+75	JbG 49	43+63	AG 51	44+40	JbG 33
98+55	TG 31	43+64	AG 51	44+41	JbG 31
		43+65	AG 51	44+42	JbG 32
		43+67	AG 51	44+43	JbG 34
		43+68	AG 51	44+44	JbG 31
		43+69	JbG 38	44+46	JbG 34
		43+70	JbG 38	44+48	JbG 31
		43+71	AG 51	44+50	JbG 32
		43+72	AG 51	44+51	JbG 38
		43+73	AG 51	44+52	JbG 31
		43+74	AG 51	44+53	JbG 32
43+01[1]	[G-20] TTTE	43+75	AG 51	44+54	JbG 33
43+02[1]	[G-21] TTTE	43+76	AG 51	44+55	JbG 38
43+03[1]	[G-22] TTTE	43+77	AG 51	44+56	JbG 34
43+04[1]	[G-23] TTTE	43+78	AG 51	44+57	JbG 32
43+05[1]	[G-24] TTTE	43+79	AG 51	44+58	JbG 32
43+06[1]	[G-25] TTTE	43+80	AG 51	44+59	JbG 32
43+07[1]	[G-26] TTTE	43+81	AG 51	44+60	JbG 32
43+08[1]	[G-27] TTTE	43+82	AG 51	44+61	JbG 32
43+09[1]	[G-28] TTTE	43+83	AG 51	44+62	JbG 33
43+10[1]	[G-29] TTTE	43+85	AG 51	44+63	JbG 33
43+11[1]	[G-30] TTTE	43+86	AG 51	44+64	JbG 32
43+12[1]	[G-70] TTTE	43+87	AG 51	44+65	JbG 34
43+13	[G-71] TTTE	43+88	AG 51	44+66	JbG 31
43+14	[G-72] TTTE	43+90[1]	JbG 38	44+67	JbG 33
43+15[1]	[G-31] TTTE	43+91[1]	JbG 32	44+68	JbG 32
43+16[1]	[G-32] TTTE	43+92[1]	JbG 31	44+69	JbG 32
43+17[1]	[G-33] TTTE	43+94[1]	JbG 31	44+70	JbG 32
43+18	JbG 34	43+95	JbG 31	44+71	JbG 31
43+19	JbG 31	43+96	JbG 31	44+72[1]	JbG 33
43+20	JbG 32	43+97[1]	JbG 31	44+73[1]	JbG 33
43+22[1]	JbG 38	43+98	JbG 31	44+75[1]	JbG 33
43+23[1]	JbG 38	43+99	JbG 31	44+76	JbG 34
43+25	[G-75] TTTE	44+00	JbG 31	44+77	JbG 32
43+26	JbG 38	44+01[1]	JbG 32	44+78	JbG 32
43+27	AG 51	44+02	JbG 31	44+79	JbG 32
43+28	JbG 38	44+03	JbG 31	44+80	JbG 33
43+29[1]	JbG 31	44+04	JbG 32	44+81	JbG 34
43+30	JbG 38	44+05[1]	JbG 38	44+82	JbG 31
43+31[1]	JbG-31	44+06	JbG 31	44+83	JbG 32
43+32	[G-73] TTTE	44+07	JbG 31	44+84	JbG 33
43+33[1]	JbG 38	44+08	JbG 38	44+85	JbG 38
43+34	TSLw 1	44+09	JbG 31	44+86	JbG 32
43+35[1]	JbG 38	44+10[1]	JbG 38	44+87	JbG 32
43+36	JbG 34	44+11	JbG 34	44+88	JbG 33
43+37[1]	JbG 38	44+12	JbG 32	44+89	JbG 33
43+38	JbG 34	44+13	JbG 38	44+90	JbG 33
43+40	JbG 32	44+14	JbG 34	44+91	JbG 33
43+41	JbG 31	44+15[1]	JbG 38	44+92	JbG 33
43+42[1]	AG 51	44+16	JbG 32	44+94	JbG 33
43+43[1]	AG 51	44+17	JbG 32	44+95	JbG 33
43+44[1]	AG 51	44+19	JbG 32	44+96	JbG 32
43+45[1]	AG 51	44+20[1]	JbG 38	44+97	JbG 33
43+46	AG 51	44+21	JbG 31	44+98	JbG 33
43+47	AG 51	44+22	JbG 31	45+00	JbG 33
		44+23	JbG 31	45+01	JbG 33
		44+24	JbG 32	45+02	JbG 33
		44+25[1]	JbG 38	45+03	JbG 33
		44+26	JbG 31	45+04	JbG 33
		44+27	JbG 31	45+05	JbG 33

45+06	JbG 33		45+80	JbG 34		46+53[2]	JbG 38
45+07	JbG 33		45+81	JbG 34		46+54[2]	JbG 38
45+08	JbG 33		45+82	JbG 34		46+55[2]	JbG 38
45+09	JbG 33		45+83	JbG 34		46+56[2]	JbG 38
45+10	JbG 33		45+84	JbG 34		46+57[2]	JbG 38
45+11	JbG 33		45+85	JbG 34		98+02	WTD 61
45+12[1]	MFG 2		45+86	JbG 34		98+03	WTD 61
45+13[1]	MFG 2		45+87	JbG 34		98+59	WTD 61
45+14[1]	MFG 2		45+88	JbG 34		98+60	WTD 61
45+15[1]	MFG 2		45+89	JbG 34		98+79[2]	WTD 61
45+16[1]	MFG 2		45+90	JbG 34		98+97[2]	WTD 61
45+17	JbG 33		45+91	JbG 34			
45+18	JbG 34		45+92	JbG 34		**Transall C-160D**	
45+19	JbG 33		45+93	JbG 34		LTG 61, Landsberg;	
45+20	JbG 32		45+94	JbG 34		LTG 62, Wunstorf;	
45+21	JbG 33		45+95	JbG 34		LTG 63, Hohn;	
45+22	JbG 33		45+96	JbG 34		WTD 61, Ingolstadt	
45+23	JbG 33		45+97	JbG 34		50+06	LTG 63
45+24	JbG 33		45+98	JbG 34		50+07	LTG 61
45+25	JbG 33		45+99[1]	JbG 34		50+08	LTG 61
45+26	TSLw 1		46+00	JbG 34		50+09	LTG 62
45+27	MFG 2		46+01	JbG 34		50+10	LTG 62
45+28	MFG 2		46+02	JbG 34		50+17	LTG 62
45+29	WTD 61		46+03	JbG 34		50+29	LTG 62
45+30	MFG 2		46+04[1]	AG 51		50+33	LTG 63
45+31	MFG 2		46+05[1]	MFG 2		50+34	LTG 63
45+32	MFG 2		46+06[1]	JbG 32		50+35	LTG 62
45+33	MFG 2		46+07	JbG 34		50+36	LTG 62
45+34	MFG 2		46+08	JbG 34		50+37	LTG 62
45+35	MFG 2		46+09	JbG 34		50+38	LTG 62
45+36	MFG 2		46+10	WTD 61		50+40	LTG 63
45+37	MFG 2		46+11	AG 51		50+41	LTG 63
45+38	MFG 2		46+12	MFG 2		50+42	LTG 63
45+39	MFG 2		46+13	AG 51		50+43	LTG 61
45+40	MFG 2		46+14	AG 51		50+44	LTG 61
45+41	MFG 2		46+15	AG 51		50+45	LTG 63
45+42	MFG 2		46+18	MFG 2		50+46	LTG 62
45+43	MFG 2		46+19	MFG 2		50+47	LTG 61
45+44	MFG 2		46+20	MFG 2		50+48	LTG 61
45+45	MFG 2		46+21	MFG 2		50+49	LTG 61
45+46	MFG 2		46+22	MFG 2		50+50	LTG 63
45+47	MFG 2		46+23[2]	JbG 32		50+51	LTG 61
45+48	MFG 2		46+24[2]	JbG 32		50+52	LTG 62
45+49	MFG 2		46+25[2]	JbG 32		50+53	LTG 62
45+50	MFG 2		46+26[2]	JbG 32		50+54	LTG 63
45+51	MFG 2		46+27[2]	JbG 32		50+55	LTG 62
45+52	MFG 2		46+28[2]	JbG 32		50+56	LTG 63
45+53	MFG 2		46+29[2]	JbG 32		50+57	LTG 61
45+54	MFG 2		46+30[2]	JbG 32		50+58	LTG 63
45+55	MFG 2		46+31[2]	JbG 32		50+59	LTG 63
45+56	MFG 2		46+32[2]	JbG 32		50+60	LTG 62
45+57	MFG 2		46+33[2]	JbG 32		50+61	LTG 63
45+59	MFG 2		46+34[2]	JbG 32		50+62	LTG 61
45+60[1]	JbG 38		46+35[2]	JbG 32		50+64	LTG 61
45+61[1]	JbG 34		46+36[2]	JbG 32		50+65	LTG 62
45+62[1]	JbG 38		46+37[2]	JbG 32		50+66	LTG 61
45+64	TSLw 1		46+38[2]	JbG 32		50+67	LTG 63
45+65	MFG 2		46+39[2]	JbG 32		50+68	LTG 61
45+66	MFG 2		46+40[2]	JbG 32		50+69	LTG 61
45+67	MFG 2		46+41[2]	JbG 38		50+70	WTD 61
45+68	MFG 2		46+42[2]	JbG 38		50+71	LTG 63
45+69	MFG 2		46+43[2]	JbG 38		50+72	LTG 61
45+70[1]	JbG 33		46+44[2]	JbG 38		50+73	LTG 62
45+71	MFG 2		46+45[2]	JbG 38		50+74	LTG 61
45+72	MFG 2		46+46[2]	JbG 38		50+75	WTD 61
45+73[1]	JbG 31		46+47[2]	JbG 38		50+76	LTG 63
45+74	MFG 2		46+48[2]	JbG 38		50+77	LTG 63
45+76	JbG 38		46+49[2]	JbG 38		50+78	LTG 62
45+77[1]	JbG 38		46+50[2]	JbG 38		50+79	LTG 63
45+78	JbG 34		46+51[2]	JbG 38		50+81	LTG 62
45+79	JbG 32		46+52[2]	JbG 38		50+82	LTG 63

50+83 LTG 62
50+84 LTG 61
50+85 LTG 63
50+86 LTG 61
50+87 LTG 63
50+88 LTG 61
50+89 LTG 62
50+90 LTG 61
50+91 LTG 62
50+92 LTG 61
50+93 LTG 61
50+94 LTG 63
50+95 LTG 63
50+96 LTG 61
50+97 LTG 62
50+98 LTG 61
50+99 LTG 61
51+00 LTG 62
51+01 LTG 62
51+02 LTG 63
51+03 LTG 62
51+04 LTG 61
51+05 LTG 62
51+06 LTG 63
51+07 LTG 62
51+08 LTG 63
51+09 LTG 63
51+10 LTG 61
51+11 LTG 62
51+12 LTG 63
51+13 LTG 61
51+14 LTG 63
51+15 LTG 61

Antonov An-26SM[1]/M[2]
JbG 32, Lechfeld
52+09[1] JbG 32
52+10[2]

Dornier Do.228
WTG 61, Ingolstadt;
MFG 5, Kiel-Holtenau
57+01 MFG 5
98+78 WTD-61

Dornier Skyservant
JbG 35, Pferdsfeld;
LTG 62, Wunstorf;
LTG 63, Hohn;
WTD 61, Ingolstadt;
MFG 5, Kiel-Holtenau
58+05 WTD 61
58+26 LTG 63
58+34 LTG 62
58+68 JbG 35
58+70 LTG 62
58+77 JbG 49
59+06 MFG 5
59+11 MFG 5
59+14 MFG 5
59+19 MFG 5
59+22 MFG 5
59+25 MFG 5

Breguet Br1151 Atlantic
**Elint*
MFG 3, Nordholz
61+01
61+02*
61+03*
61+04
61+05
61+06*
61+08
61+09
61+10
61+11
61+12
61+13
61+14
61+15
61+16
61+17
61+18
61+19*
61+20*

Westland Lynx Mk88
MFG 3, Nordholz
83+01
83+02
83+03
83+04
83+05
83+06
83+07
83+08
83+09
83+10
83+11
83+12
83+13
83+14
83+15
83+16
83+17
83+18
83+19

Westland Sea King HAS41
MFG 5, Kiel-Holtenau
89+50
89+51
89+52
89+53
89+54
89+55
89+56
89+57
89+58
89+59
89+60
89+61
89+62
89+63
89+64
89+65
89+66
89+67
89+68
89+69
89+70
89+71

Eurofighter 2000
98+29 MBB (ZH586)

English Electric Canberra B2
WTD 61, Ingolstadt
99+34

Heeresfliegertruppe
Sikorsky/VFW CH-53G
HFlgRgt-15, Rheine-Bentlage;
HFlgRgt-25, Laupheim;
HFlgRgt-35, Mendig;
HFWS, Bückeburg;
WTD 61, Ingolstadt
84+01 WTD 61
84+02 WTD 61
84+03 15
84+04 35
84+05 35
84+06 35
84+07 HFWS
84+08 35
84+09 25
84+10 25
84+11 HFWS
84+12 15
84+13 HFWS
84+14 HFWS
84+15 25
84+16 HFWS
84+17 25
84+18 HFWS
84+19 HFWS
84+20 35
84+21 HFWS
84+22 35
84+23 25
84+24 35
84+25 35
84+26 35
84+27 35
84+28 35
84+29 35
84+30 35
84+31 35
84+32 35
84+33 35
84+34 35
84+35 35
84+36 35
84+37 35
84+38 35
84+39 35
84+40 25
84+41 HFWS
84+42 25
84+43 25
84+44 25
84+45 25
84+46 25
84+47 25
84+48 25
84+49 HFWS
84+50 25
84+51 25
84+52 25
84+53 25
84+54 25
84+55 25
84+56 25
84+57 25
84+58 25
84+59 25
84+60 25
84+62 25
84+63 25
84+64 25
84+65 35

84+66	35
84+67	35
84+68	15
84+69	15
84+70	15
84+71	15
84+72	15
84+73	15
84+74	15
84+75	15
84+76	15
84+77	15
84+78	15
84+79	15
84+80	15
84+82	15
84+83	15
84+84	15
84+85	15
84+86	15
84+87	15
84+88	15
84+89	15
84+90	15
84+91	15
84+92	35
84+93	35
84+94	35
84+95	25
84+96	25
84+97	25
84+98	15
84+99	15
85+00	15
85+01	35
85+02	35
85+03	35
85+04	25
85+05	25
85+06	25
85+07	15
85+08	15
85+09	15
85+10	35
85+11	25
85+12	15

GHANA
Air Force
Short SC7 Skyvan
No 1 Transport Sqn, Takoradi
G450 [A]
G451 [B]
G452 [C]
G453 [D]
G454 [E]
G455 [F]

GREECE
Helliniki Aeroporia
Lockheed
C-130H Hercules
356 Mira, Elefsis
741
742
743
744
745
746
747
749

750
751
752

HUNGARY
Magyar Honvédseg Repülö Csapatai
Antonov An-26
Szolnok Mixed Air Carrier Regiment

202	(02202)
203	(02203)
204	(02204)
208	(02208)
209	(02209)
405	(03405)
406	(03406)
407	(03407)
603	(03603)

ISRAEL
Heyl Ha'Avir
Lockheed Hercules
C-130H
4X-FBA/102
4X-FBB/106
4X-FBC/309
4X-FBQ/420
4X-FBS/427
4X-FBT/435
4X-FBU/448
4X-FBW/436
4X-FBX/428

C-130E
4X-FBD/311
4X-FBE/304
4X-FBF/301
4X-FBG/310
4X-FBH/312
4X-FBI/314
4X-FBJ/305
4X-FBK/318
4X-FBL/313
4X-FBM/316
4X-FBN/307
4X-FBP/208

KC-130H
4X-FBY/522
4X-FBZ/545

ITALY
Aeronautica Militare Italiano
Aeritalia G222
46ª Brigata Aerea, Pisa;
14* Stormo, Pratica di Mare;
RSV, Pratica di Mare

MM62101	RS-45
MM62102	46-20
MM62104	46-91
MM62105	46-82
MM62108	46-30
MM62109	46-96
MM62110	46-81
MM62111	46-83
MM62112	46-85
MM62114	46-80
MM62115	46-22
MM62116	46-25
MM62118	46-24
MM62119	46-21
MM62120	46-90
MM62121	46-86
MM62122	46-23
MM62123	46-28
MM62124	46-88
MM62125	46-87
MM62126	46-26
MM62127	46-27
MM62130	RS-51
MM62132	46-32
MM62133	46-93
MM62134	46-33
MM62143	46-36
MM62144	46-98
MM62145	46-50
MM62146	46-51
MM62147	46-52

Aeritalia G222TCM

MM62103	46-37
MM62135	46-94
MM62136	46-97
MM62137	46-95
MM62152	
MM62153	46-99
MM61254	
MM62155	

Aeritalia G222RM

MM62107	
MM62138	
MM62139	14-20
MM62140	14-21
MM62141	14-22
MM62142	

Aeritalia-EMB AMX/AMX-T*
2* Stormo, Istrana;
3* Stormo, Villafranca;
32* Stormo, Amendola;
51* Stormo, Istrana;
RSV, Pratica di Mare

MMX595	Aeritalia
MMX596	Aeritalia
MMX597	Aeritalia
MMX599	Aeritalia
MM7089	2-10
MM7090	RS-12
MM7091	2-01
MM7092	RS-14
MM7093	
MM7094	
MM7095	51-33
MM7096	51-62
MM7097	51-35
MM7098	51-36
MM7099	2-02
MM7100	
MM7101	51-41
MM7102	
MM7103	51-34
MM7104	51-31
MM7105	2-04
MM7106	51-37
MM7107	51-44
MM7109	51-45
MM7110	2-14
MM7111	51-50
MM7112	51-52
MM7114	51-46
MM7115	51-51

MM7116	3-42		MM54459	61-13		MM54551	6*	
MM7117			MM54460	61-14		MM54553		
MM7118	2-11		MM54461	61-15		MM54554	61-95	
MM7119	3-07		MM54462	61-16				
MM7120	3-10		MM54463	61-17		**Boeing 707-328B/-3F5C***		
MM7121	3-47		MM54464	61-20		14º Stormo, Pratica di Mare;		
MM7122			MM54465	61-21		31º Stormo, Roma-Ciampino		
MM7123	3-51		MM54467	61-23		MM62148	(14)	
MM7124	3-14		MM54468	61-24		MM62149	(14)	
MM7125	3-15		MM54469	61-25		MM62150*	(31)	
MM7126	3-53		MM54470	61-26		MM62151*	14-02	
MM7127	3-22		MM54471	61-27				
MM7128	3-23		MM54472	61-30		**Breguet Br 1150 Atlantic**		
MM7129	3-24		MM54473	4*		30* Stormo, Cagliari;		
MM7130	51-43		MM54475	3*		41* Stormo, Catania		
MM7131			MM54476			MM40108	41-70	
MM7132			MM54477	9*		MM40109	30-71	
MM7133	51-57		MM54478	7*		MM40110	41-72	
MM7134	3-01		MM54479	1*		MM40111	41-73	
MM7135	51-32		MM54480	0*		MM40112	30-74	
MM7138	51-56		MM54482	5*		MM40113	30-75	
MM7139	3-02		MM54484	11*		MM40114	41-76	
MM7140	2-06		MM54485	10*		MM40115	41-77	
MM7141	51-55		MM54486	2*		MM40116	30-78	
MM7142	3-04		MM54487	61-31		MM40117	41-02	
MM7143	3-05		MM54488	61-32		MM40118	30-03	
MM7144	3-03		MM54489	61-33		MM40119	30-04	
MM7145	3-06		MM54490	61-34		MM40120	41-05	
MM7146	2-23		MM54491	61-35		MM40121	41-06	
MM7147	2-20		MM54492	61-36		MM40122	30-07	
MM7148	2-21		MM54493	61-37		MM40123	30-10	
MM7149	51-53		MM54494	61-40		MM40124	41-11	
MM7150	51-40		MM54496	61-42		MM40125	30-12	
MM7151	51-42		MM54497	61-43				
MM7152			MM54498	61-44		**Dassault Falcon 50**		
MM7153	2-16		MM54499	61-45		31* Stormo, Roma-Ciampino		
MM7154	51-54		MM54500	61-46		MM62020		
MM7155	2-24		MM54503	61-51		MM62021		
MM7156	2-22		MM54504	61-52		MM62026		
MM7157	51-51		MM54505	61-53		MM62029		
MM7158			MM54506	61-54				
MM7159			MM54507	61-55		**Grumman Gulfstream III**		
MM7160	51-30		MM54508	61-56		31* Stormo, Roma-Ciampino		
MM55024*	Aeritalia		MM54509	61-57		MM62022		
MM55025*	(RSV)		MM54510	61-60		MM62025		
MM55026*	Aeritalia		MM54511	61-61				
			MM54512	61-62		**Lockheed F-104 Starfighter**		
Aermacchi MB339			MM54513	61-63		4* Stormo, Grosseto;		
*Frecce Tricolori			MM54514	61-64		5* Stormo, Rimini;		
(313 Gruppo), Rivolto;			MM54515	61-65		9* Stormo, Grazzanise;		
61ª Brigata Aerea, Lecce;			MM54516	61-66		36* Stormo, Gioia del Colle;		
14* Stormo, Pratica di Mare;			MM54517	61-67		37* Stormo, Trapani;		
RSV, Pratica di Mare			MM54518	61-70		51* Stormo, Istrana;		
MM54438	61-93		MM54532	61-71		53* Stormo, Cameri		
MM54439	12*		MM54533	61-72		**F-104G**		
MM54440			MM54534	61-73		MM6529	4-52	
MM54442	61-95		MM54535	61-74		MM6532	4-51	
MM54443	61-50		MM54536	9*		MM6542	4-53	
MM54445	8*		MM54537			MM6552	4-50	
MM54446	61-01		MM54538	61-75		MM6576	4-45	
MM54447	61-02		MM54539	61-76		MM6589	4-49	
MM54448	61-03		MM54540	8*		**F-104S**		
MM54449	61-04		MM54541	RS-27		MM6701	36-13	
MM54450	61-94		MM54542	61-81		MM6703	51-23	
MM54451	61-86		MM54543	61-82		MM6704	5-42	
MM54452			MM54544	61-83		MM6705	9-33	
MM54453	61-05		MM54545	61-84		MM6710		
MM54454	61-06		MM54546	61-85		MM6713	53-05	
MM54455	61-07		MM54547	61-87		MM6714		
MM54456	RS-10		MM54548	61-90		MM6716		
MM54457	61-11		MM54549	61-91		MM6717	51-15	
MM54458	61-12		MM54550	61-92				

MM6719	51-06
MM6720	
MM6721	9-42
MM6722	5-45
MM6726	4-21
MM6727	9-45
MM6730	5-30
MM6731	4-10
MM6732	
MM6733	4-22
MM6734	9-43
MM6735	5-46
MM6736	
MM6737	5-43
MM6739	51-01
MM6740	5-32
MM6741	37-21
MM6742	5-14
MM6744	5-07
MM6747	37-24
MM6748	
MM6749	37-15
MM6750	37-04
MM6756	5-07
MM6758	53-10
MM6759	5-03
MM6760	5-05
MM6761	5-05
MM6762	53-05
MM6763	4-9
MM6764	5-31
MM6767	
MM6768	36-05
MM6769	4-2
MM6770	
MM6771	
MM6772	9-52
MM6773	53-14
MM6774	36-21
MM6775	51-01
MM6776	5-37
MM6778	51-15
MM6780	
MM6781	5-24
MM6782	37-15
MM6784	37-27
MM6785	
MM6786	37-21
MM6787	4-7
MM6788	5-01
MM6789	37-02
MM6791	5-06
MM6792	5-21
MM6794	37-20
MM6795	4-5
MM6796	5-15
MM6797	5-25
MM6798	37-01
MM6800	
MM6802	4-1
MM6804	
MM6807	5-41
MM6808	51-15
MM6809	9-35
MM6810	9-30
MM6812	5-36
MM6814	
MM6815	53-11
MM6816	53-14
MM6817	9-40
MM6818	
MM6819	53-01

MM6820	51-07
MM6821	5-16
MM6822	9-41
MM6823	53-02
MM6824	36-12
MM6825	36-11
MM6826	36-01
MM6827	5-27
MM6828	4-6
MM6830	5-27
MM6831	37-04
MM6833	5-22
MM6835	36-12
MM6836	5-10
MM6838	36-10
MM6839	4-6
MM6840	37-25
MM6841	
MM6842	37-26
MM6843	51-03
MM6844	37-23
MM6845	
MM6847	37-11
MM6848	
MM6849	5-33
MM6850	36-02
MM6869	4-3
MM6870	51-04
MM6872	53-15
MM6873	5-35
MM6875	5-32
MM6876	5-40
MM6878	9-31
MM6879	51-02
MM6880	4-12
MM6881	36-16
MM6886	5-02
MM6887	37-13
MM6890	4-22
MM6908	
MM6909	
MM6910	37-12
MM6912	53-03
MM6913	5-22
MM6914	5-13
MM6915	5-15
MM6916	37-03
MM6918	37-22
MM6920	5-26
MM6921	
MM6922	5-04
MM6923	9-51
MM6924	36-10
MM6925	9-35
MM6926	
MM6929	9-32
MM6930	
MM6932	4-4
MM6934	51-14
MM6935	51-05
MM6936	51-22
MM6937	51-16
MM6938	4-16
MM6939	4-20
MM6940	53-07
MM6941	51-20
MM6942	53-13
MM6943	36-20
MM6944	5-03
MM6946	37-06

TF-104G

| MM54226 | 4-23 |

MM54228	4-26
MM54232	4-27
MM54232	4-29
MM54233	4-30
MM54235	4-31
MM54237	4-32
MM54250	4-33
MM54251	4-34
MM54253	4-35
MM54254	4-36
MM54255	4-37
MM54256	4-38
MM54257	4-39
MM54258	
MM54260	4-41
MM54261	4-42
MM54552	
MM54553	4-44
MM54554	4-48
MM54555	4-45
MM54556	4-47
MM54557	4-50
MM54558	4-46

**Lockheed
C-130H Hercules**
46ª Brigata Aerea, Pisa

MM61988	46-02
MM61989	46-03
MM61990	46-04
MM61991	46-05
MM61992	46-06
MM61993	46-07
MM61994	46-08
MM61995	46-09
MM61997	46-11
MM61998	46-12
MM61999	46-13
MM62001	46-15

**McDonnell Douglas
DC9-32**
31° Stormo, Roma-Ciampino

| MM62012 | |
| MM62013 | |

**Panavia Tornado
Strike/Trainer[1]/ECR[2]**
6° Stormo, Ghedi;
36° Stormo, Gioia del Colle;
50° Stormo, Piacenza;
RSV, Pratica di Mare;
TTTE, RAF Cottesmore;
MM586

MM7002	I-92 TTTE
MM7003	6-31
MM7004	6-04
MM7005	50-04
MM7006	
MM7007	50-07
MM7008	
MM7009	50-44
MM7010	50-01
MM7011	6-11
MM7013	
MM7014	
MM7015	6-01
MM7016	6-16
MM7017	50-14
MM7018	6-02
MM7019	19
MM7020	50-12

MM7021	6-21
MM7022	6-03
MM7023	50-03
MM7024	24
MM7025	
MM7026	6-26
MM7027	
MM7028	6-14
MM7029	6-25
MM7030	
MM7031	
MM7033	
MM7034	6-34
MM7035	35
MM7036	6-06
MM7037	36-37
MM7038	36-33
MM7039	50-30
MM7040	36-35
MM7041	
MM7042	6-22
MM7043	43
MM7044	6-66
MM7046	50-36
MM7047	36-36
MM7048	36-54 (Alenia)
MM7049	50-44
MM7050	50
MM7051	36-32
MM7052	6-32
MM7053	53
MM7054	50-34
MM7055	55
MM7056	36-52
MM7057	36-54
MM7058	58
MM7059	6-35
MM7060	
MM7061	61
MM7062	62
MM7063	63
MM7064	50-43
MM7065	6-33
MM7066	66
MM7067	36-45
MM7068	36-46
MM7069	6-61
MM7070	70
MM7071	71
MM7072	50-32
MM7073	73
MM7075	50-35
MM7076	36-31
MM7078	50-32
MM7079[2]	(Alenia)
MM7080	80
MM7081	RS-01
MM7082	RS-02
MM7083	6-10
MM7084	36-42
MM7085	36-50
MM7086	36-40
MM7087	50-37
MM7088	88
MM55000	I-42 TTTE
MM55001	I-40 TTTE
MM55002	6-20
MM55003	I-43 TTTE
MM55004	I-44 TTTE
MM55005	I-45 TTTE
MM55006	50-50

MM55007	50-51
MM55008	
MM55009	6-15
MM55010	36-56
MM55011	36-55

Piaggio-Douglas PD-808/[1]PD-808-GE/[2]PD-808-RM/[3]PD-808-TA
14° Stormo, Pratica di Mare;
31° Stormo, Roma-Ciampino;
RSV, Pratica di Mare

MM577[3]	RS-48
MM578[3]	RS-49
MM61948	(14)
MM61949	(14)
MM61950	14-50
MM61951	(31)
MM61952[1]	(14)
MM61953[3]	(14)
MM61954[3]	(31)
MM61955[1]	(14)
MM61956[2]	(14)
MM61957[3]	RS-50
MM61958[1]	(14)
MM61959[1]	(14)
MM61960[1]	(14)
MM61961[1]	(14)
MM61962[1]	(14)
MM62014[2]	(14)
MM62015[2]	(14)
MM62016[2]	14-55
MM62017[2]	(14)

Marina Militare Italiano
McDonnell TAV-8B
6° Reparto Aeromobili, Taranto

MM55032	1-01
MM55033	1-02

JORDAN
Al Quwwat al-Jawwiya al Malakiya al-Urduniya
Lockheed C-130H Hercules
3 Sqn, Amman
344
345
346
347

KUWAIT
Kuwait Air Force
McDonnell Douglas DC9-32
42 Sqn, Ali Al Salem
KAF 321

McDonnell Douglas DC9-83
42 Sqn, Ali Al Salem
KAF 26

Lockheed L100-30 Hercules
41 Sqn, Kuwait International
KAF 323
KAF 324
KAF 325

LUXEMBOURG
NATO
Boeing E-3A
NAEWF, Geilenkirchen
LX-N90442
LX-N90443
LX-N90444
LX-N90445
LX-N90446
LX-N90447
LX-N90448
LX-N90449
LX-N90450
LX-N90451
LX-N90452
LX-N90453
LX-N90454
LX-N90455
LX-N90456
LX-N90457
LX-N90458
LX-N90459

Boeing 707-329C
NAEWF, Geilenkirchen
LX-N19996
LX-N20198
LX-N20199

MOROCCO
Force Aerienne Royaume Marocaine
CAP-230
Green March

04	CN-ABD
05	CN-ABF
06	CN-ABI
07	CN-ABJ
08	CN-ABK
09	CN-ABL

Lockheed C-130H Hercules

4535	CN-AOA
4551	CN-AOC
4575	CN-AOD
4581	CN-AOE
4583	CN-AOF
4713	CN-AOG
4717	CN-AOH
4733	CN-AOI
4738	CN-AOJ
4739	CN-AOK
4742	CN-AOL
4875	CN-AOM
4876	CN-AON
4877	CN-AOO
4888	CN-AOP
4892	CN-AOQ
4907	CN-AOR
4909	CN-AOS
4940	CN-AOT

NETHERLANDS
Koninklijke Luchtmacht
Agusta-Bell AB.412
SAR Flight, Leeuwarden
R-01
R-02
R-03

Fokker F-27-100 Friendship
334 Sqn, Eindhoven
C-1
C-2
C-3

Fokker F-27-300M Troopship
334 Sqn, Eindhoven
C-4
C-5
C-6
C-7
C-8
C-9
C-11
C-12

General Dynamics F-16A/F-16B*
306/311/312 Sqns, Volkel;
313/315 Sqns, Twente;
314 Sqn, Gilze-Rijen;
316 Sqn, Eindhoven;
322/323 Sqns, Leeuwarden

J-001	313 Sqn
J-002	313 Sqn
J-003	313 Sqn
J-004	313 Sqn
J-005	313 Sqn
J-006	313 Sqn
J-008	313 Sqn
J-009	313 Sqn
J-010	313 Sqn
J-011	313 Sqn
J-012	313 Sqn
J-013	313 Sqn
J-014	313 Sqn
J-015	313 Sqn
J-016	313 Sqn
J-017	313 Sqn
J-018	313 Sqn
J-019	313 Sqn
J-020	313 Sqn
J-021	315 Sqn
J-055	315 Sqn
J-057	315 Sqn
J-058	315 Sqn
J-059	315 Sqn
J-060	315 Sqn
J-061	315 Sqn
J-062	315 Sqn
J-063	315 Sqn
J-064*	315 Sqn
J-065*	315 Sqn
J-066*	315 Sqn
J-067*	313 Sqn
J-068*	313 Sqn
J-135	314 Sqn
J-136	316 Sqn
J-137	314 Sqn
J-138	314 Sqn
J-139	314 Sqn
J-140	314 Sqn
J-141	314 Sqn
J-142	316 Sqn
J-143	316 Sqn
J-144	314 Sqn
J-145	314 Sqn
J-146	314 Sqn
J-192	311 Sqn

J-193	311 Sqn
J-194	311 Sqn
J-196	311 Sqn
J-197	311 Sqn
J-198	311 Sqn
J-199	311 Sqn
J-201	314 Sqn
J-202	314 Sqn
J-203	322 Sqn
J-204	322 Sqn
J-205	322 Sqn
J-206	314 Sqn
J-207	322 Sqn
J-208*	316 Sqn
J-209*	314 Sqn
J-210*	316 Sqn
J-211*	316 Sqn
J-212	323 Sqn
J-213	322 Sqn
J-214	323 Sqn
J-215	322 Sqn
J-218	322 Sqn
J-220	322 Sqn
J-223	322 Sqn
J-226	322 Sqn
J-228	322 Sqn
J-230	322 Sqn
J-231	323 Sqn
J-232	323 Sqn
J-234	323 Sqn
J-235	323 Sqn
J-236	323 Sqn
J-240	322 Sqn
J-241	322 Sqn
J-243	322 Sqn
J-246	323 Sqn
J-248	323 Sqn
J-249	322 Sqn
J-250	323 Sqn
J-251	322 Sqn
J-253	323 Sqn
J-254	323 Sqn
J-255	323 Sqn
J-256	323 Sqn
J-259*	322 Sqn
J-260*	322 Sqn
J-261*	323 Sqn
J-262*	323 Sqn
J-264*	322 Sqn
J-265*	323 Sqn
J-266*	323 Sqn
J-267*	323 Sqn
J-270*	323 Sqn
J-360	314 Sqn
J-361	314 Sqn
J-362	314 Sqn
J-363	311 Sqn
J-364	314 Sqn
J-365	314 Sqn
J-366	316 Sqn
J-367	314 Sqn
J-368*	314 Sqn
J-369*	316 Sqn
J-508	315 Sqn
J-509	315 Sqn
J-510	315 Sqn
J-511	315 Sqn
J-512	315 Sqn
J-513	315 Sqn
J-514	313 Sqn
J-515*	315 Sqn
J-516*	315 Sqn

J-616	311 Sqn
J-617	311 Sqn
J-619	311 Sqn
J-620	311 Sqn
J-622	311 Sqn
J-623	311 Sqn
J-624	311 Sqn
J-627	306 Sqn
J-628	306 Sqn
J-630	306 Sqn
J-631	306 Sqn
J-632	306 Sqn
J-633	306 Sqn
J-635	306 Sqn
J-636	306 Sqn
J-637	306 Sqn
J-638	306 Sqn
J-640	306 Sqn
J-641	306 Sqn
J-642	306 Sqn
J-643	306 Sqn
J-644	306 Sqn
J-645	306 Sqn
J-646	306 Sqn
J-647	306 Sqn
J-648	306 Sqn
J-649*	306 Sqn
J-650*	323 Sqn
J-651*	312 Sqn
J-652*	311 Sqn
J-653*	306 Sqn
J-654*	311 Sqn
J-655*	306 Sqn
J-656*	312 Sqn
J-657*	314 Sqn
J-864	312 Sqn
J-866	312 Sqn
J-867	312 Sqn
J-868	312 Sqn
J-869	312 Sqn
J-870	312 Sqn
J-871	312 Sqn
J-872	312 Sqn
J-873	312 Sqn
J-874	312 Sqn
J-875	312 Sqn
J-876	312 Sqn
J-877	312 Sqn
J-878	312 Sqn
J-879	312 Sqn
J-881	312 Sqn
J-882*	316 Sqn
J-884*	314 Sqn
J-885*	311 Sqn

MBB Bo.105CB/ [1]Bo.105CD
299 Sqn, Deelen
B-37
B-38
B-39
B-40
B-42
B-43
B-44
B-45
B-47
B-48
B-63
B-64
B-66
B-67

B-68
B-69
B-70
B-71
B-72
B-74
B-75
B-76
B-77
B-78
B-79
B-80
B-83[1]

Pilatus PC-7
EMVO, Woensdrecht
L-01
L-02
L-03
L-04
L-05
L-06
L-07
L-08
L-09
L-10

Sud Alouette III
Grasshoppers
298 Sqn, Soesterberg;
300 Sqn, Eindhoven;
302 Sqn, Deelen;
SAR Flight, Leeuwarden
A-177
A-208
A-209
A-217
A-218
A-226
A-227
A-235
A-246
A-247
A-253
A-260
A-261
A-266
A-267
A-275
A-281
A-292
A-293
A-301
A-302
A-307
A-324*
A-336
A-342
A-343
A-350*
A-366
A-374
A-383
A-390*
A-398*
A-399
A-407
A-414
A-451
A-452
A-453*
A-464

A-465*
A-470
A-471
A-482
A-483
A-488
A-489
A-494
A-495
A-499
A-500
A-514
A-515
A-521
A-522
A-528
A-529
A-535
A-536
A-542
A-549
A-550
H-20 SAR
H-67 SAR
H-75 SAR
H-81 SAR

Marine Luchtvaart Dienst
Fokker F-27-200MPA
336 Sqn, Hato, Antilles
M-1
M-2

Lockheed
P-3C Orion
MARPAT, Valkenburg,
Sigonella and Keflavik
300
301
302
303
304
305
306
307
308
309
310
311
312

Westland SH-14D Lynx
7/860 Sqns, De Kooij
260   7 Sqn
261   7 Sqn
262   7 Sqn
264   7 Sqn
265   7 Sqn
266   860 Sqn
267   860 Sqn
268   860 Sqn
269   860 Sqn
270   860 Sqn
271   860 Sqn
272   860 Sqn
273   860 Sqn
274   860 Sqn
276   860 Sqn
277   860 Sqn
278   860 Sqn
279   860 Sqn
280   860 Sqn

281   860 Sqn
282   860 Sqn
283   860 Sqn

NEW ZEALAND
Royal New Zealand Air Force
Boeing 727-22C
40 Sqn, Whenuapai
NZ7271
NZ7272

Lockheed
C-130H Hercules
40 Sqn, Whenuapai
NZ7001
NZ7002
NZ7003
NZ7004
NZ7005

Lockheed
P-3K Orion
5 Sqn, Whenuapai
NZ4201
NZ4202
NZ4203
NZ4204
NZ4205
NZ4206

NIGERIA
Federal Nigerian Air Force
Lockheed
C-130H Hercules
Lagos
NAF-910
NAF-911
NAF-912
NAF-913
NAF-914
NAF-915
NAF-917
NAF-918
NAF-918 (NAF 916)

NORWAY
Kongelige Norske
Luftforsvaret
Dassault
Falcon 20 ECM
335 Skv, Gardermoen
041
053
0125

General Dynamics
F-16A/ F-16B
331 Skv, 334 Skv, Bodø;
332 Skv, Rygge *(y/bk)*;
338 Skv, Ørland
272   332 Skv
273   332 Skv
274   332 Skv
275   332 Skv
276   332 Skv
277   332 Skv
278   332 Skv
279   332 Skv
281   332 Skv
282   332 Skv
284   332 Skv

285	332 Skv	
288	338 Skv	
289	338 Skv	
291	338 Skv	
292	338 Skv	
293	338 Skv	
295	338 Skv	
297	338 Skv	
298	338 Skv	
299	338 Skv	
302*	338 Skv	
304*	332 Skv	
305*	332 Skv	
306*	332 Skv	
307*	332 Skv	
658	334 Skv	
659	334 Skv	
660	334 Skv	
661	334 Skv	
662	334 Skv	
663	334 Skv	
664	334 Skv	
665	334 Skv	
666	334 Skv	
667	334 Skv	
668	334 Skv	
669	334 Skv	
670	334 Skv	
671	331 Skv	
672	331 Skv	
673	331 Skv	
674	331 Skv	
675	331 Skv	
677	331 Skv	
678	331 Skv	
680	331 Skv	
681	331 Skv	
682	331 Skv	
683	331 Skv	
686	331 Skv	
687	331 Skv	
688	331 Skv	
689*	338 Skv	
690*	334 Skv	
691*	334 Skv	
692*	334 Skv	
693*	338 Skv	
711*	331 Skv	
712*	331 Skv	

Lockheed
C-130H Hercules
335 Skv, Gardermoen
952
953
954
955
956
957

Lockheed P-3C Orion
333 Skv, Andøya
3296
3297
3298
3299

Lockheed P-3N Orion
333 Skv Andøya
4576
6603

Northrop F-5A
336 Skv, Rygge
128
130
131
132
133
134
208
210
215
220
225
895
896
898
902

Northrop F-5B
336 Skv, Rygge
136
241
243
244
387
594
595
906
907
908
909

Westland Sea King
Mk43/Mk43A^A/Mk43B^B
330 Skv, Bodø
060^A
062^A
066^A
069
070^A
071^B
072^A
073^A
074^A
189
322^B

Kystvakt (Coast Guard)
Westland Lynx Mk86
337 Skv, Bardufoss
207
216
228
232
237
350

OMAN
Royal Air Force of Oman
BAC 1-11/485GD
4 Sqn, Seeb
551
552
553

Grumman G1159
Gulfstream 2
4 Sqn, Seeb
601

Lockheed
C-130H Hercules
4 Sqn, Seeb
501
502
503

Short Skyvan 3M
2 Sqn, Seeb
901
902
903
904
905
906
907
908
910
911
912
913
914
915
916

PAKISTAN
Air Force
Boeing 707-340C
68-19866 12 Sqn

PORTUGAL
Forca Aerea Portuguesa
CASA 212A/212ECM*
Aviocar
401 Esq, Sintra;
502 Esq, Sintra;
503 Esq, Lajes

6501	502 Esq
6502*	502 Esq
6503	502 Esq
6504	502 Esq
6505	502 Esq
6506	502 Esq
6507	502 Esq
6508	502 Esq
6509	401 Esq
6510	401 Esq
6511	502 Esq
6512	401 Esq
6513	503 Esq
6514	503 Esq
6515	503 Esq
6517	503 Esq
6519	401 Esq
6520	503 Esq
6521*	401 Esq
6522*	401 Esq
6523*	401 Esq
6524*	401 Esq

Dassault
Falcon 20C
504 Esq, Lisbon/Montijo
8101
8102
8103

Dassault
Falcon 50
504 Esq, Lisbon/Montijo
7401
7402
7403

Lockheed
C-130H/C-130H-30*
Hercules
501 Esq, Lisbon/Montijo
6801
6802
6803
6804
6805
6806*

Lockheed (GD)
F-16A/F-16B*
201 Esq, Montre Rea
6101
6102
6103
6104
6105
6106
6107
6108
6109
6110
6111
6112
6113
6114
6115
6116
6117
6118*
6119*
6120*

Lockheed P-3P Orion
601 Esq, Lisbon/Montijo
4801
4802
4803
4804
4805
4806

SAUDI ARABIA
Al Quwwat al-Jawwiya
as Sa' udiya
Boeing E-3A/KE3A*
Sentry
18 Sqn, Riyadh
1801
1802
1803
1804
1805
1811*
1812*
1813*
1814*
1815*
1816*
1817*
1818*

Lockheed
C-130 Hercules
1 Sqn, Riyadh;
4 Sqn, Jeddah;
16 Sqn, Jeddah

112	VC-130H	1 Sqn
451	C-130E	4 Sqn
452	C-130E	4 Sqn

455	C-130E	4 Sqn
456	KC-130H	4 Sqn
457	KC-130H	4 Sqn
458	KC-130H	4 Sqn
459	KC-130H	4 Sqn
461	C-130H	4 Sqn
462	C-130H	4 Sqn
463	C-130H	4 Sqn
464	C-130H	4 Sqn
465	C-130H	4 Sqn
466	C-130H	4 Sqn
467	C-130H	4 Sqn
468	C-130H	4 Sqn
470	C-130H	4 Sqn
471	C-130H-3	4 Sqn
472	C-130H	4 Sqn
473	C-130H	4 Sqn
474	C-130H	4 Sqn
475	C-130H	4 Sqn
1601	C-130H	16 Sqn
1602	C-130H	16 Sqn
1603	C-130H	16 Sqn
1604	C-130H	16 Sqn
1605	C-130H	16 Sqn
1606	C-130E	16 Sqn
1607	C-130E	16 Sqn
1608	C-130E	16 Sqn
1609	C-130E	16 Sqn
1610	C-130E	16 Sqn
1611	C-130E	16 Sqn
1612	C-130H	16 Sqn
1613	C-130H	16 Sqn
1614	C-130H	16 Sqn
1615	C-130H	16 Sqn
1616	KC-130H	16 Sqn
1617	KC-130H	16 Sqn
1618	C-130H	16 Sqn
1619	C-130H	16 Sqn
1620	KC-130H	16 Sqn
1621	KC-130H	16 Sqn
1622	C-130H-30	16 Sqn
1623	C-130H-30	16 Sqn
1624	C-130H	16 Sqn
1625	C-130H	16 Sqn
1626	C-130H	16 Sqn
1627	C-130H	16 Sqn
1628	C-130H	16 Sqn

SINGAPORE
Republic of Singapore Air
Force
Lockheed Hercules
122 Sqn, Changi
C-130B
720
721
724
725
C-130H
730
731
732
733
KC-130H
734
735

SLOVAKIA
Aero L.39/L.59 (L.39MS)
Albatros
LSP/2 Letka, Kosice
1 SLP/1 Letka, 2 Letka

and 3 Letka, Sliac;
2 ZDLP/3 Letka, Trencin;
White Albatros, Kosice*

0002	L.39MS	LSP
0101	L.39C	WA
0102	L.39C	WA
0103	L.39C	
0111	L.39C	WA
0112	L.39C	WA
0442	L.39C	LSP
0443	L.39C	WA
0730	L.39V	LSP
1725	L.39ZA	2 ZDLP
3905	L.39ZA	2 ZDLP
4355	L.39C	WA
4357	L.39C	WA
4701	L.39ZA	2 ZDLP

Antonov An-12BP
2 ZDLP/1 Letka, Piestany
2209

Antonov An-26
2 ZDLP/1 Letka, Piestany
2506
3208

Let 410
LSP, Kosice;
2 ZDLP/1 Letka, Piestany

0404	L.410M	2 ZDLP
0405	L.410M	2 ZDLP
0730	L.410UVP	2 ZDLP
0927	L.410T	LSP
0930	L.410T	LSP
1203	L.410FG	2 ZDLP
1511	L.410UVP	2 ZDLP
1525	L.410FG	2 ZDLP
1810	L.410UVP-E	2 ZDLP
2006	L.410UVP-E	2 ZDLP
2311	L.410UVP	2 ZDLP

Mikoyan MiG-29/UB*
1 SLP/1 Letka, Sliac
3911
7501

Sukhoi Su-25K/BK*
2 ZDLP/3 Letka, Trencin
1006
1007
1008
1027
3237*
5003
6017
6018
8072
8073
8074

Tupolev Tu-154B-2
2 ZDLP/1 Letka, Bratislava
0420

SPAIN
Ejercito del Aire
Airtech CN235
Ala 35, Getafe

T-19C-01	35-60	
T-19C-02	35-61	
T.19B-03	35-21	

147

T.19B-04	35-22
T.19B-05	35-23
T.19B-06	35-24
T.19B-07	35-25
T.19B-08	35-26
T.19B-09	35-27
T.19B-10	35-28
T.19B-11	35-29
T.19B-12	35-30
T.19B-13	35-31
T.19B-14	35-32
T.19B-15	35-33
T.19B-16	35-34
T.19B-17	35-35

Boeing 707-381B/368C*
Grupo 45, Torrejon

T.17-1	45-10
TK.17-2	45-11
T.17-3*	45-12

CASA 101 Aviojet
Ala 21, Moron;
Grupo de Escuelas de Matacan (74);
AGA, San Javier (79)
*Patrulla Aguila, San Javier**

E.25-01*	79-01	[1]
E.25-02	793-02	
E.25-03	79-03	
E.25-05	79-05	
E.25-06*	79-06	[6]
E.25-07*	79-07	[7]
E.25-08*	79-08	[8]
E.25-09	79-09	
E.25-10	79-10	
E.25-11	79-11	
E.25-12	79-12	
E.25-13*	79-13	[3]
E.25-14*	79-14	[4]
E.25-15	79-15	
E.25-16	79-16	
E.25-17	79-17	
E.25-18	79-18	
E.25-19	79-19	
E.25-20	79-20	
E.25-21*	79-21	[9]
E.25-22*	79-22	
E.25-23*	79-23	[10]
E.25-24	79-24	
E.25-25*	79-25	[5]
E.25-26*	79-26	[2]
E.25-27*	79-27	[11]
E.25-28*	79-28	[12]
E.25-29	79-29	
E.25-30	79-30	
E.25-32	74-01	
E.25-33	74-02	
E.25-34	21-04	
E.25-35	74-03	
E.25-36	79-36	
E.25-37	74-04	
E.25-38	79-38	
E.25-40	74-06	
E.25-41	79-41	
E.25-42	793-32	
E.25-43	79-43	
E.25-44	79-44	
E.25-45	79-45	
E.25-46	79-46	
E.25-47	79-47	
E.25-48	79-48	

E.25-49	79-49
E.25-50	79-40
E.25-51	74-07
E.25-52	74-08
E.25-53	411-07
E.25-54	74-10
E.25-55	74-05
E.25-56	79-37
E.25-57	74-12
E.25-58	
E.25-59	74-13
E.25-60	74-14
E.25-61	74-15
E.25-62	74-16
E.25-63	74-17
E.25-64	74-18
E.25-65	74-19
E.25-66	79-96
E.25-67	74-21
E.25-68	74-22
E.25-69	79-97
E.25-71	74-25
E.25-72	74-26
E.25-73	74-27
E.25-74	74-28
E.25-75	74-29
E.25-76	74-30
E.25-78	79-02
E.25-79	74-32
E.25-80	74-33
E.25-81	74-34
E.25-83	74-35
E.25-84	79-04
E.25-86	74-37
E.25-87	74-38
E.25-88	74-39

CASA 212 Aviocar
212 (XT.12)/212A (T.12B)/
212B (TR.12A)/212D
(TE.12B)/212E (T.12C)
Ala 35, Getafe;
Ala 37, Villanubla;
Ala 46, Gando, Las Palmas;
Grupo 72, Alcantarilla;
Grupo Esc, Matacan (74);
AGA (Ala 79), San Javier;
403 Esc, Cuatro Vientos;
408 Esc, Getafe

XT.12A-1	54-10
TR.12A-3	403-01
TR.12A-4	403-02
TR.12A-5	403-03
TR.12A-6	403-04
TR.12A-7	403-05
TR.12A-8	403-06
TE.12B-9	79-91
TE.12B-10	79-92
T.12B-12	35-01
T.12B-13	74-70
T.12B-14	46-30
T.12B-15	
T.12B-16	74-71
T.12B-17	37-03
T.12B-18	46-31
T.12B-19	46-32
T.12B-20	37-04
T.12B-21	35-05
T.12B-22	35-06
T.12B-23	72-01
T.12B-24	37-07
T.12B-25	74-72

T.12B-26	72-02
T.12B-27	46-33
T.12B-28	72-03
T.12B-29	35-08
T.12B-30	74-73
T.12B-31	46-34
T.12B-33	72-04
T.12B-34	74-74
T.12B-35	46-35
T.12B-36	37-09
T.12B-37	72-05
T.12B-38	35-10
T.12B-39	745-39
TE.12B-40	79-93
TE.12B-41	79-94
TE.12B-42	744-42
T.12C-43	46-50
T.12C-44	35-50
T.12B-46	74-46
T.12B-47	72-06
T.12B-48	37-11
T.12B-49	46-36
T.12B-50	745-50
T.12B-51	74-78
T.12B-52	72-07
T.12B-53	37-12
T.12B-54	37-13
T.12B-55	46-37
T.12B-56	74-79
T.12B-57	72-08
T.12B-58	46-38
T.12C-59	37-51
T.12C-60	37-52
T.12C-61	35-53
T.12B-63	37-14
T.12B-64	46-39
T.12B-65	74-80
T.12B-66	72-09
T.12B-67	74-81
T.12B-68	35-15
T.12B-69	37-16
T.12B-70	37-17
T.12B-71	35-18
TR.12D-72	408-01
TR.12D-73	408-02
TR.12D-74	408-03

Cessna 560 Citation VI
403 Esc, Cuatro Vientos

TR.20-01	403-11
TR.20-02	403-12

Dassault Falcon 20
Grupo 45, Torrejon

T.11-1	45-02
TM.11-2	45-03
TM.11-3	45-04
TM.11-4	45-01
T.11-5	45-05

Dassault Falcon 50
Grupo 45, Torrejon

T.16-1	45-20

Dassault Falcon 900
Grupo 45, Torrejon

T.18-1	45-40
T.18-2	45-41

Fokker F.27M
Friendship 400MPA
802 Esc, Gando

D.2-01
D.2-02
D.2-03

Lockheed P-3A/P-3B* Orion
Ala 22, Jerez

P.3-1	22-21
P.3-3	22-22
P.3-4	22-23
P.3-5	22-24
P.3-7	22-26
P.3B-8*	22-31
P.3B-9*	22-32
P.3B-10*	22-33
P.3B-11*	22-34
P.3B-12*	22-35

Lockheed Hercules C-130H/C-130H-30[1]
311 Esc/312 Esc (Ala 31), Zaragoza

TL.10-1[1]	31-01
T.10-2	31-02
T.10-3	31-03
T.10-4	31-04
T.10-8	31-05
T.10-9	31-06
T.10-10	31-07

KC-130H
312 Esc (Ala 31), Zaragosa

TK.10-5	31-50
TK.10-6	31-51
TK.10-7	31-52
TK.10-11	31-53
TK.10-12	31-54

McDonnell Douglas EF-18A/EF-18B* Hornet
Ala 12, Torrejon;
Ala 15, Zaragoza

CE.15-1*	15-70
CE.15-2*	15-71
CE.15-3*	15-72
CE.15-4*	15-73
CE.15-5*	15-74
CE.15-6*	15-75
CE.15-7*	12-70
CE.15-8*	12-71
CE.15-9*	12-72
CE.15-10*	12-73
CE.15-11*	12-74
CE.15-12*	12-75
C.15-13	12-01
C.15-14	15-01
C.15-15	15-02
C.15-16	15-03
C.15-17	15-04
C.15-18	15-05
C.15-20	15-07
C.15-21	15-08
C.15-22	15-09
C.15-23	15-10
C.15-24	15-11
C.15-25	15-12
C.15-26	15-13
C.15-27	15-14
C.15-28	15-15
C.15-29	15-16
C.15-30	15-17
C.15-31	15-18
C.15-32	15-19
C.15-33	15-20
C.15-34	15-21
C.15-35	15-22
C.15-36	15-23
C.15-37	15-24
C.15-38	15-25
C.15-39	15-26
C.15-40	15-27
C.15-41	15-28
C.15-42	15-29
C.15-43	15-30
C.15-44	12-02
C.15-45	12-03
C.15-46	12-04
C.15-47	12-05
C.15-48	12-06
C.15-49	12-07
C.15-50	12-08
C.15-51	12-09
C.15-52	12-10
C.15-53	12-11
C.15-54	12-12
C.15-55	12-13
C.15-56	12-14
C.15-57	12-15
C.15-58	12-16
C.15-59	12-17
C.15-60	12-18
C.15-61	12-19
C.15-62	12-20
C.15-63	12-21
C.15-64	12-22
C.15-65	12-23
C.15-66	12-24
C.15-67	12-25
C.15-68	12-26
C.15-69	12-27
C.15-70	12-28
C.15-72	12-30

Arma Aérea de l'Armada Espanola Cessna 550 Citation 2
Esc 004, Rota

U.20-1	01-405
U.20-2	01-406
U.20-3	01-407

SUDAN
Silakh Al Jawwiya as Sudaniya
Lockheed C-130H Hercules
1100
1101
1102
1103
1104
1105

SWEDEN
Kungliga Svenska Flygvapnet
Beechcraft Super King Air (Tp.101)
F17, Ronneby;
F21, Lulea

101002	012	F21
101003	013	F17
101004	014	F17

Grumman G.1159C Gulfstream 4 (Tp.102)
F16, Uppsala

102001	021

Lockheed C-130E Hercules (Tp.84)
F7, Satenäs

84001	841
84002	842

Lockheed C-130H Hercules (Tp.84)
F7, Satenäs

84003	843
84004	844
84005	845
84006	846
84007	847
84008	848

SAAB SF.340B (Tp.100)
F16, Uppsala

100001	001

Swearingen Metro III (Tp.88)

88003	883

Vertol 107-II-4 (Hkp.4B)
F15, Soderhamn;
F17, Ronneby

04451	91	F17
04452	92	F17
04453	93	F17
04454	94	
04455	95	F15
04456	96	
04457	97	F17
04458	98	F17
04459	99	F17
04460	90	F17

Marine Flygtjanst Vertol 107-II-5 (Hkp.4C)
1 Hkp Div, Berga

04061	61
04063	63
04064	64

Kawasaki-Vertol KV.107-II (Hkp.4C)
1 Hkp Div, Berga;
2 Hkp Div, Säve;
3 Hkp Div, Ronneby

04065	65	2 Hkp Div
04067	67	2 Hkp Div
04068	68	2 Hkp Div
04069	69	1 Hkp Div
04070	70	1 Hkp Div
04071	71	1 Hkp Div
04072	72	2 Hkp Div
04073	73	1 Hkp Div
04074	74	1 Hkp Div
04075	75	3 Hkp Div

Armen
MBB Bo.105CB (Hkp.9B)
Armeflyget 1 (AF1), Boden;
Armeflyget 2 (AF2), Malmslatt;
F6, Karlsborg (Air Force)

09201	01	AF2
09202	02	AF1
09203	03	AF2
09204	04	AF2
09205	05	AF1
09206	06	AF1
09207	07	AF1
09208	08	AF1
09209		
09210	10	AF1
09211	11	AF1
09212	12	AF1
09213	13	AF2
09214	14	AF1
09215	15	AF2
09216	16	AF2
09217	17	AF2
09218		
09219	19	AF1
09220	20	AF2
09415	95	F6
09416	96	F6

SWITZERLAND
Gates Learjet 35A
Swiss Air Force, Dubendorf
T-781
T-782

TURKEY
Turk Hava Kuvvetleri
Cessna 650 Citation VII
224 Filo, Etimesgut

93-7024	ETI-024
93-7026	ETI-026

Grumman G.1159C
Gulfstream 4
224 Filo, Etimesgut
003

Transall C.160D
221 Filo, Erkilet
019

020	12-020
021	
022	12-022
023	12-023
024	12-024
025	12-025
026	12-026
027	12-027
028	12-028
029	
030	12-030
031	12-031
032	12-032
033	12-033
034	12-034
035	12-035
036	12-036
037	12-037
038	12-038
039	12-039
040	12-040

Lockheed
C-130B Hercules
222 Filo, Erkilet
10960
10963

23496
70527
80736
91527

Lockheed
C-130E Hercules
222 Filo, Erkilet

00991	12-991
01468	12-468
01947	12-947
13186	12-186
13187	12-187
13188	12-188
13189	12-189
17949	12-949

UNITED ARAB EMIRATES
United Arab Emirates Air Force
Abu Dhabi
Lockheed
C-130H Hercules
1211
1212
1213
1214

Dubai
Lockheed
L.100-30 Hercules
311
312

Kosice-based L-39 Albatros of the Slovak Air Force 'White Albatroses' team. *Andrew P. March*

US Military Aircraft Markings

All USAF aircraft have been allocated a fiscal year (FY) number since 1921. Individual aircraft are given a serial according to the fiscal year in which they are ordered. The numbers commence at 0001 and are prefixed with the year of allocation. For example F-15C Eagle 40001 (84-001 was the first aircraft ordered in 1984. The fiscal year (FY) serial is carried on the technical data block which is usually stencilled on the left-hand side of the aircraft just below the cockpit. The number displayed on the fin is a corruption of the FY serial. Most tactical aircraft carry the fiscal year in small figures followed by the last three or four digits of the serial in large figures. For example Lakenheath-based F-15E Eagle 10311 carries 91-311/LN on its tail. Large transport and tanker aircraft such as C-130s and KC-135s sometimes display a five-figure number commencing with the last digit of the appropriate fiscal year and four figures of the production number. An example of this is KC-135R 58-0128 which displays 80128 on its fin.

USN serials follow a straightforward numerical sequence which commenced, for the present series, with the allocation of 00001 to an SB2C Helldiver by the Bureau of Aeronautics in 1940. Numbers in the 165000 series are presently being issued. They are usually carried in full on the rear fuselage of the aircraft.

UK based USAF Aircraft

The following aircraft are normally based in the UK. They are listed in numerical order of type with individual aircraft in serial number order, as depicted on the aircraft. The number in brackets is either the alternative presentation of the five-figure number commencing with the last digit of the fiscal year, or the fiscal year where a five-figure serial is presented on the aircraft. Where it is possible to identify the allocation of aircraft to individual squadrons by means of colours carried on fin or cockpit edge, this is also provided.

Lockheed U-2R
9 RW, RAF Alconbury [BB]
10329   (FY68)
01080   (FY80)
01099   (FY80)

McDonnell Douglas
F-15C Eagle/F-15D Eagle/
F-15E Strike Eagle
48FW, RAF Lakenheath [LN]
492FS blue
493FS yellow
494FS red
86-0164 (60164) F-15CY [48FW]
-    (   ) F-15C y
-    (   ) F-15C y
-    (   ) F-15C y
-    (   ) F-15C y
-    (   ) F-15C y
-    (   ) F-15C y
-    (   ) F-15C y
-    (   ) F-15C y
-    (   ) F-15C y
-    (   ) F-15C y

86-0182 (60182)	F-15D	y
- ( )	F-15D	y
90-0248 (00248)	F-15E	m
		[48 FW]
90-0251 (00251)	F-15E	bl
		[492 FS]
90-0255 (00255)	F-15E	bl
90-0256 (00256)	F-15E	bl
90-0257 (00257)	F-15E	bl
90-0258 (00258)	F-15E	bl
90-0259 (00259)	F-15E	bl
90-0260 (00260)	F-15E	bl
90-0261 (00261)	F-15E	bl
90-0262 (00262)	F-15E	bl
91-0300 (10300)	F-15E	bl
91-0301 (10301)	F-15E	bl
91-0302 (10302)	F-15E	bl
91-0303 (10303)	F-15E	bl
91-0304 (10304)	F-15E	bl
91-0305 (10305)	F-15E	bl
91-0306 (10306)	F-15E	
91-0307 (10307)	F-15E	bl
91-0308 (10308)	F-15E	bl
91-0309 (10309)	F-15E	bl
91-0310 (10310)	F-15E	bl
91-0311 (10311)	F-15E	bl

91-0312 (10312)	F-15E	bl
91-0313 (10313)	F-15E	r
		[3rd AF]
91-0314 (10314)	F-15E	r
		[494 FS]
91-0315 (10315)	F-15E	r
91-0316 (10316)	F-15E	r
91-0317 (10317)	F-15E	r
91-0318 (10318)	F-15E	r
91-0319 (10319)	F-15E	r
91-0320 (10320)	F-15E	r
91-0321 (10321)	F-15E	r
91-0322 (10322)	F-15E	r
91-0323 (10323)	F-15E	r
91-0324 (10324)	F-15E	r
91-0325 (10325)	F-15E	bl
91-0326 (10326)	F-15E	bl
91-0327 (10327)	F-15E	r
91-0328 (10328)	F-15E	r
91-0329 (10329)	F-15E	bl
91-0330 (10330)	F-15E	r
91-0331 (10331)	F-15E	r
91-0332 (10332)	F-15E	bl
91-0333 (10333)	F-15E	r
91-0334 (10334)	F-15E	r
91-0335 (10335)	F-15E	r

Sikorsky MH-53J		Lockheed C-130 Hercules		Boeing KC-135R
352 SOG/21 SOS		7 SOS*		Stratotanker
RAF Alconbury		67 SOS/353 SOG		100ARW, 351 ARS [D]
01626	(FY70)	RAF Alconbury		RAF Mildenhall (r/w/bl)
01629	(FY70)	37814 (FY63)	C-130E	10313 (FY61)
10357	(FY68)	40476 (FY84)	MC-130H*	10321 (FY61)
10923	(FY68)	60223 (FY66)	HC-130P	14833 (FY64)
14431	(FY66)	61699 (FY86)	MC-130H*	23558 (FY62)
14993	(FY67)	70023 (FY87)	MC-130H*	23561 (FY62)
95784	(FY69)	80193 (FY88)	MC-130H*	23577 (FY62)
95789	(FY69)	95820 (FY69)	HC-130N	38003 (FY63)
95791	(FY69)	95823 (FY69)	HC-130N	38875 (FY63)
95793	(FY69)	95826 (FY69)	HC-130N	80128 (FY58)
95795	(FY69)	95827 (FY69)	HC-130N	

UK based US Navy Aircraft

Beech UC-12M
Super King Air
Naval Air Facility, Mildenhall [8G]
3837 (163837)
3840 (163840)
3843 (163843)

European based USAF Aircraft

These aircraft are normally based in Western Europe with the USAFE. They are shown in numerical order of type designation, with individual aircraft in serial number order as carried on the aircraft. An alternative five-figure presentation of the serial is shown in brackets where appropriate. Fiscal year (FY) details are also provided if necessary. The unit allocation and operating bases are given for most aircraft.

McDonnell Douglas
F-4G Phantom
SP: 52FW Spangdahlem, Germany
81 FS yellow/black

69-258	(90258)	y
69-259	(90259)	y
69-263	(90263)	y
69-267	(97267)	y
69-286	(90286)	y
69-556	(97556)	y
69-558	(97558)	y

McDonnell Douglas
C-9A Nightingale
75ALS, 86 Wg Ramstein, Germany
SHAPE, Chievres, Belgium[1]
FY71

10876[1] (VIP)	
10879	
10880	
10881	
10882	

Fairchild A-10A Thunderbolt II
SP: 52FW Spangdahlem, Germany
510 FS black

81-951	(10951)
81-952	(10952)
81-954	(10954)
81-956	(10956)
81-962	(10962)
81-963	(10963)
81-966	(10966)
81-976	(10976)
81-978	(10978)
81-980	(10980)
81-983	(10983)
81-984	(10984)
81-988	(10988)
81-991	(10991)
81-992	(10992)
82-649	(20649)
82-650	(20650)
82-654	(20654)
82-655	(20655)
82-656	(20656)

Beech C-12
[1]JUSMG, Ankara, Turkey
[2]US Embassy Flight, Athens

31216	(FY73)[1]	C-12C
31218	(FY73)[2]	C-12A
60173	(FY76)[1]	C-12C

McDonnell Douglas
F-15C/F-15D Eagle
BT: 36FW Bitburg, Germany
22FS red

IS: 57FS/35 Wg Keflavik, Iceland
black/white

79-011	(90011)	F-15D	BT r
79-012	(90012)	F-15D	BT r
79-021	(90021)	F-15C	IS bk
79-022	(90022)	F-15C	BT r
79-025	(90025)	F-15C	BT y
79-035	(90035)	F-15C	BT r
79-036	(90036)	F-15C	[36FW]
79-037	(90037)	F-15C	BT r
79-057	(90057)	F-15C	BT r/y
79-058	(90058)	F-15C	BT r
79-064	(90064)	F-15C	BT y
79-068	(90068)	F-15C	BT y
79-072	(90072)	F-15C	BT r
79-073	(90073)	F-15C	BT r
79-076	(90076)	F-15C	BT r
79-077	(90077)	F-15C	BT y
79-078	(90078)	F-15C	BT r
80-003	(00003)	F-15C	BT r
80-004	(00004)	F-15C	BT r
80-005	(00005)	F-15C	BT r
80-010	(00010)	F-15C	BT r
80-011	(00011)	F-15C	BT r
80-012	(00012)	F-15C	BT y
80-015	(00015)	F-15C	BT r/y
80-021	(00021)	F-15C	IS bk
80-022	(00022)	F-15C	r
			[22FS]
80-026	(00026)	F-15C	BT r
80-029	(00029)	F-15C	IS bk
80-031	(00031)	F-15C	BT r
80-035	(00035)	F-15C	IS bk
			[35Wg]
80-038	(00038)	F-15C	IS bk
80-039	(00039)	F-15C	IS bk
80-040	(00040)	F-15C	IS bk
80-041	(00041)	F-15C	IS bk
80-042	(00042)	F-15C	IS bk
80-046	(00046)	F-15C	[A.F.I.]
80-047	(00047)	F-15C	IS bk
80-048	(00048)	F-15C	IS bk
80-050	(00050)	F-15C	[A.F.I.]
80-052	(00052)	F-15C	IS bk
			[57FS]
80-056	(00056)	F-15D	IS bk
80-057	(00057)	F-15D	IS bk
81-047	(10047)	F-15C	IS bk
81-061	(10061)	F-15D	IS bk
84-001	(40001)	F-15C	BT y
			[53FS]
84-002	(40002)	F-15C	BT y
84-003	(40003)	F-15C	BT r/y
84-004	(40004)	F-15C	BT y
84-005	(40005)	F-15C	BT y
84-006	(40006)	F-15C	BT y
84-007	(40007)	F-15C	BT y
84-008	(40008)	F-15C	BT y
84-009	(40009)	F-15C	BT r/y
			[36FW]

84-010	(40010)	F-15C	BT y
84-013	(40013)	F-15C	BT y
84-014	(40014)	F-15C	BT y
84-015	(40015)	F-15C	BT y
84-016	(40016)	F-15C	BT y
84-019	(40019)	F-15C	BT y
84-020	(40020)	F-15C	BT y
84-021	(40021)	F-15C	BT y
84-022	(40022)	F-15C	r
			[22FS]
84-023	(40023)	F-15C	BT y
84-024	(40024)	F-15C	BT y
84-025	(40025)	F-15C	BT y
84-026	(40026)	F-15C	BT y
84-027	(40027)	F-15C	BT y
84-043	(40043)	F-15D	BT y
84-044	(40044)	F-15D	BT y

Lockheed (GD)
F-16C/F-16D*
RS: 86Wg Ramstein, Germany
512FS green/black
526FS red/black
SP: 52FW Spangdahlem, Germany
23FS blue/white
81FS yellow
480FS red/white

85-400	(51400)	RS	gn
85-422	(51422)	RS	r
85-426	(51426)	[526FS] r	
85-428	(51428)	RS	gn
85-438	(51438)	RS	gn
85-450	(51450)	RS	r
85-453	(51453)	RS	r
85-455	(51455)	RS	gn
85-457	(51457)	RS	r
85-461	(51461)	RS	r
85-464	(51464)	RS	r
85-465	(51465)	RS	r
85-471	(51471)	RS	gn
85-474	(51474)	RS	gn
85-476	(51476)	RS	r
85-477	(51477)	RS	r
85-480	(51480)	RS	gn
86-044	(60044)*	RS	gn
86-049	(60049)*	RS	gn
86-209	(60209)	RS	r
86-255	(60255)	RS	gn
86-270	(60270)	RS	[86FW] gn
86-288	(60288)	SP	y
86-303	(60303)	RS	gn
86-313	(60313)	RS	r
86-327	(60327)	SP	bl
86-342	(60342)	RS	gn
86-350	(60350)	SP	r
86-361	(60361)	SP	bl
86-364	(60364)	SP	bl
86-365	(60365)	SP	bl
86-369	(60369)	SP	r
87-219	(70219)	SP	bl

87-220	(70220)	RS gn	90-831	(00831)	SP [52FW] r	40082*
87-221	(70221)	RS gn	90-833	(00833)	SP r	40083*
87-227	(70227)	RS gn	90-843	(00843)*	SP r	40084
87-232	(70232)	RS gn	90-846	(00846)*	SP r	40085
87-233	(70233)	SP y	90-847	(00847)*	SP r	40086
87-242	(70242)	[86 Wg]	90-849	(00849)*	SP r	40087
87-248	(70248)	RS gn	91-336	(10336)	SP	40108
87-250	(70250)	RS gn	91-337	(10337)	SP r [52FW]	40109
87-259	(70259)	RS gn	91-342	(10342)	SP r	40110
87-260	(70260)	SP bl	91-343	(10343)	SP r	40111
87-268	(70268)	SP r	91-344	(10344)	SP r [480FS]	40112
87-270	(70270)	[52FW] m	91-345	(10345)	SP	
87-276	(70276)	RS gn	91-346	(10346)	SP bl	

Boeing CT-43A
76 ALS, 86 Wg Ramstein, Germany
31149 (FY73)

87-281	(70281)	SP [81FS] y	91-347	(10347)	SP bl
87-287	(70287)	SP y	91-348	(10348)	SP bl
87-338	(70338)	SP y	91-349	(10349)	SP bl
87-340	(70340)	SP y	91-351	(10351)	SP bl

Lockheed C-130E Hercules
37 ALS, 435 AW Rhein Main, Germany

87-347	(70347)	RS gn	91-352	(10352)	SP [52FW] m	01260	(FY70)
87-372	(70372)*	SP y	91-353	(10353)	SP [23FS] bl	01264	(FY70)
87-383	(70383)*	RS r	91-354	(10354)	SP bl	01271	(FY70)
87-385	(70385)*	RS gn	91-355	(10355)	SP bl	01274	(FY70)
87-389	(70389)*	SP y	91-356	(10356)	SP bl	10935	(FY68)
88-152	(80152)*	RS r	91-462	(10462)*	SP	10938	(FY68)
88-174	(80174)*	RS	91-463	(10463)*	SP	10943	(FY68)
88-397	(80397)	SP y	91-464	(10464)*	SP bl	10947	(FY68)
88-400	(80400)	SP r	91-465	(10465)*	SP bl	17681	(FY64)
88-410	(80410)	RS r				18240	(FY64)
88-526	(80526)*	RS r [526FS]	**Grumman C-20A**			37885	(FY63)
88-550	(80550)	RS r	**Gulfstream III**			37887	(FY63)
89-009	(92009)	RS r	76ALS, 86Wg Ramstein,			40502	(FY64)
89-011	(92011)	RS r	Germany			40527	(FY64)
89-029	(92029)	RS r	FY83			40533	(FY64)
89-032	(92032)	RS r	30500			40550	(FY64)
89-036	(92036)	RS r	30501			96566	(FY69)
89-134	(92134)	RS r	30502			96582	(FY69)
89-137	(92137)	RS r				96583	(FY69)
90-709	(00709)	RS r					
90-796	(00796)*	RS r	**Gates C-21A**				
90-800	(00800)*	RS r	**Learjet**				
90-813	(00813)	SP r	76ALS, 86Wg Ramstein,				
90-818	(00818)	SP r	Germany				
90-827	(00827)	SP r	*7005ABS/HQ USEUCOM,				
90-828	(00828)	SP r	Stuttgart, Germany				
90-829	(00829)	SP r	FY84				
			40081*				

European based US Navy Aircraft

Lockheed P-3 Orion
CINCAFSE, NAF Sigonella, Italy
CinCLANT, NAS Norfolk, Virginia
VQ-2, NAF Rota, Spain

148888	EP-3E	[23]
149668	EP-3E	[21]
150495	UP-3A	NAF Keflavik
150496	VP-3A	CinCLANT
150505	EP-3E	[24]
150511	VP-3A	CinCAFSE
150515	VP-3A	CinCAFSE
152740	UP-3B	VQ-2
157320	EP-3E	[26]
157325	EP-3E	VQ-2
160770	P-3C	VQ-2

Beech UC-12M Super King Air
[1] NAF Sigonella, Italy
[2] NAF Rota, Spain
3838 (163838) [1]
3839 (163839) [2]
3841 (163841) [1]
3842 (163842) [2]
3844 (163844) [1]

NA CT-39G Sabreliner
NAF Sigonella, Italy
159361 [31]
159362 [32]
159363 [33]

European based US Army Aircraft

Beech C-12 Super King Air
(¹=C-12C, ²=C-12D, ³=RC-12K)
56 Av Co, Coleman Barracks
7th ATC, Grafenwohr
207 AvCo, Heidelberg
HQ/USEUCOM, Stuttgart
6th Avn Det, Vicenza, Italy
3-58 Avn, Wiesbaden
5-158 Avn, Wiesbaden
1MIB, Wiesbaden
Berlin Brigade

22253[1]	(FY73)	HQ/USEUCOM
22254[1]	(FY73)	207 AvCo
22255[1]	(FY73)	6 Av Det
22260[1]	(FY73)	7th ATC
22261[1]	(FY73)	5-158 Avn
22262[1]	(FY73)	Berlin Brig.
22549[1]	(FY76)	HQ/USEUCOM
22550[1]	(FY76)	HQ/USEUCOM
22556[1]	(FY76)	6 Avn Det
22557[1]	(FY76)	207AvCo
22564[1]	(FY76)	56 AvCo
22931[1]	(FY77)	6 Avn Det
22932[1]	(FY77)	6 Avn Det
22944[1]	(FY77)	56 AvCo
22950[1]	(FY77)	56 AvCo
23126[1]	(FY78)	207AvCo
23127[1]	(FY78)	207AvCo
23128[1]	(FY78)	207AvCo
24380[2]	(FY84)	207AvCo
50147[3]	(FY85)	1MIB
50148[3]	(FY85)	1MIB
50150[3]	(FY85)	1MIB
50151[3]	(FY85)	1MIB
50152[3]	(FY85)	1MIB
50153[3]	(FY85)	1MIB
50154[3]	(FY85)	1MIB
50155[3]	(FY85)	1MIB

Beech U-21A/U-21D* King Air

18006	(FY66)	6th Avn Det
18010	(FY66)	5-158 Avn
18012	(FY66)	5-158 Avn
18013	(FY66)	Berlin Brigade
18014	(FY66)	56 AvCo
18058	(FY67)	V Corps
18078	(FY67)	5-158 Avn
18080	(FY67)	56 AvCo
18110*	(FY67)	3-58Avn

Boeing-Vertol CH-47D Chinook
'B' Co, 3rd Avn, Mainz-Finthen;
'B' Co, 6 Batt, 158 Av Reg't, Coleman Barracks;
'A' Co, 5 Batt, 159 Av Reg't Giebelstadt
'E' Co, 502 Avn Reg't, Aviano
FY86
61674 6/158 BCo
61676 3-BCo
FY87
70072 /5/159ACO
70073 3-BCo
70075 6/158 BCo
70076 6/158 BCo
70077 3-BCo

70078 3-BCo
70079 5/159 ACo
70080 5/159 ACo
70081 5/159 ACo
70082 5/159 ACo
70083 5/159 ACo
70084 5/159 ACo
70085 5/159 ACo
70086 5/159 ACo
70087 5/159 ACo
70088 5/159 ACo
70089 5/159 ACo
70090 5/159 ACo
70091 5/159 ACo
70092 5/159 ACo
70093 5/159 ACo
70094 5/159 ACo
70096 6/158 BCo
70097 6/158 BCo
70098 6/158 BCo
70099 6/158 BCo
70100 6/158 BCo
70101 6/158 BCo
70103 6/158 BCo
70104 6/158 BCo
70105 6/158 BCo
70106 6/158 BCo
70107 6/158 BCo
70109 6/158 BCo
70110 6/158 BCo
70111 6/158 BCo
70112 6/158 BCo
FY88
80098 502 ECo
80099 502 ECo
80100 502 ECo
80101 502 ECo
80102 502 ECo
80103 502 ECo
80104 502 ECo
80106 502 ECo
FY89
90138 502 ECo
90139 502 ECo
90140 502 ECo
90141 502 ECo
90142 502 ECo
90143 502 ECo
90144 502 ECo
90145 502 ECo

Sikorsky UH-60A Black Hawk
7-1 Avn, Ansbach
45 Med Co, Ansbach
TF Skyhawk, Ansbach
357th Avn Det/SHAPE, Chievres
2-3 Avn, Giebelstadt
23rd TF, Giebelstadt
7th Btn, 158 Avn Reg't, Giebelstadt
15th Med Det (HA), Grafenwohr
'H'Co, 1st Avn Reg't, Hanau
7-227 Avn, Hanau
207th Aviation Co, Heidelberg
2-6 Cavalry, Illesheim
236th Med Co (HA), Landstuhl
8th Btn, 158 Avn Reg't, Wiesbaden
3-6, 5-6 Cavalry, Wiesbaden
159th Med Co, Wiesbaden

FY77	
22723	236 Med Co
22727	236 Med Co
FY78	
22969	236 Med Co
22986	236 Med Co
22990	7-1 Avn
22991	45 Med Co
22995	159 Med Co
22996	236 Med Co
22997	159 Med Co
23000	159 Med Co
23001	236 Med Co
23003	159 Med Co
FY79	
23271	159 Med Co
FY80	
23427	
23428	
23431	23rd TF
23432	
23433	
23434	236 Med Co
23436	
23439	7-1 Avn
23440	
23442	
23489	
23490	7-158 Avn
23496	7-1 Avn
FY81	
23548	7-1 Avn
23551	236 Med Co
23568	8-158 Avn
23571	
23572	5-6 Cav
23573	159 Med Co
23582	
23583	
23584	
23585	
23587	
23589	
23590	7-227 Avn
23592	236 Med Co
23594	7-1 Avn
23595	
23596	236 Med Co
23597	159 Med Co
23602	
23603	
23605	
23606	
23607	
23608	159 Med Co
23609	227 Avn
23610	
23613	7-1 Avn
23614	
23615	236 Med Co
23616	7-1 Avn
23617	
23618	7-1 Avn
23622	23rd TF
23623	7-158 Avn
23625	

Serial	Unit
23626	5-6 Cav
FY82	
23647	1 HCo
23660	
23661	
23662	TF Skyhawk
23663	7-1 Avn
23664	1 HCo
23665	
23666	
23667	
23668	
23669	
23672	236 Med Co
23673	7-158 Avn
23675	236 Med Co
23676	236 Med Co
23682	7-227 Avn
23684	6-159 CCo
23685	236 Med Co
23686	7-227 Avn
23690	7-158 Avn
23691	
23692	
23693	236 Med Co
23695	7-158 Avn
23697	
23699	7-158 Avn
23701	
23702	7-1 Avn
23703	
23704	
23721	
23722	8-158 Avn
23723	159 Med Co
23726	159 Med Co
23727	236 Med Co
23728	236 Med Co
23729	7-1 Avn
23730	236 Med Co
23731	45 Med
23733	7-1 Avn
23734	7-227 Avn
23735	236 Med Co
23736	236 Med Co
23737	7-158 Avn
23738	236 Med Co
23741	
23743	159 Med Co
23744	7-1 Avn
23745	159 Med Co
23746	159 Med Co
23748	7-1 Avn
23749	159 Med Co
23750	159 Med Co
23751	45 Med Co
23753	159 Med Co
23754	7-1 Avn
23755	7-1 Avn
23756	159 Med Co
23761	7-227 Avn
FY83	
23855	
23869	
FY86	
24498	7-227 Avn
24506	7-227 Avn
24530	45 Med Co
24532	2-6 Cav
24533	
24538	
24547	7-1 Avn
24550	236 Med Co

Serial	Unit
24551	235 Med Co
24552	4-11 ACR
24553	6/158 BCo
24554	7-227 Avn
24555	
24570	
FY87	
24579	
24581	236 Med Co
24583	357 Av Det
24584	357 Av Det
24589	207 Av Co
24621	3-1 Avn
24634	
24642	
24643	7-158 Avn
24644	
24645	
24646	7-1 Avn
24647	7-1 Avn
24656	
26000	
26001	
26002	159 Med Co
26003	7-1 Avn
26004	7-1 Avn
FY88	
26019	
26020	4-229 Avn
26021	3-H Co
26023	6-6 Cav
26024	
26025	
26027	
26028	
26031	
26034	4-229 Avn
26038	
26039	
26040	
26041	
26051	3-H Co
26052	7-227 Avn
26054	236 Med Co
26056	3-H Co
26061	
26063	
26067	7-227 Avn
26068	7-227 Avn
26070	
26071	7-227 Avn
26072	7-227 Avn
26073	
26074	
26075	7-227 Avn
26077	
26080	3-1 Avn
26085	2-227 Avn
26086	3-227 Avn
FY89	
26138	
26142	
26145	
26146	
26151	2-1 Avn
26153	3-1 Avn
26155	2-3 Avn
26164	2-1 Avn
26165	2-1 Avn

McD AH-64A Apache
1-1 Avn, Ansbach
2-1 Avn, Ansbach

3rd Avn, Giebelstadt
2-227 Avn, 3-227 Avn, Hanau
2-6 Cav, 6-6 Cav, Illesheim
4-229 Avn, Illesheim
5-6 Cav, Wiesbaden

Serial	Unit
FY84	
24204	3-227 Avn
24218	2-6 Cav
24244	2-3 Avn
24247	
24250	3-227 Avn
24254	
24257	4-229 Avn
24260	2-6 Cav
24262	2-6 Cav
24266	2-6 Cav
24277	
24290	2-6 Cav
24293	2-6 Cav
24296	2-6 Cav
24297	2-6 Cav
24299	
24303	2-6 Cav
24304	2-6 Cav
24308	2-6 Cav
FY85	
25352	1-1 Avn
25357	2-6 Cav
25397	5-6 Cav
25424	2-3 Avn
25430	
25460	3-1 Avn
25465	2-3 Avn
25469	5-6 Cav
25470	2-227 Avn
25471	5-6 Cav
25472	2-227 Avn
25473	1-1 Avn
25474	2-227 Avn
25475	5-6 Cav
25476	5-6 Cav
25478	1-1 Avn
25479	3-1 Avn
25480	2-227 Avn
25482	
25485	5-6 Cav
FY86	
8940	4-229 Avn
8941	4-229 Avn
8942	4-229 Avn
8943	4-229 Avn
8946	4-229 Avn
8947	4-229 Avn
8948	4-229 Avn
8949	4-229 Avn
8950	4-229 Avn
8951	4-229 Avn
8952	4-229 Avn
8955	4-229 Avn
8956	3-1 Avn
8957	4-229 Avn
8959	4-229 Avn
8960	4-229 Avn
8961	4-229 Avn
8970	3-227 Avn
8981	
8983	227 Avn
9010	2-1 Avn
9011	2-1 Avn
9019	
9026	5-6 Cav
9029	2-227 Avn
9030	

Serial	Unit	Serial	Unit	Serial	Unit
9032	2-1 Avn	440	3-227 Avn	503	2-227 Avn
9033	2-227 Avn	441	3-227 Avn	504	2-227 Avn
9037	2-1 Avn	442	3-1 Avn	505	3-227 Avn
9038		443	3-227 Avn	506	2-227 Avn
9039	1-1 Avn	444	2-227 Avn	507	3-227 Avn
9041	2-227 Avn	445	3-227 Avn	FY88	
9048	2-1 Avn	446	3-227 Avn	197	3-227 Avn
FY87		447	3-227 Avn	198	2-227 Avn
407		449	3-227 Avn	199	2-227 Avn
408	2-1 Avn	451	2-227 Avn	204	6-6 Cav
409	3-1 Avn	455	2-227 Avn	212	6-6 Cav
410	3-227 Avn	457	2-227 Avn	213	6-6 Cav
412	2-1 Avn	459	2-1 Avn	214	6-6 Cav
413		465	1 Avn	215	6-6 Cav
415	3-227 Avn	467		216	6-6 Cav
417		470	2-1 Avn	217	6-6 Cav
418	227 Avn	471		218	6-6 Cav
419	2-1 Avn	473	2-1 Avn	222	6-6 Cav
420	3-1 Avn	474	2-1 Avn	225	6-6 Cav
423		475	227 Avn	228	6-6 Cav
428	3-1 Avn	476	2-1 Avn	229	6-6 Cav
432	2-1 Avn	477		232	6-6 Cav
433	3-227 Avn	478	2-1 Avn	233	6-6 Cav
434	3-227 Avn	479	2-1 Avn	234	6-6 Cav
435	227 Avn	481	2-1 Avn	236	6-6 Cav
436	3-1 Avn	482	2-1 Avn	238	6-6 Cav
437		487	2-227 Avn	243	6-6 Cav
438	3-227 Avn	496		246	6-6 Cav
439	3-1 Avn	498	5-6 Cav	250	6-6 Cav

US Army Beech RC-12K Super King Air is based at Wiesbaden. *Andrew P. March*

The following aircraft are normally based in the USA but are likely to be seen visiting the UK from time to time. The presentation is in numerical order of the type, commencing with the B-**1B** and concluding with the C-**141**. The aircraft are listed in numerical progression by the serial actually carried externally. Fiscal year information is provided, together with details of mark variations and in some cases operating units. Where base-code letter information is carried on the aircrafts' tails, this is detailed with the squadron/base data; for example the 7th Wing's B-1B 30069 carries the letters DY on its tail, thus identifying the Wing's home base as Dyess AFB, Texas.

Rockwell B-1B Lancer
7 Wg Dyess AFB, Texas [DY]
28 BW Ellsworth AFB,
South Dakota [EL]
319 BG Grand Forks AFB,
North Dakota [GF]
384 BW McConnell AFB,
Kansas [OZ]
410 TS EdwardsAFB, California

FY83	
30065	7 Wg
30066	7 Wg
30067	7 Wg
30068	7 Wg
30069	7 Wg
30070	7 Wg
30071	7 Wg
FY84	
40049	410 TS
40050	7 Wg
40051	7 Wg
40053	7 Wg
40054	7 Wg
40055	7 Wg
40056	7 Wg
40057	7 Wg
40058	7 Wg
FY85	
50059	7 Wg
50060	28 BW
50061	28 BW
50062	7 Wg
50064	28 BW
50065	7 Wg
50066	28 BW
50067	7 Wg
50068	410 TS
50069	7 Wg
50070	7 Wg
50071	7 Wg
50072	7 Wg
50073	28 BW
50074	7 Wg
50075	28 BW
50077	28 BW
50078	28 BW
50079	28 BW
50080	384 BW
50081	384 BW
50082	7 Wg
50083	28 BW
50084	28 BW
50085	28 BW
50086	28 BW
50087	28 BW
50088	28 BW

50089	28 BW
50090	28 BW
50091	28 BW
50092	28 BW
FY86	
60093	28 BW
60094	28 BW
60095	7 Wg
60096	28 BW
60097	319 BG
60098	28 BW
60099	28 BW
60100	7 Wg
60101	384 BW
60102	28 BW
60103	7 Wg
60104	28 BW
60105	319 BG
60107	319 BG
60108	28 BW
60109	7 Wg
60110	319 BG
60111	319 BG
60112	319 BG
60113	319 BG
60114	319 BG
60115	384 BW
60116	319 BG
60117	319 BG
60118	319 BG
60119	319 BG
60120	319 BG
60121	319 BG
60122	319 BG
60123	319 BG
60124	384 BW
60125	384 BW
60126	384 BW
60127	384 BW
60128	384 BW
60129	384 BW
60130	384 BW
60131	319 BG
60132	7 Wg
60133	28 BW
60134	384 BW
60135	384 BW
60136	384 BW
60137	384 BW
60138	384 BW
60139	384 BW
60140	384 BW

Boeing E-3 Sentry
961 AW&CS/18 Wg (*or*)
  Kadena AB, Japan [ZZ]

962 AW&CS (*gn*)		
552 ACW		
Elmendorf AFB, Alaska [AK]		
963 AW&CS (*bk*)		
964 AW&CS (*r*)		
965 AW&CS (*y*)		
966 AW&CS (TS) (*bl*)		
Tinker AFB, Oklahoma [OK]		
FY80		
00137	E-3C	*r*
00138	E-3C	*y*
00139	E-3C	*bk*
FY81		
10004	E-3C	*bk*
10005	E-3C	*r*
FY71		
11407	E-3B	*bl*
11408	E-3B	*y*
FY82		
20006	E-3C	*y*
20007	E-3C	*y*
FY83		
30008	E-3C	*or*
30009	E-3C	*bk*
FY73		
31674	JE-3C	Boeing
31675	E-3B	*r*
FY75		
50556	E-3B	*bk*
50557	E-3B	*r*
50558	E-3B	*y*
50559	E-3B	*r*
50560	E-3B	*r*
FY76		
61604	E-3B	*y*
61605	E-3B	*bl*
61606	E-3B	*m*
61607	E-3B	*m*
FY77		
70351	E-3B	*gn*
70352	E-3B	*r*
70353	E-3B	*bl*
70354	E-3B	*bk*
70355	E-3B	*r*
70356	E-3B	*y*
FY78		
80576	E-3B	*bk*
80577	E-3B	*r*
80578	E-3B	*y*
FY79		
90001	E-3B	*bk*
90002	E-3B	*bl*
90003	E-3B	*bk*

Boeing E-4B
1ACCS/55 RW

Offutt AFB, Nebraska [OF]

31676	(FY73)
31677	(FY73)
40787	(FY74)
50125	(FY75)

Lockheed C-5 Galaxy

60 AW Travis AFB, California
97 AMW Altus AFB, Oklahoma
137 ALS/105 AG
Stewart AFB, New York (*bl*)
433 AW/68 ALS Kelly AFB, Texas*
436 AW Dover AFB, Delaware
439 AW/337 ALS
Westover AFB, Massachusetts*
(*=AFRES: Air Force Reserve)

C-5A Galaxy
FY70

00445	433 AW*
00446	433 AW*
00447	439 AW*
00448	439 AW*
00449	97 AMW
00450	433 AW*
00451	97 AMW
00452	436 AW
00453	60 AW
00454	436 AW
00455	436 AW
00456	97 AMW
00457	60 AW
00458	97 AMW
00459	60 AW
00460	436 AW
00461	433 AW*
00462	60 AW
00463	436 AW
00464	97 AMW
00465	436 AW
00467	436 AW

FY66

68304	439 AW*
68305	433 AW*
68306	433 AW*
68307	433 AW*

FY67

70167	439 AW*
70168	439 AW*
70169	137 ALS
70170	137 ALS
70171	433 AW*
70173	137 ALS
70174	137 ALS

FY68

80211	439 AW*
80212	137 ALS
80213	60 AW
80214	436 AW
80215	439 AW*
80216	60 AW
80217	436 AW
80219	439 AW*
80220	433 AW*
80221	433 AW*
80222	439 AW*
80223	433 AW*
80224	137 ALS
80225	439 AW*
80226	137 ALS

FY69

90001	60 AW
90002	433 AW*

90003	439 AW*
90004	433 AW*
90005	439 AW*
90006	137 ALS
90007	433 AW*
90008	137 ALS
90009	137 ALS
90010	60 AW
90011	439 AW*
90012	137 ALS
90013	439 AW*
90014	60 AW
90015	137 ALS
90016	433 AW*
90017	439 AW*
90018	60 AW
90019	439 AW*
90020	439 AW*
90021	137 ALS
90022	439 AW*
90023	60 AW
90024	97 AMW
90025	60 AW
90026	60 AW
90027	436 AW

C-5B Galaxy
FY83

31285	436 AW

FY84

40059	436 AW
40060	60 AW
40061	436 AW
40062	60 AW

FY85

50001	436 AW
50002	60 AW
50003	436 AW
50004	60 AW
50005	436 AW
50006	60 AW
50007	436 AW
50008	60 AW
50009	436 AW
50010	60 AW

FY86

60011	436 AW
60012	60 AW
60013	436 AW
60014	60 AW
60015	436 AW
60016	60 AW
60017	436 AW
60018	60 AW
60019	436 AW
60020	436 AW
60021	60 AW
60022	60 AW
60023	436 AW
60024	60 AW
60025	436 AW
60026	60 AW

FY87

70027	436 AW
70028	60 AW
70029	436 AW
70030	60 AW
70031	436 AW
70032	60 AW
70033	436 AW
70034	60 AW
70035	436 AW

70036	60 AW
70037	436 AW
70038	60 AW
70039	436 AW
70040	60 AW
70041	436 AW
70042	60 AW
70043	436 AW
70044	60 AW
70045	436 AW

Boeing E-8A J-STARS

Grumman, Melbourne, Florida
FY86

60416	(N770JS)
60417	(N8411)

McDonnell-Douglas KC-10A Extender

4 Wg Seymour-Johnson AFB, North Carolina [SJ]
22 ARW March AFB, California
458 OG Barksdale AFB, Louisiana

FY82

20191	22 ARW	
20192	4 Wg	*r/bk*
20193	22 ARW	

FY83

30075	458 OG	
30076	22 ARW	
30077	4 Wg	*r/bk*
30078	22 ARW	
30079	458 OG	
30080	22 ARW	
30081	458 OG	
30082	458 OG	

FY84

40185	22 ARW	
40186	458 OG	
40187	22 ARW	
40188	458 OG	
40189	22 ARW	
40190	458 OG	
40191	22 ARW	
40192	458 OG	

FY85

50027	22 ARW	
50028	458 OG	
50029	4 Wg	*k*
50030	4 Wg	
50031	4 Wg	*k*
50032	458 OG	
50033	458 OG	
50034	458 OG	

FY86

60027	458 OG	
60028	4 Wg	
60029	4 Wg	*bk*
60030	4 Wg	
60031	4 Wg	*bk*
60032	4 Wg	*bk*
60033	4 Wg	*r*
60034	4 Wg	*bk*
60035	4 Wg	*bk*
60036	4 Wg	*r*
60037	4 Wg	*bk*
60038	4 Wg	*r*

FY87

70117	22 ARW
70118	22 ARW
70119	22 ARW
70120	22 ARW

70121	~4 Wg	bk
70122	4 Wg	r
70123	4 Wg	r
70124	4 Wg	r

FY79

90433	458 OG
90434	458 OG
91710	458 OG
91711	458 OG
91712	458 OG
91713	458 OG
91946	22 ARW
91947	22 ARW
91948	22 ARW
91949	22 ARW
91950	22 ARW
91951	22 ARW

McDonnell-Douglas C-17 Globemaster III
417 TS Edwards AFB, California [ED]
437 AW Charleston AFB, South Carolina

FY90

00532	C-17A	437 AW
00533	C-17A	
00534	C-17A	
00535	C-17A	

FY87

70025	YC-17A	417 TS

FY88

80265	C-17A	417 TS
80266	C-17A	417 TS
80267	C-17A	

FY89

91189	C-17A	417 TS
91190	C-17A	417 TS
91191	C-17A	
91192	C-17A	437 AW

Boeing C-18A/EC-18B[1]/ EC-18D[2]
(Air Force Systems Command)
Wright-Patterson AFB, Ohio

FY81

10891[1]	4950 TW
10892[1]	4950 TW
10893[2]	4950 TW
10894[1]	4950 TW
10895[2]	4950 TW
10896[1]	4950 TW
10898	4950 TW

Grumman C-20 Gulfstream III/IV[1]
89 AW Andrews AFB, Maryland
US Army Andrews AFB, Maryland

FY91

10108[1]	C-20F	US Army

FY85

50049	C-20C	89 AW
50050	C-20C	89 AW

FY86

60200	C-20B	89 AW
60201	C-20B	89 AW
60202	C-20B	89 AW
60203	C-20B	89 AW
60204	C-20B	89 AW
60205	C-20B	89 AW
60206	C-20B	89 AW
60403	C-20B	89 AW

FY87

70139	C-20E	US Army
70140	C-20E	US Army

Boeing C-22B/C-22C[1]
201 ALS Andrews AFB, Maryland
310 ALS Howard AFB, Panama

FY83

34610	201 ALS
34612	201 ALS
34615	201 ALS
34616	201 ALS
34618[1]	310 ALS

Boeing VC-25A
89 AW Andrews AFB, Maryland

FY82

28000 (Air Force One)	

FY92

29000	

Boeing CT-43A
12 FTW Randolph AFB, Texas [RA] (*bk/y*)
200 ALS Buckley ANGB, Colorado

FY71

11403	12 FTW
11404	12 FTW
11405	12 FTW
11406	12 FTW

FY72

20283	
20284	200 ALS
20287	200 ALS
20288	200 ALS

FY73

31150	12 FTW
31151	12 FTW
31152	12 FTW
31153	12 FTW
31154	200 ALS
31155	12 FTW
31156	12 FTW

Boeing B-52G Stratofortress
2 BW Barksdale AFB, Louisiana [LA]
42 BW Loring AFB, Maine [LZ]
93 BW Castle AFB, California [CA]
366 Wg Castle AFB, California [MO]
410 BW KI Sawyer AFB, Michigan [KI]
419 TS Edwards AFB, California [ED]
6512 TS (AFSC), Wright-Patterson AFB, Ohio

FY57

76471	2 BW
76472	2 BW
76476	93 BW
76480	2 BW
76488	
76495	2 BW
76497	366 Wg
76498	2 BW
76503	2 BW
76511	2 BW
76515	2 BW
76520	366 Wg

FY58

80158	2 BW
80160	2 BW
80163	93 BW
80164	
80165	
80170	2 BW
80173	2 BW
80176	
80181	2 BW
80182	
80191	93 BW
80192	42 BW
80195	42 BW
80197	42 BW
80202	2 BW
80203	366 Wg
80206	42 BW
80210	93 BW
80211	2 BW
80212	366 Wg
80213	93 BW
80214	93 BW
80216	42 BW
80218	42 BW
80221	93 BW
80222	2 BW
80223	42 BW
80226	42 BW
80227	2 BW
80229	2 BW
80230	42 BW
80231	
80233	93 BW
80234	
80235	419 TS
80236	2 BW
80239	2 BW
80240	93 BW
80242	366 Wg
80244	2 BW
80245	2 BW
80248	93 BW
80250	2 BW
80253	42 BW
80255	42 BW
80257	42 BW
80258	93 BW

FY59

92565	93 BW
92566	2 BW
92567	
92568	
92569	366 Wg
92570	366 Wg
92572	93 BW
92573	42 BW
92577	2 BW
92580	2 BW
92581	2 BW
92583	
92585	42 BW
92586	419 TS
92588	93 BW
92589	93 BW
92590	2 BW
92591	2 BW
92594	2 BW
92595	93 BW
92598	366 Wg
92599	93 BW
92602	2 BW

Boeing B-52H Stratofortress

2 BW Barksdale AFB, Louisiana [LA]
5 BW Minot AFB, North Dakota [MT]
92 BW Fairchild AFB, Washington [FC]
410 BW KI Sawyer AFB, Michigan [KI]
416 BW Griffiss AFB, New York [GR]
419 TS Edwards AFB, California [ED]

FY60

00001	2 BW
00002	410 BW
00003	410 BW
00004	
00005	410 BW
00007	2 BW
00008	410 BW
00009	2 BW
00010	2 BW
00011	410 BW
00012	416 BW
00013	410 BW
00014	2 BW
00015	92 BW
00016	2 BW
00017	2 BW
00018	2 BW
00019	2 BW
00020	2 BW
00021	416 BW
00022	92 BW
00023	92 BW
00024	416 BW
00025	2 BW
00026	
00028	92 BW
00029	
00030	416 BW
00031	2 BW
00032	2 BW
00033	416 BW
00034	5 BW
00035	
00036	410 BW
00037	2 BW
00038	410 BW
00041	2 BW
00042	2 BW
00043	2 BW
00044	92 BW
00045	92 BW
00046	5 BW
00047	410 BW
00048	416 BW
00049	2 BW
00050	419 TS
00051	
00052	92 BW
00053	
00054	410 BW
00055	5 BW
00056	
00057	5 BW
00058	92 BW
00059	410 BW
00060	416 BW
00061	92 BW
00062	2 BW

FY61

10001	92 BW
10002	2 BW
10003	92 BW
10004	
10005	92 BW
10006	92 BW
10007	5 BW
10008	92 BW
10009	92 BW
10010	5 BW
10011	
10012	410 BW
10013	2 BW
10014	416 BW
10015	416 BW
10016	
10017	92 BW
10018	92 BW
10019	
10020	416 BW
10021	416 BW
10022	92 BW
10023	5 BW
10024	410 BW
10025	416 BW
10026	92 BW
10027	2 BW
10028	2 BW
10029	
10031	92 BW
10032	2 BW
10034	410 BW
10035	
10036	92 BW
10038	2 BW
10039	92 BW
10040	92 BW

Lockheed C-130 Hercules

1 SOS Kadena AB, Japan
3 Wg Elmendorf AFB, Alaska [AK]
7 ACCS Keesler AFB, Missouri [KS]
7 SOS RAF Alconbury, UK
7 Wg Dyess AFB, Texas [DY]
8 SOS Hurlburt Field, Florida
9 SOS Eglin AFB, Florida
15 SOS Hurlburt Field, Florida
16 SOS Hurlburt Field, Florida
16 SOW Hurlburt Field, Florida
17 SOS Kadena AB, Japan
23 Wg Pope AFB, North Carolina [FT]
41 ECS Davis-Monthan AFB, Arizona [DM] (bl)
43 ECS Davis-Monthan AFB, Arizona [DM] (r)
67 SOS RAF Alconbury, UK
71 RQS Patrick AFB, Florida [FF]
310 ALS, Howard AFB, Canal Zone
314 AW Little Rock AFB, Arkansas [LK] (r/w)
374 AW Yokota AB, Japan [YJ]
418 TS Edwards AFB, California [ED]
435 AW Rhein-Main AB, Germany
542 CTW Kirtland AFB, New Mexico

102 RQS New York ANG
105 ALS Tennessee ANG
109 ALS Minnesota ANG
115 ALS California ANG
129 RQS California ANG
130 ALS West Virginia ANG
135 ALS Maryland ANG
139 ALS New York ANG
142 ALS Delaware ANG
143 ALS Rhode Island ANG
144 ALS Alaska ANG
154 ALS Arkansas ANG
156 ALS North Carolina ANG
158 ALS Georgia ANG
164 ALS Ohio ANG
165 ALS Kentucky ANG
167 ALS West Virginia ANG
180 ALS Missouri ANG
181 ALS Texas ANG
185 ALS Oklahoma ANG
187 ALS Wyoming ANG
193 SOS Pennsylvania ANG
210 RQS Alaska ANG
63 ALS Selfridge ANGB, Michigan *
64 ALS Chicago O'Hare, Illinois [VO] *
95 ALS Milwaukee, Wisconsin [MK] *
96 ALS St Paul, Minnesota [MS] (pr) *
301 RQS Patrick AFB, Florida [FF] *
303 ALS March AFB, California *
304 RQS Portland, Oregon [PD] *
327 ALS NAS Willow Grove, Pennsylvania [WG] *
328 ALS Niagara Falls, New York [NF] *
357 ALS Maxwell AFB, Alabama [MX] *
700 ALS Dobbins AFB, Georgia [DB] *
711 SOS Duke Field, Florida *
731 ALS Peterson AFB, Colorado [PP] *
757 ALS Youngstown, Ohio [YO] *
758 ALS Pittsburgh, Pennsylvania [PI] *
815 ALS Keesler, Missouri [KT] *
(*=AFRES: Air Force Reserve)

FY90

00161	MC-130H	
00162	MC-130H	
00163	AC-130U	16 SOW
00164	AC-130U	16 SOW
00165	AC-130U	16 SOW
00166	AC-130U	
00167	AC-130U	

FY60

00294	C-130B	731 ALS*
00310	C-130B	731 ALS*

FY80

00320	C-130H	158 ALS
00321	C-130H	158 ALS
00322	C-130H	158 ALS
00323	C-130H	158 ALS
00324	C-130H	158 ALS
00325	C-130H	158 ALS
00326	C-130H	158 ALS

Serial	Type	Unit	Serial	Type	Unit	Serial	Type	Unit
00331	C-130H	158 ALS	10967	C-130B	303 ALS*	20059	C-130H	144 ALS
00332	C-130H	158 ALS	10968	C-130B	303 ALS*	20060	C-130H	144 ALS
FY90						20061	C-130H	144 ALS
01057	C-130H	105 ALS	*FY91*					
01058	C-130H	105 ALS	11231	C-130H	165 ALS	*FY72*		
			11232	C-130H	165 ALS	21288	C-130E	374 AW
FY70			11233	C-130H	165 ALS	21289	C-130E	374 AW
01259	C-130E	23 Wg	11234	C-130H	165 ALS	21290	C-130E	374 AW
01260	C-130E	435 AW	11235	C-130H	165 ALS	21291	C-130E	314 AW
01261	C-130E	23 Wg	11236	C-130H	165 ALS	21292	C-130E	314 AW
01262	C-130E	23 Wg	11237	C-130H	165 ALS	21293	C-130E	314 AW
01263	C-130E	23 Wg	11238	C-130H	165 ALS	21294	C-130E	314 AW
01264	C-130E	435 AW	11239	C-130H	165 ALS	21295	C-130E	314 AW
01265	C-130E	23 Wg	11651	C-130H	165 ALS	21296	C-130E	314 AW
01266	C-130E	23 Wg	11652	C-130H	165 ALS	21298	C-130E	314 AW
01267	C-130E	23 Wg	11653	C-130H	165 ALS	21299	C-130E	374 AW
01268	C-130E	23 Wg				21302	HC-130H	
01269	C-130E	23 Wg	*FY61*					
01270	C-130E	23 Wg	12358	C-130E	115 ALS	*FY92*		
01271	C-130E	435 AW	12359	C-130E	115 ALS	21531	C-130H	327ALS
01272	C-130E	23 Wg	12360	WC-130E	815 ALS*	21532	C-130H	327ALS
01273	C-130E	23 Wg	12361	C-130E	109 ALS	21533	C-130H	327ALS
01274	C-130E	435 AW	12362	C-130E	314 AW	21534	C-130H	327ALS
01275	C-130E	23 Wg	12363	C-130E	314 AW	21535	C-130H	327ALS
01276	C-130E	23 Wg	12364	C-130E	731 ALS*	21536	C-130H	327ALS
			12365	WC-130E	815 ALS*	21537	C-130H	327ALS
FY90			12366	WC-130E	815 ALS*	21538	C-130H	327ALS
01791	C-130H	164 ALS	12367	C-130E	115 ALS			
01792	C-130H	164 ALS	12368	C-130E	96 ALS	*FY62*		
01793	C-130H	164 ALS	12369	C-130E	314 AW	21784	C-130E	154 ALS
01794	C-130H	164 ALS	12370	C-130E	115 ALS	21786	C-130E	109 ALS
01795	C-130H	164 ALS	12371	C-130E	143 ALS	21787	C-130E	154 ALS
01796	C-130H	164 ALS	12372	C-130E	115 ALS	21788	C-130E	154 ALS
01797	C-130H	164 ALS	12635	C-130B	187 ALS	21789	C-130E	731 ALS*
01798	C-130H	164 ALS	12636	C-130B	156 ALS	21790	C-130E	154 ALS
02103	HC-130H	210 RQS	12638	C-130B	156 ALS	21791	EC-130E	7 ACCS
09107	C-130H	757 ALS*	12639	C-130B		21792	C-130E	115 ALS
09108	C-130H	757 ALS*	12640	C-130B	156 ALS	21793	C-130E	115 ALS
			12647	C-130B	303 ALS*	21794	C-130E	731 ALS*
FY81						21795	C-130E	154 ALS
10626	C-130H	700 ALS	*FY64*			21798	C-130E	154 ALS*
10627	C-130H	700 ALS	14852	HC-130P	542 CTW	21799	C-130E	63 ALS
10628	C-130H	700 ALS	14853	HC-130P	71 RQS	21801	C-130E	115 ALS
10629	C-130H	700 ALS	14854	HC-130P	542 CTW	21803	C-130E	731 ALS*
10630	C-130H	700 ALS	14855	HC-130H	304 RQS*	21804	C-130E	154 ALS
10631	C-130H	700 ALS	14856	HC-130P	304 RQS*	21806	C-130E	96 ALS*
			14857	HC-130P	514 TS	21807	C-130E	731 ALS*
FY68			14858	HC-130P	17 SOS	21808	C-130E	731 ALS*
10934	C-130E	23 Wg	14859	EC-130H	41 ECS	21810	C-130E	731 ALS*
10935	C-130E	435 AW	14860	HC-130P	304 RQS*	21811	C-130E	115 ALS
10937	C-130E	23 Wg	14861	WC-130H	815 ALS*	21812	C-130E	109 ALS
10938	C-130E	435 AW	14862	EC-130H	41 ECS	21816	C-130E	96 ALS*
10939	C-130E	23 Wg	14863	HC-130P	71 RQS	21817	C-130E	109 ALS
10940	C-130E	23 Wg	14864	HC-130P	71 RQS	21818	EC-130E	7 ACCS
10941	C-130E	23 Wg	14865	HC-130P	304 RQS*	21819	C-130E	310 ALS
10942	C-130E	23 Wg	14866	C-130H	815 ALS*	21820	C-130E	731 ALS*
10943	C-130E	435 AW	17680	C-130E	314 AW	21821	C-130E	314 AW
10947	C-130E	435 AW	17681	C-130E	435 AW	21822	C-130E	310 ALS
10948	C-130E	314 AW	18240	C-130E	435 AW	21823	C-130E	731 ALS*
10949	C-130E	314 AW				21824	C-130E	154 ALS
10950	C-130E	314 AW	*FY91*			21825	EC-130E	7 ACCS
			19141	C-130H	328 ALS	21826	C-130E	109 ALS
FY61			19142	C-130H	328 ALS	21827	C-130E	314 AW
10949	C-130B	156 ALS	19143	C-130H	328 ALS	21828	C-130E	310 ALS
10950	C-130B	156 ALS	19144	C-130H	328 ALS	21829	C-130E	109 ALS
10951	C-130B	757 ALS*				21830	C-130E	731 ALS*
10954	C-130B	303 ALS*	*FY82*			21832	EC-130E	7 ACCS
10956	C-130B	303 ALS*	20054	C-130H	144 ALS	21833	C-130E	115 ALS
10957	C-130B	303 ALS*	20055	C-130H	144 ALS	21834	C-130E	96 ALS*
10958	C-130B	303 ALS*	20056	C-130H	144 ALS	21835	EC-130E	96 ALS*
10959	C-130B	731 ALS*	20057	C-130H	144 ALS	21836	EC-130E	7 ACCS
10962	C-130B	156 ALS	20058	C-130H	144 ALS	21837	C-130E	109 ALS
						21838	C-130E	731 ALS*

Serial	Type	Unit
21839	C-130E	96 ALS*
21842	C-130E	115 ALS
21843	MC-130E	1 SOS
21844	C-130E	96 ALS*
21846	C-130E	109 ALS
21847	C-130E	96 ALS*
21848	C-130E	96 ALS*
21849	C-130E	303 ALS*
21850	C-130E	327 ALS*
21851	C-130E	115 ALS
21852	C-130E	96 ALS*
21855	MC-130E	8 SOS
21856	C-130E	109 ALS
21857	EC-130E	7 ACCS
21858	C-130E	731 ALS*
21859	C-130E	167 ALS
21860	C-130E	731 ALS*
21862	C-130E	115 ALS
21863	EC-130E	7 ACCS
21864	C-130E	109 ALS
21866	C-130E	731 ALS*
23487	C-130B	757 ALS*
23493	C-130B	303 ALS*

FY83

Serial	Type	Unit
30486	C-130H	139 ALS
30487	C-130H	139 ALS
30488	C-130H	139 ALS
30489	C-130H	139 ALS
30490	LC-130H	139 ALS
30491	LC-130H	139 ALS
30492	LC-130H	139 ALS
30493	LC-130H	139 ALS
31212	MC-130H	412 TW

FY73

Serial	Type	Unit
31580	EC-130H	43 ECS
31581	EC-130H	43 ECS
31582	C-130H	374 AW
31583	EC-130H	43 ECS
31584	EC-130H	41 ECS
31585	EC-130H	41 ECS
31586	EC-130H	41 ECS
31587	EC-130H	41 ECS
31588	EC-130H	41 ECS
31590	EC-130H	43 ECS
31592	EC-130H	43 ECS
31594	EC-130H	41 ECS
31595	EC-130H	43 ECS
31597	C-130H	374 AW
31598	C-130H	374 AW

FY53

Serial	Type	Unit
33129	AC-130A	711 SOS*

FY63

Serial	Type	Unit
37764	C-130E	328 ALS*
37765	C-130E	314 AW
37767	C-130E	314 AW
37768	C-130E	314 AW
37769	C-130E	327ALS*
37770	C-130E	328 ALS*
37771	C-130E	314 AW
37773	EC-130E	193 SOS
37776	C-130E	327 ALS*
37777	C-130E	167 ALS
37778	C-130E	314 AW
37779	C-130E	327 ALS*
37781	C-130E	314 AW
37782	C-130E	143 ALS
37783	EC-130E	193 SOS
37784	C-130E	314 AW
37785	MC-130E	1 SOS
37786	C-130E	314 AW
37788	C-130E	143 ALS
37790	C-130E	314 AW
37791	C-130E	314 AW
37792	C-130E	167 ALS
37793	C-130E	314 AW
37794	C-130E	314 AW
37795	C-130E	314 AW
37796	C-130E	314 AW
37799	C-130E	167 ALS
37800	C-130E	374 AW
37803	C-130E	23 Wg
37804	C-130E	815 ALS*
37805	C-130E	314 AW
37806	C-130E	23 Wg
37807	C-130E	314 AW
37808	C-130E	23 Wg
37809	C-130E	143 ALS
37811	C-130E	167 ALS
37812	C-130E	23 Wg
37813	C-130E	67 SOS
37814	C-130E	193 SOS
37815	C-130E	193 SOS
37816	C-130E	815 ALS*
37817	C-130E	167 ALS
37818	C-130E	374 AW
37819	C-130E	314 AW
37820	C-130E	23 Wg
37821	C-130E	328 ALS*
37822	C-130E	327 ALS*
37823	C-130E	143 ALS
37824	C-130E	135 ALS
37825	C-130E	327 ALS*
37826	C-130E	193 SOS
37828	C-130E	23 Wg
37829	C-130E	314 AW
37830	C-130E	314 AW
37831	C-130E	303 ALS*
37832	C-130E	327 ALS*
37833	C-130E	327 ALS*
37834	C-130E	314 AW
37836	C-130E	314 AW
37837	C-130E	374 AW
37838	C-130E	314 AW
37839	C-130E	314 AW
37840	C-130E	143 ALS
37841	C-130E	314 AW
37842	C-130E	1 SOS
37845	C-130E	23 Wg
37846	C-130E	23 Wg
37847	C-130E	154 ALS
37848	C-130E	327 ALS*
37849	C-130E	23 Wg
37850	C-130E	314 AW
37851	C-130E	167 ALS
37852	C-130E	328 ALS*
37853	C-130E	327ALS*
37854	C-130E	314 AW
37856	C-130E	303 ALS*
37857	C-130E	374 AW
37858	C-130E	167 ALS
37859	C-130E	143 ALS
37860	C-130E	314 AW
37861	C-130E	314 AW
37863	C-130E	328 ALS*
37864	C-130E	314 AW
37865	C-130E	374 AW
37866	C-130E	314 AW
37867	C-130E	327 ALS*
37868	C-130E	143 ALS
37869	EC-130E	193 SOS
37871	C-130E	23 Wg
37872	C-130E	167 ALS
37874	C-130E	314 AW
37876	C-130E	314 AW
37877	C-130E	167 ALS
37879	C-130E	374 AW
37880	C-130E	314 AW
37882	C-130E	314 AW
37883	C-130E	327 ALS*
37884	C-130E	23 Wg
37885	C-130E	435 AW
37887	C-130E	435 AW
37888	C-130E	314 AW
37889	C-130E	143 ALS
37890	C-130E	23 Wg
37891	C-130E	314 AW
37892	C-130E	327 ALS*
37893	C-130E	314 AW
37894	C-130E	314 AW
37895	C-130E	135 ALS
37896	C-130E	314 AW
37897	C-130E	167 ALS
37898	C-130E	8 SOS
37899	C-130E	23 Wg
39810	C-130E	23 Wg
39811	C-130E	314 AW
39812	C-130E	314 AW
39813	C-130E	193 SOS
39814	C-130E	314 AW
39815	C-130E	193 SOS
39816	EC-130E	193 SOS
39817	EC-130E	193 SOS

FY84

Serial	Type	Unit
40204	C-130H	700ALS*
40205	C-130H	700ALS*
40206	C-130H	142 ALS
40207	C-130H	142 ALS
40208	C-130H	142 ALS
40209	C-130H	142 ALS
40210	C-130H	142 ALS
40211	C-130H	142 ALS
40212	C-130H	142 ALS
40213	C-130H	142 ALS
40475	MC-130H	418 TS
40476	MC-130H	7 SOS

FY64

Serial	Type	Unit
40495	C-130E	23 Wg
40496	C-130E	23 Wg
40497	C-130E	374 AW
40498	C-130E	23 Wg
40499	C-130E	23 Wg
40500	C-130E	AFLC
40502	C-130E	435 AW
40503	C-130E	374 AW
40504	C-130E	23 Wg
40510	C-130E	135 ALS
40512	C-130E	154 ALS
40513	C-130E	314 AW
40514	C-130E	135 ALS
40515	C-130E	135 ALS
40517	C-130E	23 Wg
40518	C-130E	314 AW
40519	C-130E	314 AW
40520	C-130E	135 ALS
40521	C-130E	135 ALS
40523	MC-130E	
40524	C-130E	314 AW
40525	C-130E	23 Wg
40526	C-130E	115 ALS
40527	C-130E	435 AW
40529	C-130E	23 Wg

Serial	Type	Unit
40530	C-130E	314 AW
40531	C-130E	23 Wg
40533	C-130E	435 AW
40534	C-130E	374 AW
40535	C-130E	314 AW
40537	C-130E	23 Wg
40538	C-130E	314 AW
40539	C-130E	23 Wg
40540	C-130E	23 Wg
40541	C-130E	23 Wg
40542	C-130E	23 Wg
40544	C-130E	135 ALS
40550	C-130E	435 AW
40551	MC-130E	8 SOS
40552	WC-130E	815 ALS*
40553	WC-130E	815 ALS*
40554	WC-130E	815 ALS*
40555	MC-130E	
40556	C-130E	374 AW
40557	C-130E	314 AW
40559	MC-130E	8 SOS
40560	C-130E	314 AW
40561	MC-130E	
40562	MC-130E	8 SOS
40565	MC-130E	1 SOS
40566	MC-130E	16 SOW
40567	MC-130E	8 SOS
40568	MC-130E	8 SOS
40569	C-130E	314 AW
40570	C-130E	23 Wg
40571	MC-130E	1 SOS
40572	MC-130E	8 SOS

FY54:

Serial	Type	Unit
41623	AC-130A	711 SOS*
41628	AC-130A	711 SOS*
41630	AC-130A	711 SOS*
41634	C-130A	155 ALS
41637	C-130A	155 ALS

FY74

Serial	Type	Unit
41658	C-130H	3 Wg
41659	C-130H	3 Wg
41660	C-130H	374 AW
41661	C-130H	374 AW
41662	C-130H	7 Wg
41663	C-130H	7 Wg
41664	C-130H	7 Wg
41665	C-130H	7 Wg
41666	C-130H	7 Wg
41667	C-130H	7 Wg
41668	C-130H	3 Wg
41669	C-130H	7 Wg
41670	C-130H	7 Wg
41671	C-130H	7 Wg
41673	C-130H	7 Wg
41674	C-130H	7 Wg
41675	C-130H	7 Wg
41676	C-130H	3 Wg
41677	C-130H	7 Wg
41679	C-130H	7 Wg
41680	C-130H	7 Wg
41682	C-130H	374 AW
41684	C-130H	374 AW
41685	C-130H	374 AW
41687	C-130H	7 Wg
41688	C-130H	7 Wg
41689	C-130H	7 Wg
41690	C-130H	3 Wg
41691	C-130H	7 Wg
41692	C-130H	3 Wg
42061	C-130H	7 Wg
42062	C-130H	3 Wg
42063	C-130H	7 Wg
42065	C-130H	7 Wg
42066	C-130H	3 Wg
42067	C-130H	7 Wg
42069	C-130H	7 Wg
42070	C-130H	3 Wg
42071	C-130H	3 Wg
42072	C-130H	7 Wg
42130	C-130H	7 Wg
42131	C-130H	3 Wg
42132	C-130H	7 Wg
42133	C-130H	374 AW
42134	C-130H	7 Wg

FY55

Serial	Type	Unit
50011	AC-130A	711 SOS*
50014	AC-130A	711 SOS*
50022	C-130A	4950 TW
50029	AC-130A	711 SOS*
50036	C-130A	63 ALS*
50046	AC-130A	711 SOS*

FY85

Serial	Type	Unit
50011	MC-130H	8 SOS
50012	MC-130H	15 SOS
50035	C-130H	357 ALS*
50036	C-130H	357 ALS*
50037	C-130H	357 ALS*
50038	C-130H	357 ALS*
50039	C-130H	357 ALS*
50040	C-130H	357 ALS*
50041	C-130H	357 ALS*
50042	C-130H	357 ALS*

FY65

Serial	Type	Unit
50962	C-130H	7 ACCS
50963	WC-130H	815 ALS*
50964	C-130H	815 ALS*
50966	WC-130H	815 ALS*
50967	C-130H	815 ALS*
50968	WC-130H	815 ALS*
50969	C-130H	815 ALS*
50970	HC-130P	304 RQS*
50971	HC-130P	304 RQS*
50972	C-130H	815 ALS*
50973	HC-130P	71 RQS
50974	HC-130P	102 RQS
50975	HC-130P	542 CTW
50976	C-130H	815 ALS*
50977	C-130H	815 ALS*
50978	HC-130P	102 RQS
50979	NC-130H	514 TS
50980	WC-130H	815 ALS*
50981	HC-130P	304 RQS*
50982	HC-130P	71 RQS
50983	HC-130P	129 RQS
50984	WC-130H	815 ALS*
50985	C-130H	815 ALS*
50986	C-130H	71 RQS
50987	HC-130P	542 CTW
50988	HC-130P	102 RQS
50989	EC-130H	41 ECS
50991	HC-130P	9 SOS
50992	HC-130P	17 SOS
50993	HC-130P	9 SOS
50994	HC-13OP	9 SOS

FY85

Serial	Type	Unit
51361	C-130H	181 ALS
51362	C-130H	181 ALS
51363	C-130H	181 ALS
51364	C-130H	181 ALS
51365	C-130H	181 ALS
51366	C-130H	181 ALS
51367	C-130H	181 ALS
51368	C-130H	181 ALS

FY66

Serial	Type	Unit
60212	HC-130P	542 CTW
60213	HC-130P	542 CTW
60215	HC-130P	9 SOS
60216	HC-130P	9 SOS
60217	HC-130P	9 SOS
60219	HC-130P	542 CTW
60220	HC-130P	129 RQS
60221	HC-130P	129 RQS
60222	HC-130P	129 RQS
60223	HC-130P	67 SOS
60224	HC-130P	129 RQS
60225	HC-130P	9 SOS

FY86

Serial	Type	Unit
60410	C-130H	758 ALS*
60411	C-130H	758 ALS*
60412	C-130H	758 ALS*
60413	C-130H	758 ALS*
60414	C-130H	758 ALS*
60415	C-130H	758 ALS*
60418	C-130H	758 ALS*
60419	C-130H	758 ALS*

FY56

Serial	Type	Unit
60469	AC-130A	711 SOS*
60498	C-130A	155 ALS
60509	AC-130A	711 SOS*
60522	C-130A	711 SOS*
60524	C-130A	155 ALS
60525	C-130A	155 ALS
60547	C-130A	155 ALS

FY86

Serial	Type	Unit
61391	C-130H	180 ALS
61392	C-130H	180 ALS
61393	C-130H	180 ALS
61394	C-130H	180 ALS
61395	C-130H	180 ALS
61396	C-130H	180 ALS
61397	C-130H	180 ALS
61398	C-130H	180 ALS
61699	MC-130H	7 SOS

FY87

Serial	Type	Unit
70023	MC-130H	7 SOS
70024	MC-130H	15 SOS
70125	MC-130H	15 SOS
70126	MC-130H	15 SOS
70127	MC-130H	8 SOS
70128	AC-130U	418 TS

FY57

Serial	Type	Unit
70463	C-130A	155 ALS
70465	C-130A	155 ALS
70526	C-130B	412 TW

FY67

Serial	Type	Unit
77184	C-130H	310 ALS

FY87

Serial	Type	Unit
79281	C-130H	64 ALS*
79282	C-130H	64 ALS*
79283	C-130H	64 ALS*
79284	C-130H	64 ALS*
79285	C-130H	64 ALS*
79286	C-130H	64 ALS*
79287	C-130H	64 ALS*
79288	C-130H	64 ALS*

80191	MC-130H	542 CTW
80192	MC-130H	542 CTW
80193	MC-130H	7 SOS
80194	MC-130H	
80195	MC-130H	15 SOS
80264	MC-130H	AFSC

FY58

80711	C-130B	187 ALS
80714	C-130B	187 ALS
80716	C-130B	412 TW
80728	C-130B	156 ALS
80729	C-130B	156 ALS
80731	C-130B	164 ALS
80734	C-130B	187 ALS
80738	C-130B	731 ALS*
80747	C-130B	165 ALS
80751	C-130B	156 ALS
80753	C-130B	156 ALS
80754	C-130B	187 ALS

FY78

80806	C-130H	185 ALS
80807	C-130H	185 ALS
80808	C-130H	185 ALS
80809	C-130H	185 ALS
80810	C-130H	185 ALS
80811	C-130H	185 ALS
80812	C-130H	185 ALS
80813	C-130H	185 ALS
81301	C-130H	130 ALS
81302	C-130H	130 ALS
81303	C-130H	130 ALS
81304	C-130H	130 ALS
81305	C-130H	130 ALS
81306	C-130H	130 ALS
81307	C-130H	130 ALS
81308	C-130H	130 ALS
81803	MC-130H	AFSC
82101	HC-130H	210 RQS
82102	HC-130H	210 RQS
84401	C-130H	95 ALS*
84402	C-130H	95 ALS*
84403	C-130H	95 ALS*
84404	C-130H	95 ALS*
84405	C-130H	95 ALS*
84406	C-130H	95 ALS*
84407	C-130H	95 ALS*
84408	C-130H	95 ALS*

FY89

90280	MC-130H	AFSC
90281	MC-130H	AFSC
90282	MC-130H	AFSC
90283	MC-130H	AFSC

FY79

90473	C-130H	144 ALS
90474	C-130H	
90475	C-130H	
90476	C-130H	157 FS
90477	C-130H	158 ALS
90478	C-130H	199 FS
90479	C-130H	185 ALS
90480	C-130H	122 FS

FY89

90509	AC-130U	AFSC
90510	AC-130U	418 TS
90511	AC-130U	418 TS
90512	AC-130U	
90513	AC-130U	
90514	AC-130U	
91051	C-130H	105 ALS
91052	C-130H	105 ALS
91053	C-130H	105 ALS
91054	C-130H	105 ALS
91055	C-130H	105 ALS
91056	C-130H	105 ALS
91181	C-130H	155 ALS
91182	C-130H	155 ALS
91183	C-130H	155 ALS
91184	C-130H	155 ALS
91185	C-130H	155 ALS
91186	C-130H	155 ALS
91187	C-130H	155 ALS
91188	C-130H	155 ALS

FY59

91524	C-130B	757 ALS*
91528	C-130B	156 ALS
91529	C-130B	165 ALS
91530	C-130B	303 ALS*
91531	C-130B	731 ALS*
91532	C-130B	757 ALS*
91533	C-130B	156 ALS
91535	C-130B	757 ALS*
91536	C-130B	156 ALS
91537	C-130B	303 ALS*

FY69

95819	HC-130N	9 SOS
95820	HC-130N	67 SOS
95821	HC-130N	17 SOS
95822	HC-130N	17 SOS
95823	HC-130N	67 SOS
95824	HC-130N	301 RQS*
95825	HC-130N	17 SOS
95826	HC-130N	67 SOS
95827	HC-130N	67 SOS
95828	HC-130N	9 SOS
95829	HC-130N	301 RQS*
95830	HC-130N	301 RQS*
95831	HC-130N	505 CTW
95832	HC-130N	9 SOS
95833	HC-130N	301 RQS*

FY69

96566	C-130E	435 AW
96568	AC-130H	16 SOS
96569	AC-130H	16 SOS
96570	AC-130H	16 SOS
96572	AC-130H	16 SOS
96573	AC-130H	16 SOS
96574	AC-130H	16 SOS
96575	AC-130H	16 SOS
96576	AC-130H	16 SOS
96577	AC-130H	16 SOS
96579	C-130E	314 AW
96580	C-130E	23 Wg
96582	C-130E	435 AW
96583	C-130E	435 AW

FY89

99101	C-130H	757 ALS*
99102	C-130H	757 ALS*
99103	C-130H	757 ALS*
99104	C-130H	757 ALS*
99105	C-130H	757 ALS*
99106	C-130H	757 ALS*

Boeing C-135/C-137

6 Wg Eielson AFB, Alaska
8 ADCS/552 ACW, Tinker AFB, Oklahoma [OK]
18 Wg Kadena AB, Japan [ZZ]
19 ARW Robins AFB, Georgia
28 ARS/43 OG Ellsworth AFB, South Dakota (bl)
41 ARS/380 OG Griffiss AFB, New York
42 ARS/380 OG Loring AFB, Maine
43 ARS/453 OG Fairchild AFB, Washington (bl)
43 ARW Malmstrom AFB, Montana
46 ARS/305 OG KI Sawyer AFB, Michigan
55 RW Offutt AFB, Nebraska [OF]
65 ALS, Hickam AFB, Hawaii
89 AW Andrews AFB, Maryland
93 ARS/398 OG Castle AFB, California
100 ARW RAF Mildenhall, UK [D] (r/w/bl)
305 ARW Grissom AFB, Indiana
350 ARS/43 ARW Beale AFB, California [BB] (y/bk)
366 Wg Mountain Home AFB, Idaho [MO] (y/gn)
380 ARW Plattsburgh AFB, New York
384 ARS/19 OG McConnell AFB, Kansas (y/r)
453 OG Fairchild AFB, Washington (b)
457 OG/19 ARW Altus AFB, Oklahoma (y/gn)
458 OG Barksdale AFB, Louisiana [LA]
509 ARS/380 OG Griffiss AFB, New York (or)
905 ARS/319 ARW Grand Forks AFB, North Dakota
906 ARS/43 OG Minot AFB, North Dakota (bl)
917 ARS/43 OG Dyess AFB, Texas [DY]
4950 TW Wright-Patterson AFB, Ohio

ANG, Air National Guard:

108 ARS Illinois ANG
116 ARS Washington ANG (bl)
117 ARS Kansas ANG (bl/y)
126 ARS Wisconsin ANG
132 ARS Maine ANG
133 ARS New Hampshire ANG
136 ARS New York ANG
141 ARS New Jersey ANG (y)
145 ARS Ohio ANG (r/w)
146 ARS Pennsylvania ANG (y/bk)
147 ARS Pennsylvania ANG (bk/y)
150 ARS New Jersey ANG (bl)
151 ARS Tennessee ANG (or)
153 ARS Mississippi ANG (bl/y)
166 ARS Ohio ANG (bl/w)
168 ARS Alaska ANG (bl)
173 ARS Nebraska ANG
191 ARS Utah ANG
196 ARS California ANG (bl/w)
197 ARS Arizona ANG
203 ARS Hawaii ANG

* AFRES, Air Force Reserve:
63 ARS/434 Wg, Selfridge
  ANGB, Michigan (*gn*)
72 ARS/434 Wg, Grissom AFB,
  Indiana (*bl*)
74 ARS/434 Wg, Grissom AFB,
  Indiana (*r*)
314 ARS/452 ARW, Beale AFB,
  California
336 ARS/452 ARW, March AFB,
  California (*y*)

Serial	Type	Unit
FY60		
00313	KC-135R	905 ARS
00314	KC-135R	305 ARW
00315	KC-135R	126 ARS
00316	KC-135E	116 ARS
00318	KC-135R	19 ARW
00319	KC-135R	19 ARW
00320	KC-135R	43 ARS
00321	KC-135R	28 ARS
00322	KC-135R	72 ARS*
00323	KC-135R	380 ARW
00324	KC-135R	905 ARS
00325	KC-135R	398 OG
00326	KC-135A	917 ARS
00327	KC-135E	191 ARS
00328	KC-135R	453 OG
00329	KC-135R	203 ARS
00331	KC-135R	93 ARS
00332	KC-135R	457 OG
00333	KC-135R	305 ARW
00334	KC-135R	126 ARS
00335	KC-135Q	458 OG
00336	KC-135Q	18 Wg
00337	KC-135Q	458 OG
00339	KC-135Q	917 ARS
00341	KC-135R	145 ARS
00342	KC-135Q	350 ARS
00343	KC-135Q	380 ARW
00344	KC-135Q	458 OG
00345	KC-135Q	917 ARS
00346	KC-135Q	458 OG
00347	KC-135R	384 ARS
00348	KC-135R	43 ARW
00349	KC-135A	46 ARS
00350	KC-135R	43 ARW
00351	KC-135R	43 ARW
00353	KC-135R	28 ARS
00355	KC-135A	917 ARS
00356	KC-135R	305 ARW
00357	KC-135R	305 ARW
00358	KC-135R	43 ARW
00359	KC-135R	74 ARS*
00360	KC-135R	43 ARW
00362	KC-135R	305 ARW
00363	KC-135R	74 ARS*
00364	KC-135R	74 ARS*
00365	KC-135R	366 Wg
00366	KC-135R	18 Wg
00367	KC-135R	145 ARS
00371	NC-135E	4950 TW
00372	C-135E	4950 TW
00374	EC-135E	4950 TW
00375	EC-135E	4950 TW
00377	KC-135A	4950 TW
00378	C-135A	55 RW
FY61		
10264	KC-135R	166 ARS
10266	KC-135R	42 ARS
10267	KC-135R	384 ARS
10268	KC-135E	314 ARS*
10270	KC-135E	72 ARS*
10271	KC-135E	63 ARS*
10272	KC-135E	74 ARS*
10275	KC-135R	905 ARS
10276	KC-135R	384 ARS
10277	KC-135R	366 Wg
10280	KC-135E	336 ARS*
10281	KC-135E	197 ARS
10284	KC-135R	453 OG
10288	KC-135R	28 ARS
10290	KC-135R	203 ARS
10292	KC-135R	384 ARS
10293	KC-135R	305 ARW
10294	KC-135R	42 ARS
10295	KC-135R	457 OG
10298	KC-135R	126 ARS
10299	KC-135R	43 ARW
10300	KC-135R	457 OG
10302	KC-135R	453 OG
10303	KC-135E	336 ARS*
10304	KC-135R	384 ARS
10305	KC-135R	305 ARW
10306	KC-135R	43 ARW
10307	KC-135R	19 ARW
10308	KC-135R	398 OG
10309	KC-135R	126 ARS
10310	KC-135R	384 ARS
10311	KC-135R	457 OG
10312	KC-135R	28 ARS
10313	KC-135R	100 ARW
10314	KC-135R	19 ARW
10315	KC-135R	28 ARS
10317	KC-135R	906 ARS
10318	KC-135R	398 OG
10320	KC-135R	509 ARS
10321	KC-135R	100 ARW
10323	KC-135R	18 Wg
10324	KC-135R	384 ARS
10325	KC-135A	906 ARS
10326	EC-135E	4950 TW
10327	EC-135N	CinC CC
10329	EC-135E	4950 TW
10330	EC-135E	4950 TW
12662	RC-135S	55 RW
12663	RC-135S	55 RW
12665	WC-135B	55 RW
12666	WC-135B	
12667	TC-135B	55 RW
12668	C-135C	89 AW
12669	C-135C	4950 TW
12670	WC-135B	55 RW
12672	OC-135B	55 RW
12673	OC-135B	55 RW
12674	OC-135B	55 RW
FY64		
14828	KC-135R	384 ARS
14829	KC-135R	509 ARS
14830	KC-135R	906 ARS
14831	KC-135R	453 OG
14832	KC-135R	203 ARS
14833	KC-135R	100 ARW
14834	KC-135R	453 OG
14835	KC-135R	384 ARS
14836	KC-135R	43 ARW
14837	KC-135R	917 ARS
14838	KC-135R	380 ARW
14839	KC-135R	906 ARS
14840	KC-135R	166 ARS
14841	RC-135V	55 RW
14842	RC-135V	55 RW
14843	RC-135V	55 RW
14844	RC-135V	55 RW
14845	RC-135V	55 RW
14846	RC-135V	55 RW
14847	RC-135U	55 RW
14848	RC-135V	55 RW
14849	RC-135U	55 RW
FY67		
19417	EC-137D	19 Wg
FY62		
23498	KC-135R	453 OG
23499	KC-135R	398 OG
23500	KC-135R	126 ARS
23502	KC-135R	380 ARW
23503	KC-135R	509 ARS
23504	KC-135R	319 ARW
23505	KC-135A	509 ARS
23506	KC-135R	19 ARW
23507	KC-135R	457 OG
23508	KC-135R	42 ARS
23509	KC-135R	
23510	KC-135R	74 ARS*
23511	KC-135R	145 ARS
23512	KC-135R	509 ARS
23513	KC-135R	366 Wg
23514	KC-135R	203 ARS
23515	KC-135R	384 ARS
23517	KC-135R	380 ARW
23518	KC-135R	305 ARW
23519	KC-135R	18 Wg
23520	KC-135R	19 ARW
23521	KC-135R	72 ARS*
23523	KC-135R	19 ARW
23524	KC-135A	457 OG
23525	KC-135A	906 ARS
23526	KC-135R	457 OG
23527	KC-135E	150 ARS
23528	KC-135R	906 ARS
23529	KC-135R	453 OG
23530	KC-135R	72 ARS*
23531	KC-135R	145 ARS
23533	KC-135R	43 ARW
23534	KC-135R	19 ARW
23537	KC-135R	43 ARW
23538	KC-135R	43 ARW
23539	KC-135A	917 ARS
23540	KC-135R	28 ARS
23541	KC-135R	305 ARW
23542	KC-135R	28 ARS
23543	KC-135R	305 ARW
23544	KC-135R	380 ARW
23545	KC-135R	19 ARW
23546	KC-135R	43 ARW
23547	KC-135R	398 OG
23548	KC-135R	398 OG
23549	KC-135R	398 OG
23550	KC-135R	19 ARW
23551	KC-135R	509 ARS
23552	KC-135R	19 ARW
23553	KC-135R	905 ARS
23554	KC-135R	19 ARW
23555	KC-135A	46 ARS
23556	KC-135R	19 ARW
23557	KC-135R	19 ARW
23558	KC-135R	100 ARW
23559	KC-135R	398 OG
23560	KC-135A	906 ARS
23561	KC-135R	100 ARW
23562	KC-135R	380 ARW
23563	KC-135A	906 ARS
23564	KC-135R	28 ARS
23565	KC-135R	905 ARS
23566	KC-135E	168 ARS
23567	KC-135R	46 ARS

Serial	Type	Unit
23568	KC-135R	380 ARW
23569	KC-135R	19 ARW
23571	KC-135R	145 ARS
23572	KC-135R	366 ARW
23573	KC-135R	509 ARS
23575	KC-135R	43 ARW
23576	KC-135R	19 ARW
23577	KC-135R	100 ARW
23578	KC-135R	453 OG
23580	KC-135R	509 ARS
23581	EC-135C	55 RW
23582	EC-135C	55 RW
23585	EC-135C	55 RW
24125	C-135B	
24126	C-135B	
24127	C-135B	65 ALS
24129	TC-135S	55 RW
24130	C-135B	55 RW
24131	RC-135W	55 RW
24132	RC-135W	55 RW
24133	TC-135S	6 Wg
24134	RC-135W	55 RW
24135	RC-135W	55 RW
24138	RC-135W	55 RW
24139	RC-135C	55 RW
26000	C-137C	89 AW
FY72		
27000	C-137C	89 AW
FY63		
37976	KC-135R	319 ARW
37977	KC-135R	18 Wg
37978	KC-135R	906 ARS
37979	KC-135R	457 OG
37980	KC-135R	43 ARW
37981	KC-135R	457 OG
37982	KC-135R	43 ARW
37984	KC-135R	457 OG
37985	KC-135R	380 ARW
37986	KC-135R	906 ARS
37987	KC-135R	319 ARW
37988	KC-135R	453 OG
37991	KC-135R	28 ARS
37992	KC-135R	43 ARW
37993	KC-135R	166 ARS
37995	KC-135R	19 ARW
37996	KC-135R	305 ARW
37997	KC-135R	384 ARS
37998	KC-135R	917 ARS
37999	KC-135R	319 ARW
38000	KC-135A	458 OG
38002	KC-135R	19 ARW
38003	KC-135R	100 ARW
38004	KC-135R	366 Wg
38005	KC-135R	398 OG
38006	KC-135R	905 ARS
38007	KC-135R	457 OG
38008	KC-135R	19 ARW
38009	KC-135R	46 ARS
38010	KC-135A	46 ARS
38011	KC-135R	905 ARS
38012	KC-135A	398 OG
38013	KC-135R	453 OG
38014	KC-135R	380 ARW
38015	KC-135R	43 ARW
38016	KC-135A	398 OG
38017	KC-135R	453 OG
38018	KC-135R	42 ARS
38019	KC-135R	380 ARW
38020	KC-135R	
38021	KC-135R	305 ARW
38022	KC-135R	42 ARS
38023	KC-135R	453 OG
38024	KC-135R	305 ARW
38025	KC-135R	905 ARS
38026	KC-135R	126 ARS
38027	KC-135R	43 ARW
38028	KC-135R	305 ARW
38029	KC-135R	126 ARS
38030	KC-135R	203 ARS
38031	KC-135R	19 ARW
38032	KC-135R	305 ARW
38034	KC-135A	917 ARS
38035	KC-135R	509 ARS
38036	KC-135R	19 ARW
38037	KC-135R	398 OG
38038	KC-135R	509 ARS
38039	KC-135R	43 ARW
38040	KC-135R	28 ARS
38041	KC-135R	72 ARS*
38043	KC-135R	384 ARS
38044	KC-135R	906 ARS
38045	KC-135R	906 ARS
38046	EC-135C	55 RW
38047	EC-135C	55 RW
38048	EC-135C	55 RW
38049	EC-135C	55 RW
38050	EC-135C	55 RW
38052	EC-135C	55 RW
38053	EC-135C	55 RW
38054	EC-135C	55 RW
38055	KC-135J	55 RW
38058	KC-135D	168 ARS
38060	KC-135D	168 ARS
38061	KC-135D	168 ARS
38871	KC-135R	398 OG
38872	KC-135R	380 ARW
38873	KC-135R	380 ARW
38874	KC-135R	28 ARS
38875	KC-135R	100 ARW
38876	KC-135R	453 OG
38877	KC-135R	319 ARW
38878	KC-135R	457 OG
38879	KC-135A	906 ARS
38880	KC-135R	457 OG
38881	KC-135A	46 ARS
38883	KC-135R	18 Wg
38884	KC-135R	398 OG
38885	KC-135A	46 ARS
38886	KC-135R	509 ARS
38887	KC-135A	906 ARS
38888	KC-135A	917 ARS
39792	RC-135V	55 RW
FY55		
53118	EC-135K	8 ADCS
53120	NKC-135A	4950 TW
53122	NKC-135A	4950 TW
53125	EC-135Y	CinC CC
53128	NKC-135A	412 TW
53132	NKC-135E	4950 TW
53134	NKC-135A	USN/FTRG
53135	NKC-135A	4950 TW
53136	KC-135A	917 ARS
53141	KC-135E	196 ARS
53142	KC-135A	398 OG
53143	KC-135E	197 ARS
53145	KC-135E	314 ARS*
53146	KC-135E	141 ARS
FY85		
56973	C-137C	89 AW
56974	C-137C	89 AW
FY56		
63591	KC-135A	380 ARW
63593	KC-135E	133 ARS
63595	KC-135A	458 OG
63596	NKC-135A	USN/FTRG
63600	KC-135A	398 OG
63604	KC-135E	117 ARS
63606	KC-135E	132 ARS
63607	KC-135E	151 ARS
63609	KC-135E	151 ARS
63611	KC-135E	146 ARS
63612	KC-135E	146 ARS
63614	KC-135A	
63620	KC-135A	906 ARS
63621	KC-135A	
63622	KC-135E	132 ARS
63623	KC-135E	336 ARS*
63624	KC-135A	46 ARS
63625	KC-135A	917 ARS
63626	KC-135E	133 ARS
63630	KC-135E	146 ARS
63631	KC-135E	117 ARS
63638	KC-135E	197 ARS
63639	KC-135A	917 ARS
63640	KC-135E	132 ARS
63641	KC-135A	196 ARS
63642	KC-135A	906 ARS
63643	KC-135E	151 ARS
63645	KC-135E	314 ARS*
63648	KC-135E	146 ARS
63650	KC-135E	133 ARS
63652	KC-135A	917 ARS
63654	KC-135E	132 ARS
63658	KC-135E	117 ARS
FY57		
71418	KC-135R	153 ARS
71419	KC-135R	453 OG
71421	KC-135E	116 ARS
71422	KC-135E	63 ARS*
71423	KC-135E	147 ARS
71425	KC-135E	151 ARS
71426	KC-135E	168 ARS
71427	KC-135R	145 ARS
71428	KC-135E	196 ARS
71429	KC-135E	117 ARS
71430	KC-135E	453 OG
71431	KC-135E	141 ARS
71432	KC-135R	380 ARW
71433	KC-135A	197 ARS
71434	KC-135E	116 ARS
71435	KC-135E	453 OG
71436	KC-135E	133 ARS
71437	KC-135E	
71438	KC-135E	72 ARS*
71440	KC-135E	319 ARW
71441	KC-135E	108 ARS
71443	KC-135E	132 ARS
71445	KC-135E	141 ARS
71447	KC-135E	146 ARS
71448	KC-135E	168 ARS
71450	KC-135E	132 ARS
71451	KC-135E	168 ARS
71452	KC-135E	197 ARS
71453	KC-135R	42 ARS
71454	KC-135R	43 ARW
71455	KC-135E	151 ARS
71456	KC-135R	453 OG
71458	KC-135E	108 ARS
71459	KC-135E	116 ARS
71460	KC-135E	117 ARS
71461	KC-135R	457 OG
71462	KC-135R	166 ARS
71463	KC-135E	117 ARS
71464	KC-135E	141 ARS
71465	KC-135E	168 ARS
71468	KC-135E	336 ARS*

Serial	Type	Unit	Serial	Type	Unit	Serial	Type	Unit
71469	KC-135R	166 ARS	80023	KC-135R	398 OG	80106	KC-135R	398 OG
71471	KC-135E	132 ARS	80024	KC-135E	146 ARS	80107	KC-135E	191 ARS
71472	KC-135R	42 ARS	80025	KC-135A	398 OG	80108	KC-135E	314 ARS*
71473	KC-135R	509 ARS	80027	KC-135R	905 ARS	80109	KC-135R	153 ARS
71474	KC-135R	305 ARW	80028	KC-135A	46 ARS	80110	KC-135E	141 ARS
71475	KC-135E	197 ARS	80030	KC-135R	509 ARS	80111	KC-135E	141 ARS
71478	KC-135E	151 ARS	80032	KC-135E	150 ARS	80112	KC-135Q	350 ARS
71479	KC-135E	336 ARS*	80034	KC-135R	380 ARW	80113	KC-135R	384 ARS
71480	KC-135E	108 ARS	80035	KC-135R	384 ARS	80114	KC-135R	398 OG
71482	KC-135E	117 ARS	80036	KC-135A	917 ARS	80115	KC-135R	150 ARS
71483	KC-135R	18 Wg	80037	KC-135E	147 ARS	80116	KC-135E	197 ARS
71484	KC-135E	197 ARS	80038	KC-135R	453 OG	80117	KC-135Q	380 ARW
71485	KC-135E	151 ARS	80040	KC-135E	150 ARS	80118	KC-135R	453 OG
71486	KC-135R	319 ARW	80041	KC-135E	63 ARS*	80119	KC-135R	28 ARS
71487	KC-135R	72 ARS*	80042	KC-135Q	380 ARW	80120	KC-135R	457 OG
71488	KC-135R	457 OG	80043	KC-135Q	191 ARS	80121	KC-135R	
71491	KC-135E	132 ARS	80044	KC-135E	141 ARS	80122	KC-135R	453 OG
71492	KC-135E	151 ARS	80045	KC-135Q	458 OG	80123	KC-135R	384 ARS
71493	KC-135R	43 ARW	80046	KC-135Q	350 ARS	80124	KC-135R	305 ARW
71494	KC-135E	168 ARS	80047	KC-135Q	380 ARW	80125	KC-135Q	350 ARS
71495	KC-135E	197 ARS	80049	KC-135Q	380 ARW	80126	KC-135R	305 ARW
71496	KC-135E	197 ARS	80050	KC-135Q	380 ARW	80128	KC-135R	100 ARW
71497	KC-135E	191 ARS	80051	KC-135R	398 OG	80129	KC-135Q	350 ARS
71499	KC-135R	453 OG	80052	KC-135E	336 ARS*	80130	KC-135R	126 ARS
71501	KC-135E	116 ARS	80053	KC-135E	314 ARS*	86971	C-137B	89 AW
71502	KC-135E	42 ARS	80054	KC-135Q	458 OG	86972	C-137B	89 AW
71503	KC-135E	151 ARS	80055	KC-135Q	350 ARS	*FY59*		
71504	KC-135E	63 ARS*	80056	KC-135R	153 ARS	91444	KC-135R	145 ARS
71505	KC-135E	132 ARS	80057	KC-135E	108 ARS	91445	KC-135E	116 ARS
71506	KC-135R	509 ARS	80058	KC-135E	314 ARS*	91446	KC-135R	153 ARS
71507	KC-135E	141 ARS	80059	KC-135R	153 ARS	91447	KC-135E	63 ARS*
71508	KC-135R	509 ARS	80060	KC-135Q	458 OG	91448	KC-135E	196 ARS
71509	KC-135E	146 ARS	80061	KC-135Q	380 ARW	91449	KC-135A	46 ARS
71510	KC-135E	191 ARS	80062	KC-135Q	917 ARS	91450	KC-135E	133 ARS
71511	KC-135E	314 ARS*	80063	KC-135R	42 ARS	91451	KC-135E	63 ARS*
71512	KC-135E	336 ARS*	80064	KC-135E	314 ARS*	91452	KC-135E	116 ARS
71514	KC-135R	126 ARS	80065	KC-135Q	380 ARW	91453	KC-135R	145 ARS
72589	KC-135E	55 RW	80066	KC-135R	19 ARS	91455	KC-135R	153 ARS
72593	KC-135R	43 ARW	80067	KC-135E	108 ARS	91456	KC-135R	141 ARS
72594	KC-135E	108 ARS	80068	KC-135E	108 ARS	91457	KC-135E	147 ARS
72595	KC-135E	147 ARS	80069	KC-135Q	380 ARW	91458	KC-135R	145 ARS
72596	KC-135A	906 ARS	80071	KC-135Q	350 ARS	91459	KC-135R	
72597	KC-135R	153 ARS	80072	KC-135Q	350 ARS	91460	KC-135Q	917 ARS
72598	KC-135E	336 ARS*	80073	KC-135R	509 ARS	91461	KC-135R	457 OG
72599	KC-135R	453 OG	80074	KC-135Q	350 ARS	91462	KC-135Q	458 OG
72600	KC-135E	116 ARS	80075	KC-135R	72 ARS	91463	KC-135R	453 OG
72601	KC-135E	151 ARS	80076	KC-135R	74 ARS*	91464	KC-135Q	917 ARS
72602	KC-135E	150 ARS	80077	KC-135Q	917 ARS	91466	KC-135R	319 ARW
72603	KC-135E	336 ARS*	80078	KC-135E	150 ARS	91467	KC-135Q	380 ARW
72604	KC-135E	146 ARS	80079	KC-135R	906 ARS	91468	KC-135Q	917 ARS
72605	KC-135R	457 OG	80080	KC-135E	191 ARS	91469	KC-135R	43 ARS
72606	KC-135E	150 ARS	80082	KC-135E	116 ARS	91470	KC-135Q	458 OG
72607	KC-135E	147 ARS	80083	KC-135R	453 OG	91471	KC-135Q	458 OG
72608	KC-135E	147 ARS	80084	KC-135Q	350 ARS	91472	KC-135R	457 OG
FY58			80085	KC-135E	336 ARS*	91473	KC-135E	132 ARS
80001	KC-135R	457 OG	80086	KC-135Q	350 ARS	91474	KC-135Q	917 ARS
80003	KC-135E	108 ARS	80087	KC-135E	150 ARS	91475	KC-135R	43 ARW
80004	KC-135E	153 ARS	80088	KC-135Q	458 OG	91476	KC-135R	457 OG
80005	KC-135E	117 ARS	80089	KC-135Q	350 ARS	91477	KC-135E	63 ARS*
80006	KC-135E	191 ARS	80090	KC-135E	314 ARS*	91478	KC-135R	153 ARS
80008	KC-135E	141 ARS	80091	KC-135A	906 ARS	91479	KC-135E	146 ARS
80009	KC-135R	126 ARS	80092	KC-135R	509 ARS	91480	KC-135Q	350 ARS
80010	KC-135R	153 ARS	80093	KC-135R	42 ARS	91482	KC-135R	384 ARS
80011	KC-135R	305 ARW	80094	KC-135Q	350 ARS	91483	KC-135R	166 ARS
80012	KC-135E	191 ARS	80095	KC-135Q	458 OG	91484	KC-135E	147 ARS
80013	KC-135E	63 ARS*	80096	KC-135E	314 ARS*	91485	KC-135E	150 ARS
80014	KC-135E	108 ARS	80098	KC-135R	398 OG	91486	KC-135A	906 ARS
80015	KC-135E	42 ARS	80099	KC-135Q	350 ARS	91487	KC-135E	108 ARS
80016	KC-135R	453 OG	80100	KC-135R		91488	KC-135R	457 OG
80017	KC-135E	146 ARS	80102	KC-135Q	305 ARW	91489	KC-135E	191 ARS
80018	KC-135R	305 ARW	80103	KC-135Q	350 ARS	91490	KC-135Q	458 OG
80020	KC-135E	116 ARS	80104	KC-135R	509 ARS	91492	KC-135R	453 OG
80021	KC-135R	126 ARS	80105	KC-135A	906 ARS	91493	KC-135E	132 ARS

Reg	Type	Unit		Reg	Unit		Reg	Unit
91495	KC-135R	18 Wg		40611	437 AW		50254	60 AW
91496	KC-135E	147 ARS		40612	437 AW		50256	60 AW
91497	KC-135E	150 ARS		40613	438 AW		50257	60 AW
91498	KC-135R	366 Wg		40614	183 ALS		50258	62 AW
91499	KC-135E	196 ARS		40615	437 AW		50259	60 AW
91500	KC-135R	380 ARW		40616	438 AW		50260	60 AW
91501	KC-135A			40617	97 AMW		50261	356 ALS*
91502	KC-135R	380 ARW		40618	437 AW		50263	62 AW
91503	KC-135E	141 ARS		40619	437 AW		50264	97 AMW
91504	KC-135Q	2 Wg		40620	756 ALS*		50265	60 AW
91505	KC-135E	133 ARS		40621	438 AW		50266	437 AW
91506	KC-135E	147 ARS		40622	183 ALS		50267	62 AW
91507	KC-135R	28 ARS		40623	438 AW		50268	60 AW
91508	KC-135R	380 ARW		40625	438 AW		50269	437 AW
91509	KC-135E	133 ARS		40626	438 AW		50270	437 AW
91510	KC-135Q	917 ARS		40627	183 ALS		50271	756 ALS*
91511	KC-135R	398 OG		40628	438 AW		50272	437 AW
91512	KC-135Q	458 OG		40629	437 AW		50273	437 AW
91513	KC-135Q	458 OG		40630	438 AW		50275	437 AW
91514	KC-135E	55 RW		40631	437 AW		50276	438 AW
91515	KC-135R	384 ARS		40632	183 ALS		50277	62 AW
91516	KC-135E	117 ARS		40633	438 AW		50278	63 AW
91517	KC-135R	380 ARW		40634	97 AMW		50279	437 AW
91518	EC-135K	8 ADCS		40635	62 AW		50280	438 AW
91519	KC-135E	146 ARS		40637	183 ALS		59397	62 AW
91520	KC-135Q	350 ARS		40638	438 AW		59399	62 AW
91521	KC-135R	384 ARS		40639	438 AW		59400	97 AMW
91522	KC-135R	380 ARW		40640	183 ALS		59401	437 AW
91523	KC-135Q	350 ARS		40642	97 AMW		59402	438 AW
				40643	60 AW		59403	60 AW
				40644	438 AW		59404	62 AW
				40645	756 ALS*		59405	438 AW
				40646	437 AW		59406	63 AW
				40649	437 AW		59408	437 AW
				40650	438 AW		59409	438 AW
				40651	438 AW		59411	438 AW
				40653	62 AW		59412	356 ALS*

Lockheed C-141B Starlifter

*AFRES, Air Force Reserve
60 AW Travis AFB, California
62 AW McChord AFB, Washington
63 AW Norton AFB, California
97 AMW Altus AFB, Oklahoma (r/y)
155 ALS/164 AG Memphis, Tennessee ANG (r)
183 ALS/172 AG Jackson Field AFB, Mississippi ANG
356 ALS/907 AG, Wright-Patterson AFB, Ohio *
437 AW Charleston AFB, South Carolina (bl/y)
438 AW McGuire AFB, New Jersey (bl/w)
445 AW March AFB, California (r/y) *
756 ALS/459 AW Andrews AFB, Maryland * (bk)

Reg	Unit		Reg	Unit		Reg	Unit
FY61			FY65			59413	438 AW
12778	155 ALS		50216	756 ALS*		59414	63 AW
FY63			50217	437 AW		FY66	
38075	60 AW		50218	437 AW		60128	60 AW
38076	438 AW		50219	60 AW		60129	62 AW
38078	97 AMW		50220	438 AW		60130	183 ALS
38079	437 AW		50221	438 AW		60131	437 AW
38080	155 ALS		50222	155 ALS		60132	438 AW
38081	62 AW		50223	438 AW		60133	438 AW
38082	62 AW		50224	438 AW		60134	356 ALS*
38083	438 AW		50225	445 AW*		60135	438 AW
38084	445 AW*		50226	756 ALS*		60136	445 AW*
38085	445 AW*		50227	63 AW		60137	62 AW
38086	62 AW		50228	438 AW		60138	97 AMW
38087	62 AW		50229	445 AW*		60139	155 ALS
38088	97 AMW		50230	60 AW		60140	438 AW
38089	62 AW		50231	438 AW		60141	62 AW
38090	438 AW		50232	63 AW		60144	438 AW
FY64			50234	60 AW		60145	62 AW
40609	97 AMW		50235	62 AW		60146	438 AW
40610	437 AW		50236	60 AW		60147	60 AW
			50237	60 AW		60148	60 AW
			50238	60 AW		60149	437 AW
			50239	60 AW		60151	445 AW*
			50240	62 AW		60152	63 AW
			50241	62 AW		60153	756 ALS*
			50242	60 AW		60154	97 AMW
			50243	63 AW		60155	438 AW
			50244	62 AW		60156	62 AW
			50245	60 AW		60157	155 ALS
			50247	60 AW		60158	62 AW
			50248	445 AW*		60159	62 AW
			50249	60 AW		60160	60 AW
			50250	60 AW		60161	62 AW
			50251	60 AW		60162	438 AW
			50252	60 AW		60163	438 AW

60164	183 ALS	60198	62 AW	FY67	
60165	62 AW	60199	438 AW	70001	62 AW
60166	438 AW	60200	62 AW	70002	437 AW
60167	437 AW	60201	63 AW	70003	62 AW
60168	437 AW	60202	437 AW	70004	437 AW
60169	438 AW	60203	97 AMW	70005	62 AW
60171	97 AMW	60204	438 AW	70007	438 AW
60172	62 AW	60205	62 AW	70009	62 AW
60173	438 AW	60206	62 AW	70010	437 AW
60174	756 ALS*	60207	438 AW	70011	437 AW
60175	62 AW	60208	62 AW	70012	437 AW
60177	356 ALS*	60209	437 AW	70013	438 AW
60178	438 AW	67944	60 AW	70014	438 AW
60179	62 AW	67945	437 AW	70015	63 AW
60180	97 AMW	67946	62 AW	70016	437 AW
60181	445 AW*	67947	438 AW	70018	62 AW
60182	445 AW*	67948	438 AW	70019	438 AW
60183	438 AW	67949	62 AW	70020	438 AW
60184	62 AW	67950	438 AW	70021	155 ALS
60185	183 ALS	67951	62 AW	70022	60 AW
60186	97 AMW	67952	63 AW	70023	356 ALS*
60187	437 AW	67953	356 ALS*	70024	155 ALS
60189	62 AW	67954	356 ALS*	70025	438 AW
60190	183 ALS	67955	437 AW	70026	437 AW
60191	60 AW	67956	438 AW	70027	438 AW
60192	62 AW	67957	445 AW*	70028	62 AW
60193	445 AW*	67958	62 AW	70029	155 ALS
60194	437 AW	67959	60 AW	70031	356 ALS*
60195	438 AW			70164	60 AW
60196	437 AW			70165	438 AW
60197	62 AW			70166	356 ALS (VIP)

US based USN/USMC Aircraft

Boeing E-6A
Sea Control Wing 1 (SCW-1),
  Tinker AFB, Oklahoma

162782	SCW-1
162783	SCW-1
162784	SCW-1
163918	SCW-1
163919	SCW-1
163920	SCW-1
164386	SCW-1
164387	SCW-1
164388	SCW-1
164404	SCW-1
164405	SCW-1
164406	SCW-1
164407	SCW-1
164408	SCW-1
164409	SCW-1
164410	SCW-1

McDonnell Douglas
C-9B Skytrain II
VR-46 Atlanta, Georgia
VR-51 Glenview NAS, Illinois
VR-52 Willow Grove NAS Pennsylvania
VR-55 Alameda NAS, California
VR-56 Norfolk NAS, Virginia
VR-57 North Island NAS, California
VR-58 Jacksonville NAS, Florida
VR-59 Dallas, Texas
VR-60 Memphis NAS, Tennessee
VR-61 Whidbey Island NAS, Washington
VR-62 Detroit, Michigan
SOES Cherry Point MCAS, North Carolina

159113 [RU]	VR-55
159114 [RX]	VR-57
159115 [RX]	VR-57
159116 [RX]	VR-57
159117 [JU]	VR-56
159118 [JU]	VR-56
159119 [JU]	VR-56
159120 [RU]	VR-55
160046	SOES
160047	SOES
160048 [JV]	VR-58
160049 [JV]	VR-58
160050 [JV]	VR-58
160051 [RU]	VR-55
161266 [RY]	VR-59
161529 [RY]	VR-59
161530 [RY]	VR-59
162753 [RV]	VR-51
162754 [RV]	VR-51
163036 [JT]	VR-52
163037 [JT]	VR-52
163208 [JS]	VR-46
163511 [JW]	VR-62
163512 [JS]	VR-46
163513 [JW]	VR-62
164605 [RT]	VR-60
164606 [RT]	VR-60
164607 [RS]	VR-61
164608 [RS]	VR-61

Grumman C-20D Gulfstream III/
C-20G Gulfstream IV*
CFLSW Andrews AFB, Maryland
163691
163692

165093*
165094*
165151*
165152*
165153*

Lockheed C-130 Hercules
VRC-50 North Island NAS, California
VR-53 Martinsburg, West Virginia
VR-54 New Orleans NAS, Louisiana
VMGR-152 Futenma MCAS, Japan
VMGR-234 Glenview NAS, Illinois
VMGR-252 Cherry Point MCAS, North Carolina
VMGRT-253 Cherry Point MCAS, North Carolina
VMGR-352 El Toro MCAS, California
VMGR-452 Stewart Field, New York

147572 [QB]	KC-130F	VMGR-352
147573 [QD]	KC-130F	VMGR-152
148246 [GR]	KC-130F	VMGRT-253
148247 [QD]	KC-130F	VMGR-152
148248 [QD]	KC-130F	VMGR-152
148249 [GR]	KC-130F	VMGRT-253
148890 [GR]	KC-130F	VMGRT-253
148891 [BH]	KC-130F	VMGR-252
148892 [GR]	KC-130F	VMGRT-253
148893 [QH]	KC-130F	VMGR-234
148894 [GR]	KC-130F	VMGRT-253
148895 [BH]	KC-130F	VMGR-252
148896 [BH]	KC-130F	VMGR-252
148897 [BH]	KC-130F	VMGR-252
148898 [BH]	KC-130F	VMGR-252
148899 [BH]	KC-130F	VMGR-252
149787 [RG]	KC-130F	VRC-50
149788 [BH]	KC-130F	VMGR-252
149789 [BH]	KC-130F	VMGR-252
149790	C-130F	
149791 [QB]	KC-130F	VMGR-352
149792 [QB]	KC-130F	VMGR-352
149793 [RG]	KC-130F	VRC-50
149794	C-130F	
149795 [QB]	KC-130F	VMGR-352
149796 [QB]	KC-130F	VMGR-352
149797	C-130F	
149798 [QB]	KC-130F	VMGR-352
149799 [QD]	KC-130F	VMGR-152
149800 [QB]	KC-130F	VMGR-352
149801	C-130F	NS Adak
149803 [GR]	KC-130F	VMGRT-253
149804 [GR]	KC-130F	VMGRT-253
149805 [RG]	C-130F	VRC-50
149806 [GR]	KC-130F	VMGRT-253
149807 [QD]	KC-130F	VMGR-152
149808 [BH]	KC-130F	VMGR-252
149811 [GR]	KC-130F	VMGRT-253
149812 [QD]	KC-130F	VMGR-152
149815 [QB]	KC-130F	VMGR-352
149816 [QB]	KC-130F	VMGR-352
150684 [GR]	KC-130F	VMGRT-253
150686 [BH]	KC-130F	VMGR-252
150687	KC-130F	
150688 [GR]	KC-130F	VMGRT-253
150689 [QB]	KC-130F	VMGR-352
150690 [QD]	KC-130F	VMGR-152
151891	TC-130G	Blue Angels
160013 [QB]	KC-130R	VMGR-352
160014 [QB]	KC-130R	VMGR-352
160015 [QB]	KC-130R	VMGR-152

160016 [QB]	KC-130R	VMGR-352	164106 [NY]	KC-130T	VMGR-452
160017 [QB]	KC-130R	VMGR-352	164180 [QH]	KC-130T	VMGR-234
160018 [QB]	KC-130R	VMGR-352	164181 [NY]	KC-130T	VMGR-452
160019 [QB]	KC-130R	VMGR-352	164441 [QH]	KC-130T	VMGR-234
160020 [QB]	KC-130R	VMGR-352	164442 [QH]	KC-130T	VMGR-234
160021 [QB]	KC-130R	VMGR-352	164597 [NY]	KC-130T-30	VMGR-452
160022 [QB]	KC-130R	VMGR-352	164598 [QH]	KC-130T-30	VMGR-234
160240 [QB]	KC-130R	VMGR-352	164759 [NY]	KC-130T	VMGR-452
160625 [BH]	KC-130R	VMGR-252	164760 [NY]	KC-130T	VMGR-234
160626 [BH]	KC-130R	VMGR-252	164762 [CW]	C-130T	VR-54
160627 [BH]	KC-130R	VMGR-252	164763 [CW]	C-130T	VR-54
160628 [BH]	KC-130R	VMGR-252	164993 [CW]	C-130T	VR-54
162308 [QH]	KC-130T	VMGR-234	164994 [WV]	C-130T	VR-53
162309 [QH]	KC-130T	VMGR-234	164995 [CW]	C-130T	VR-54
162310 [QH]	KC-130T	VMGR-234	164996 [WV]	C-130T	VR-53
162311 [QH]	KC-130T	VMGR-234	164997 [WV]	C-130T	VR-53
162785 [QH]	KC-130T	VMGR-234	164998 [WV]	C-130T	VR-53
162786 [QH]	KC-130T	VMGR-234	164999 [NY]	KC-130T	VMGR-452
163022 [QH]	KC-130T	VMGR-234	165000 [QH]	KC-130T	VMGR-234
163023 [QH]	KC-130T	VMGR-234	165158	C-130T	
163310 [NY]	KC-130T	VMGR-452	165159	C-130T	
163311 [NY]	KC-130T	VMGR-452	165160	C-130T	
163591 [NY]	KC-130T	VMGR-452	165161	C-130T	
163592 [NY]	KC-130T	VMGR-452	165162	KC-130T	
164105 [NY]	KC-130T	VMGR-452	165163	KC-130T	

F-15E Strike Eagle 91-0311 of 492FS/48FW based at RAF Lakenheath. *PRM*

Boeing B-1B Lancer in the colours of 7Wg at Dyess AFB, Texas. *PRM*

ADDENDUM

Serial	Type (code/other identity)	Owner/operator, location or fate
BH229	Hawker Hurricane IIb	Privately owned, Washington, West Sussex
DP872	Fairey Barracuda II (fuselage)	FAA Museum, Yeovilton
DR393	Hawker Hurricane IIa (P3351)	Privately owned, Washington, W Sussex
EJ693	Hawker Tempest V [SA-J]	Sold to the USA, 1992
FM118	Avro Lancaster B.X <ff>	Privately owned, Gosport, Hants
FT323	NA Harvard II (FAP.1513)	Privately owned, Cranfield
WH796	EE Canberra PR7 <ff>	Privately owned, Stock, Essex
WH801	EE Canberra T22 <ff>	Privately owned, Stock, Essex
WH803	EE Canberra T22 <ff>	Privately owned, Stock, Essex
WH981	EE Canberra E15 [CN]	Scrapped At Wyton, September 1993
WJ603	EE Canberra B2 (8664M) <ff>	Privately owned, Stock, Essex
WJ731	EE Canberra B2T [BK]	RAF Wyton, Fire Section
WJ874	EE Canberra T4	RAF No 360 Sqn, Wyton
WJ945	Vickers Varsity T1 (G-BEDV) [21]	Imperial War Museum, Duxford
WK111	EE Canberra T17 [EA]	RAF Wyton, wfu
WK144	EE Canberra B2 (8689M) <ff>	Privately owned, Stock, Essex
WV318	Hawker Hunter T7B [A]	RAF ASF, Lossiemouth
WV395	Hawker Hunter F4 (8001M)	BAe Dunsfold, Fire Section
WV495	Percival Provost T1 (7697M) [P-C]	Sold to the USA
WV795	Hawker Sea Hawk FGA6 (8151M) ◉	Privately owned, Bournemouth
WV856	Hawker Sea Hawk FGA6 [163]	FAA Museum, stored RNAS Yeovilton
WW138	DH Sea Venom FAW22 [227/Z]	FAA Museum, stored RNAS Yeovilton
WZ476	DH Vampire T11 (XE985)	Repainted as XE985
WZ581	DH Vampire T11 <ff>	Privately owned, Ruislip
WZ679	Auster AOP9 (7863M)	Painted as XP248
WZ769	Slingsby Grasshopper TX1	Privately owned, stored Rufforth
WZ868	DH Chipmunk T10	Privately owned, Audley End
XA127	DH Sea Vampire T22 <ff>	FAA Museum, stored RNAS Yeovilton
XA129	DH Sea Vampire T22	FAA Museum, stored Wroughton
XA286	Slingsby Cadet TX3	Privately owned, stored Rufforth
XA290	Slingsby Cadet TX3	Privately owned, stored Rufforth
XA466	Fairey Gannet COD4 [777/LM]	FAA Museum, stored Wroughton
XB446	Grumman Avenger ECM6B [992/C]	FAA Museum, stored Wroughton
XD317	VS Scimitar F1 [112/R]	FAA Museum, stored Wroughton
XD375	DH Vampire T11 (7887) [72]	Privately owned, Fakenham
XD614	DH Vampire T11 <ff>	No 424 Sqn ATC, Southampton
XD857	Vickers Valiant B(K) 1 <ff>	Privately owned, Rayleigh, Essex
XE340	Hawker Sea Hawk FGA6 [131/Z]	Royal Scottish Museum of Flight, E Fortune
XE650	Hawker Hunter FGA9 (G-9-449) <ff>	Macclesfield Historical Av'n Soc, Chelford
XE682	Hawker Hunter GA11	Burnt at Culdrose
XE985	DH Vampire T11 (WZ476)	Mosquito Aircraft Museum
XE998	DH Vampire T11 [36]	Privately owned, Aston Juxtra Mondrum
XF383	Hawker Hunter F6 (8706M) <ff>	Privately owned, Duxford
XG194	Hawker Hunter FGA9 (8839M) [55] <rf>	RAF North Luffenham Training Area
XG209	Hawker Hunter F6 (8709M) [69]	RAF Halton Fire Section
XG325	EE Lightning F1 <ff>	Privately owned, Rayleigh, Essex
XG462	Bristol Belvedere HC1 <ff>	IHM, Weston-super-Mare
XG523	Bristol Sycamore HR14 <ff>	North-East Aircraft Museum, Usworth
XG737	DH Sea Venom FAW22 [220/Z]	Vampire Rest'n Grp, Wellesbourne Mountford
XH563	Avro Vulcan B2MRR <ff>	Privately owned, Banchory
XJ396	WS55 Whirlwind HAR10	Burnt at Farnborough
XJ582	DH Sea Vixen FAW2 (8139M) [702]	Scrapped at Stock, November 1991
XJ758	WS55 Whirlwind HAR10 (8464M) <ff>	Privately owned, Oswestry
XK421	Auster AOP9 (8365M) (frame)	Stratford Aircraft Collection, Long Marston
XK741	Folland Gnat F1 (fuselage)	Midland Air Museum, Coventry
XK824	Slingsby Grasshopper TX1	Sold to Germany
XL160	HP Victor K2 (8910M)	To Standard PTA, 1994
XL163	HP Victor K2 (8916M)	Privately owned, Stock, Essex
XL568	Hawker Hunter T7A [C]	RAF, stored Lossiemouth
XL580	Hawker Hunter T8M [723]	RN, stored Yeovilton
XL603	Hawker Hunter T8M [724]	RN, stored Yeovilton

Serial	Type (code/other identity)	Owner/operator, location or fate
XL616	Hawker Hunter T7 [D]	RAF, stored Lossiemouth
XL954	Percival Pembroke C1 (9042M/N4234C)	Privately owned, Tatenhill
XM330	WS58 Wessex HAS1	*Scrapped at Farnborough*
XM363	Hunting Jet Provost T3 <ff>	RAF Cranwell
XM417	Hunting Jet Provost T3 (8054BM)	RAF North Luffenham Training Area
XM656	Avro Vulcan B2 (8757M) <ff>	Privately owned, Stock, Essex
XM923	WS58 Wessex HAS3	*Burnt at Fleetlands*
XN308	WS55 Whirlwind HAS7	RNAS Yeovilton Fire Section
XN332	Saro P531 (G-APNV) [759]	FAA Museum, stored RNAS Yeovilton
XN385	WS55 Whirlwind HAS7	Privately owned, Bournemouth
XN606	Hunting Jet Provost T3A (9121M) [51]	*Sold to USA, 1993*
XN692	DH Sea Vixen FAW2 [125/E]	RNAS Yeovilton
XN694	DH Sea Vixen FAW2	*Scrapped at Llandbedr*
XN769	EE Lightning F2 (8402M) [Z]	*Scrapped at West Drayton, January 1994*
XN930	HS Buccaneer S1 (8180M) [632/LM] <ff>	Privately owned, Stock, Essex
XM981	HS Buccaneer S2B	RAF, stored Lossiemouth
XP116	WS58 Wessex HAS3 [520]	*Scrapped at Lee-on-Solent*
XP137	WS58 Wessex HAS3 [CU]	RN, ETS, Culdrose
XP248	Auster AOP9 (7863M/WZ679)	Privately owned, Little Gransden
XP393	WS55 Whirlwind HAR10 [U]	*Burnt at Farnborough*
XP399	WS55 Whirlwind HAR10	Privately owned, Kettering
XP516	HS Gnat T1 (8580M) [16]	*Scrapped at Farnborough, 1992*
XP534	HS Gnat T1 (8620M) [64]	Kennet Aircraft, Cranfield
XP857	WS Scout AH1	*Burnt at Middle Wallop*
XP893	WS Scout AH1	AAC Middle Wallop, BDRT
XP902	WS Scout AH1	AAC Middle Wallop, BDRT
XP908	WS Scout AH1 [Y]	AAC, stored Sek Kong
XR140	AW Argosy E1 (8579M) (fuselage)	*Burnt at Halton*
XR396	DH Comet C4 (8882M/G-BDIU) (fuselage)	RAF Kinloss, BDRT
XR501	WS58 Wessex HC2	RAF No 22 Sqn, E Flt, Coltishall
XS153	WS58 Wessex HAS3 [662/PO]	*To AAC Sennelager, BDRT*
XS416	BAC Lightning T5 <ff>	Privately owned, New Waltham, Humberside
XS458	BAC Lightning T5 [DY]	*Sold to Cyprus, November 1993*
WS488	WS58 Wessex HU5 (9056M) [XK]	RAF No 2 SoTT, Cosford
XS538	WS Wasp HAS1 [451]	RN, Predannack Fire School
XS590	DH Sea Vixen FAW2 [131/E]	FAA Museum, stored RNAS Yeovilton
XS610	HS Andover E3	RAF Northolt
XS791	HS Andover CC2	RAF, stored Northolt
XS794	HS Andover CC2	RAF, stored Northolt
WS865	WS58 Wessex HAS1 [529/CU]	*Burnt at Lee-on-Solent, 1993*
XS881	WS58 Wessex HAS1 [046/CU]	RNAS Yeovilton, Fire Section
XT280	HS Buccaneer S2B	RAF ASF, Lossiemouth
XT453	WS58 Wessex HU5 [A]	RNAS Yeovilton
XT455	WS58 Wessex HU5 [U]	RNAS Lee-on-Solent, Fire Section
XT485	WS58 Wessex HU5 [621/PO]	*Burnt at Lee-on-Solent, 1993*
XT487	WS58 Wessex HU5 [815/LS]	*Burnt at Lee-on-Solent, 1993*
XT602	WS58 Wessex HC2	RAF No 22 Sqn, St Mawgan
XT614	WS Scout AH1 [C]	AAC, stored Sek Kong
XT624	WS Scout AH1 [D]	AAC, stored Sek Kong
XT628	WS Scout AH1 [E]	AAC, stored Sek Kong
XT630	WS Scout AH1 [X]	AAC, stored Sek Kong
XT636	WS Scout AH1 [F]	ACC, stored Sek Kong
XT645	WS Scout AH1 (fuselage)	AAC Thorney Island, BDRT
XT667	WS58 Wessex HC2 [F]	*Written off, off Hong Kong, 17 Sept 1993*
XT769	WS58 Wessex HU5 [823]	FAA Museum, stored RNAS Yeovilton
XT903	McD Phantom FGR2 [X]	RAF Leuchars, BDRT
XV106	BAC VC10 C1K	RAF No 10 Sqn, Brize Norton
XV131	WS Scout AH1 [Y]	AAC Middle Wallop, BDRT
XV181	Lockheed Hercules C1p (mod)	MoD(PE), Marshall, Cambridge
XV269	DHC Beaver AL1 (8011M)	*Scrapped at Middle Wallop, 1990*
XV281	HS Harrier GR3	BAe Warton, instructional use
XB338	HS Buccaneer S2A (8774M) <ff>	RAF Exhibition Flight, St Athan
XV350	HS Buccaneer S2B	East Midlands Aeropark
XV420	McD Phantom FGR2 [0]	
XV631	WS Wasp HAS1	*Scrapped at Farnborough, 1992*
XV651	WS61 Sea King HAS5 [591]	RN No 706 Sqn, Culdrose

Serial	Type (code/other identity)	Owner/operator, location or fate
XV654	WS61 Sea King HAS6 [705/PW] (wreck)	RN AIU, Lee-on-Solent
XV672	WS61 Sea King AEW2A [183/R]	RNAY Fleetlands
XV673	WS61 Sea King HAS5 [588]	RN No 706 Sqn, Culdrose
XW295	BAC Jet Provost TSA [29]	*Sold to Australia, 1993*
XW296	BAC Jet Provost T5 [Q]	RAF, stored Shawbury
XW352	BAC Jet Provost T5 [R]	Privately owned, stored Tamworth
XW357	BAC Jet Provost T5A [5]	*Sold to Australia, 1993*
XW362	BAC Jet Provost T5A (91..M) [17]	*Sold to Australia, 1993*
XW363	BAC Jet Provost T5A [36]	BAe Training School, Warton
XW374	BAC Jet Provost T5A [38]	*Sold to Australia, 1993*
XW406	BAC Jet Provost T5A [23]	*Sold to Australia, 1993*
XW408	BAC Jet Provost T5A [24]	Privately owned, stored Tamworth
XW435	BAC Jet Provost T5A [4]	*Sold to Australia, 1993*
XW612	WS Scout AH1 [A]	AAC, stored Sek Kong
XW613	WS Scout AH1 [B]	AAC, stored Sek Kong
XW797	WS Scout AH1 [G]	AAC, stored Sek Kong
XW860	WS Gazelle HT2	AAC SAE, Middle Wallop
XX885	HS Buccaneer S2B	RAF, stored Lossiemouth
XX889	HS Buccaneer S2B	RAF No 208 Sqn, Lossiemouth
XX892	HS Buccaneer S2B	RAF ASF, Lossiemouth
XX893	HS Buccaneer S2B	RAF, stored Lossiemouth
XX901	HS Buccaneer S2B	RAF ASF, Lossiemouth
ZA130	WS61 Sea King HAS5 [587]	RN No 706 Sqn, Culdrose
ZA134	WS61 Sea King HAS5 [598]	RN No 706 Sqn, Culdrose
ZA136	WS61 Sea King HAS6 [015]	RN No 820 Sqn, Culdrose
ZA137	WS61 Sea King HAS5 [597]	RN No 706 Sqn, Culdrose
ZD636	WS61 Sea King HAR5 [825]	RN No 771 Sqn, Culdrose
ZD939	Panavia Tornado F2 [AS]	BAe Warton, instructional use
ZD982	B-V Chinook HC2 [BI]	Boeing, Philadelphia (conversion)
ZE692	BAe Sea Harrier FRS1 [000/R]	RN No 801 Sqn, Yeovilton
ZF116	WS61 Sea King HC4	MoD(PE), A&AEE Boscombe Down
ZF120	WS61 Sea King HC4 [20]	RN No 772 Sqn, Portland
ZF514	Shorts Tucano T1	RAF No 1 FTS, Linton-on-Ouse
ZG506	BAe Harrier GR7 [AF]	RAF No 3 Sqn, Laarbruch
ZG754	Panavia Tornado GRIT [AW]	RAF, stored St Athan (damaged)
ZG778	Panavia Tornado F3 [BG]	RAF No 29 Sqn, Coningsby
ZG797	Panavia Tornado F3 [BF]	RAF No 29 Sqn, Coningsby
ZG821	WS61 Sea King HC4 [UN]	RN No 845 Sqn, Yeovilton
ZG914	WS Lynx AH9	AAC No 653 Sqn, Wattisham

Symbol <ff> denotes front fuselage only

Shorts Tucano T.1 ZF145 in the display colours of No.1 FTS. Listen as Ossa, Daniel J. Marsh